SKOOB DIRECTORY

SKOOB DIRECTORY

OF SECONDHAND BOOKSHOPS IN THE BRITISH ISLES

Sixth Edition

SKOOB BOOKS LTD
LONDON

General Editor: M.P.Ong
Assistant editors: Miles Lanham
Adam Wilson
Mina Pang
C.Y.Loh
Design: © Mark Lovell
Managing Director: Ike Ong

Published by:
Skoob Books Ltd
11a - 17 Sicilian Avenue
Southampton Row
Holborn
London WC1A 2QH
Fax: 0171 404 4398
E mail: books @ skoob.demon.co.uk
Web site: http://www.bozell.com.my/bozell/Skoob.skoob.html

ISBN 1 871438 13 6

Printed by WSOY, Finland

IN MEMORIAM

George Jeffery

CONTENTS

DIRECTORY CONTENTS

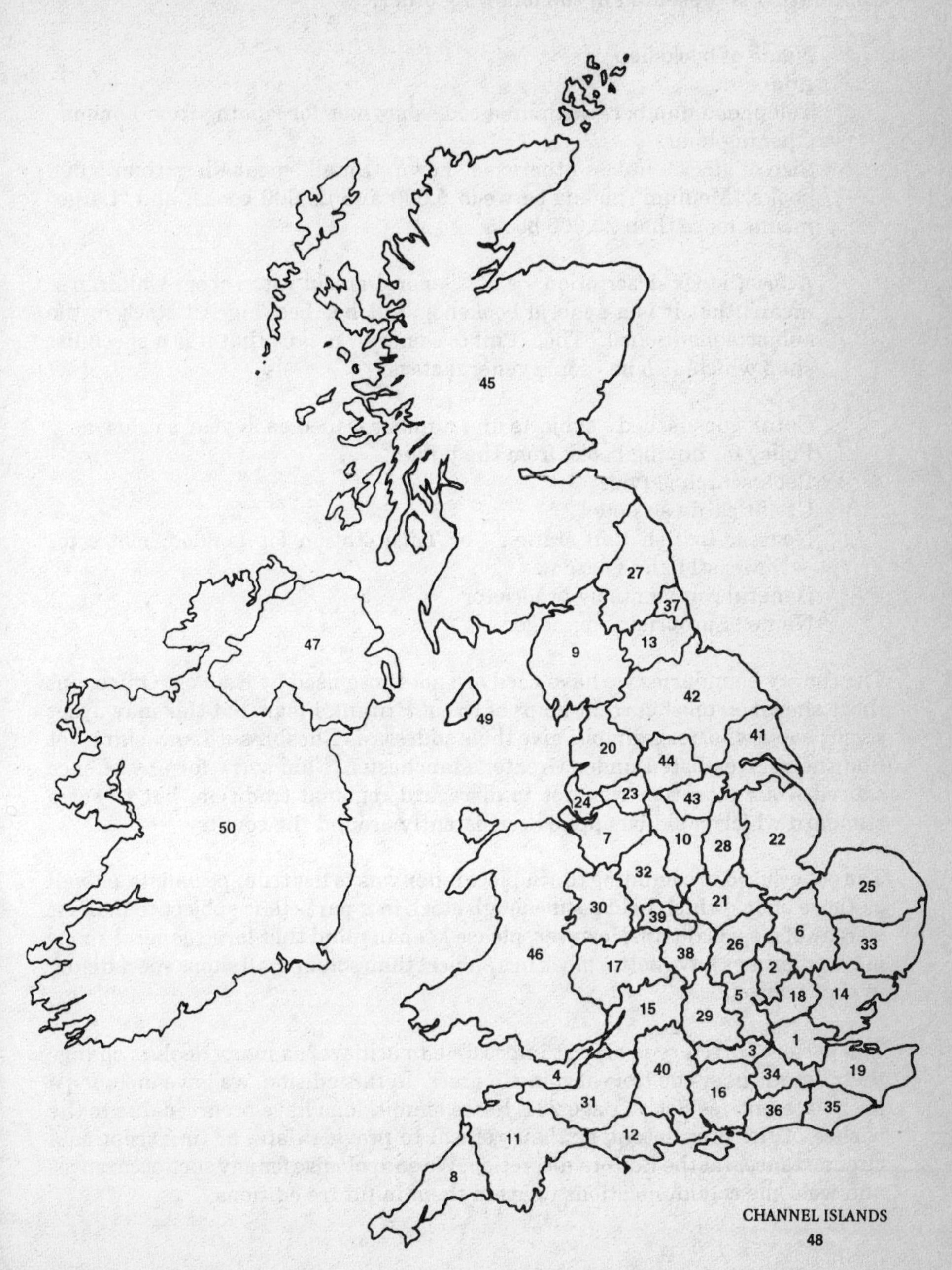
45
27
37
13
9
47
49
42
41
20
44
24
23
43
50
7
10
28
22
32
25
30
39
21
6
33
46
17
38
26
2
5
18
14
15
29
1
3
4
40
34
19
31
16
36
35
12
11
8
CHANNEL ISLANDS
48

DIRECTORY LAYOUT AND ABBREVIATIONS

Information is presented in the following order:-

Name of bookshop
Address
Telephone number - with area code shown as for ringing from London
Opening hours
Size of stock - unless otherwise shown, "Small" means less than 5,000 books, "Medium" means between 5,000 and 20,000 books, and "Large" means more than 20,000 books.

A brief stock description - e.g. "General stock: Lit, Topog, Children's" means that it is a general bookshop, but has best/biggest stock in the subjects mentioned. "Theo, Phil & General" means that it is a specialist shop which also has some general stock.

Catalogues issued - subjects and number issued each year as shown
Policy for buying books from the public
Book search service
Credit cards accepted
Nearest British Rail station - or Tube station for London, metro for Newcastle and Glasgow
General comments by proprietor
Name of proprietor/manager

The county boundaries we have used are not those used by the Post Office, but those shown on most current maps of Great Britain. I fear that this may upset some people who, for example, give their address as Cheshire or Lancashire, yet find themselves listed under Greater Manchester. I am sorry for any offence caused - our intention was not to disregard regional tradition, but to set a standard which could be applied consistently around the country.

The policy used in compiling the Subject Index was to list true specialists, as well as those shops which held good enough stock in a particular subject to make it worthy of a special trip. However, please keep in mind that large general shops may sometimes have better stock in a subject than some small shops specialising in that subject.

The perfect *Directory* is almost impossible to achieve, as many dealers change their details near the time of going to press. In this edition, we have included a short late-entries list on page 201. Some ommissions have occurred due to the wishes of the proprietors, or their refusal to provide data, or (in exceptional circumstances) at the Editors' discretion. We do apologise for any such occurences and welcome communications to avoid them in future editions.

GENERAL ABBREVIATIONS

Cat - catalogues
pa - per annum
occ - occasional
Est - established

BR - British Rail
ec - early closing
cc - credit cards:

A = Access
M = Mastercard
V = Visa
Am = American Express
D = Diners Club
E = Eurocard
J = JCB
S = Switch

SUBJECT ABBREVIATIONS

1sts - First Editions
Alt - Alternative
Anthrop - Anthropology
Arch - Archeology
Atec - Architecture
Atqn - Antiquarian
Avia - Aviation
Biblio - Bibliograghy
Biog - Biography
Br - British
Bus - Business
Cartog - Cartography
Chem - Chemistry
Chld - Childrens
Crime - Crime Fiction
Dec Art - Decorative Art
Det - Detective Fiction
E Europe - Eastern Europe
Econ - Economics
Educ - Education
Eng - English
Eso - Esoterica
Eur - European

Fem - Feminist
Fict - Fiction
Folio - Folio Society
For - Foreign
Fr - French
Gard - Gardening
Geog - Geography
Geol - Geology
Ger - German
Hbk - Hardbacks
Hist - History
Illus - Illustrated Books
Ir - Irish
Lang - Language
Ling - Linguistics
Lit - Literature
Lit Crit - Literary criticism
Maths - Mathematics
Med - Medicine
Mid E - Middle East
Mil - Military
Mod - Modern
Mount - Mountaineering
Mus - Music

Nat Hist - Natural History
Occ - Occult
OP - Out of Print
O/S - Ordnance Survey
Pbk - Paperbacks
Perf Arts - Performing Arts
Phil - Philosophy
Photo - Photography
Po - Poetry
Pol - Politics
Psy - Psychology
Rel - Religion
SF - Science Fiction
Scot - Scottish
Sci - Science
Soc Sci - Social Sciences
Tech - Technical
Theol - Theology
Topog - Topography
Trans - Transport
TV - Television

eg. C19th - eg. Nineteenth Century

The subject abbreviations included above are intended as a basic guide to the listing of specialist subjects which have been greatly increased in this edition.

FOREWORD

To find a particular book has become much more difficult in the Nineties and many booksellers no longer provide the service whereby they stock as many books as are available on a subject, as they used to do. Guided by the pearl of accounting wisdom that says a bookshop would make more by limiting its selection to a third, and only sell titles where there is a demand of ten or more, those bookshops which provide the facilities of choice and range are becoming a luxury of the past. As a result, the bookshops which fulfil that demand for a large selection of books on a subject have to triple their prices to achieve the previous year's turnover to stay afloat. The beauty of secondhand bookshops is that we stock one copy of many titles, unlike the new bookshops and supermarkets who sell the limited best-sellers. Consumers are buying fewer books and the proportion of books sold to the number in stock is diminishing. To match sales of the previous year, most secondhand booksellers have to double their stock size and increase their prices.

Many new bookshops are businesses whose proprietors work *on* the business with the intention of selling it, hopefully to a chain, but they do not work *in* the business. The Body Shop success is the role model. Providing a service with social benefits is totally discounted, there being no profit in that as today's government policy goes. The demise of the Net Book Price Agreement has made matters worse. Independent bookshops, not having the advantage of high-volume purchases, are not able to compete with large chains who are achieving discounts as much as seventy-five per cent compared to their minute thirty-five per cent. The price war will devastate the small independent bookshops who provide a service to remote communities. Publishers and distributors are not supportive and single orders are often declined or penalised by a reduced discount, e.g. ten per cent, and postage is added. The Royal Mail no longer exists, thanks to the wisdom of the Conservative Party, and the Post Office charges would turn the sale into a loss.

Publishers forge ahead to bring out new titles so as to satisfy the demands of the 'Americanised' marketing departments as they compete for the diminishing market. Competition for recreation time from C.D. ROMs, Computer games and nouveau-tech modems encourages the obsession, but the gems of the back-list are overlooked. Often reprints are ignored when the demand does not fulfil the minimum print-run policy of the conglomerates. As such, specialist scholarly works and academic books are often produced with a published price of, for example, seventy-five pounds. Many publishers and sometimes non-profit making organisations such as University Presses have set this precedent. The out-of-print book has become a rare item and a luxury.

Secondhand booksellers are the source for books which are no longer in print and so unavailable from new bookshops. The pricing policy varies between organisations. Some choose to apply the replacement price (£30 - £49), others charge the replacement value should the tome be reprinted (£50 - £80); specialists deem such items as rare items equivalent to the luxurious antiquarian fine bindings or furniture (£90 - £150). Some specialists stock only out-of-print titles and have a pricing policy of fifty pounds for hardbacks and fifteen pounds for paper.

That a book could be located by 'letting one's fingers do the walking' is a fallacy created by the media. Herein lies the irresponsibility of the television advertisement: both the book in question and the author are fictitious. The story-line which portrays an author finding a book by telephone has given the public an unrealistic expectation that all bookshops should fulfil their whims. *Touché* to the publishers who had the enterprise to create the fictitious title and make it available to the amusement of all. An exercise in Postmodernism *par excellence*. The niche has created the new industry of the Book Finding Service. As reported in *The Times* of 17th November 1995, £3,600 was charged to find the book *Language in Infancy and Children* by A.C. Crittenden (cost £10.95). A book-finder on Channel Four boasts of charging £60 per hour for his expertise. Skoob Books has one of the highest turnovers of titles in the British Isles and has developed a Booksearch Department to cope with the increasing demand. To qualify for this service, the consumer has to purchase a copy of this Directory at the published price, post-free. Their requirements are researched by our Booksearch Department as well as other agencies. On locating the specified title, the customer will be charged and the book despatched. Prospectors are asked to specify the maximum affordable price as we do not control the pricing policy of the shops from whom we obtain requested books. Thanks, again, to the vision of Margaret Thatcher and John Major who have created this disillusion; rents have escalated and taxes on business premises have tripled. Government propaganda has not helped small businesses in the reduction of interest rates when banks are charging a higher minimum rate despite the Government minimum lending rate being reduced.

We apologise for any inaccuracies in this edition as many bookshops could have closed by the time we get into print. The last thing proprietors would want to do is to announce that their bookshop is no longer commercially viable when they hope to sell it as a going concern. Thus, be warned that some may have vanished without a trace on your arrival at the premises.

In the era of Postmodernist bookselling, chain-shops and supermarkets, this is your friendly old corner shop thanking you, our customers, for your patronage during the last sixteen years, and we hope to serve you for many more.

I would like to thank Judith & John Clute, the late Christopher Johnson, Barrie Buxton, Tim Donnelly, Debra A. Hamilton, Brian Lake, Paul Minet, Martin Stone, Nigel Burwood and Marco of Any Amount of Books, Gino of Pordes, David Pritchard-Jones, Eric Morton, Elisabeth & Robin Summers, Tim Watson of The Stoke Newington Church Street Bookshop, David Houston, George Jeffery IV and all who have helped to make this publication possible.

Ike Ong
1996

INTRODUCTION

Dear Reader, do not let the apparently dyslexic title fool you, for between these covers can be found true literary nirvana: the *Skoob Directory* is the answer to J.R. Hartley's prayers.

There is nothing more fascinating than the unpredictable pursuit of the secondhand book, and for the biographer, the thrill of the chase has a heady reward. To find an elusive volume is a joy unsurpassed, save by the yet more ecstatic find, that of a tome intimately connected to one's subject. As a teenager, one of my haunts was Sidney Wright's emporium (est 1905) nestling under the gloomy glazed arches of the Royal Arcade in Boscombe, a genteel satellite of Bournemouth. With its raised trays of romances and paperbacks displayed invitingly outside, and rows of rarer volumes displayed behind its curved glass windows, the shop constituted an extra-mural extension of my education.

It saw me through many periods: an early fascination with the Napoleonic Wars; a later diversion into Art Nouveau; and a mature (if that's the right word) obsession with the 1920s aesthetes. While deeply engaged on a biography of Stephen Tennant - brightest of the Bright Young Things, lover to Siegfried Sassoon and latterly a decorative recluse - I was delving one day in the bowels of the shop's basement. A slim black-and-white chequerboard bound book virtually fell into my hands: *The White Wallet*, a 1928 compendium of a verse put together by Stephen's mother, Pamela Glenconner (a Wyndham 'Soul', and one of Sargent's Three Graces), illustrated with Beardsleyesque line drawings by her fey and precocious young son. I have never seen this book before or since, and it has provided elegant vignettes for my first published book, *Serious Pleasures*, I can only contend that Stephen Tennant's spirit guided me to that shelf.

It is the phenomenon experienced by the sort of biographer who seeks a certain empathy with his or her subject; Margaret Forster once told me how Daphne du Maurier's *Rebecca* had practically leapt at her off a bookshelf on the day that a letter arrived inviting her to write the dame's life. When I began the work on my biography of Noel Coward, it seemed that bookshops of the Home Counties - so cosily reminiscent of Miss Marple tales - had foreknowledge of my arrival and had cunningly placed relevant volumes at my personal shelf eye-level. Indeed, I felt like Miss Marple herself as all manner of obscure theatrical and literary memoirs beckoned me down complex lines of connection in Coward's life, sometimes to personal encounters. In Lawrence Oxley's shop in Alresford, Hampshire I found the American composer, Ned Rorem's *Paris Diary*; the book set off a trail which ended at the author's Central Park apartment in New York, to hear a first hand account of his amorous encounter with Coward in 1950s Paris. The same shop came up trumps with a signed first edition of the memoirs of Eva Le Gallienne (actress-director daughter of Wilde's friend Richard Le Gallienne, she was sometime lover to Coward's designer, Gladys Calthrop), which I snapped up for the princely sum of three pounds and fifty pence.

Along the coast, in one of Hastings's many Dickensian treasure troves, a life of the actress Meggie Albanesi (a contemporary of Coward's who died tragically young) was acquired for even less, and provided clues to the discovery that the apparently virginal *ingenue* had led a less-than-pure life and in fact died from a botched abortion. Only through browsing the pick 'n' mix of some dead person's effects can one come across such gems. Readers have such bookshops to blame for those tantalising footnotes which sketch the eccentricites of minor characters; whole literary circles might have fallen into obscurity were it not for the magpie habits of the literary recyclers.

It is a reciprocal arrangement, in which we customers should exhibit certain qualities, pre-eminent of which is forebearance. To adopt Miss Austen's syntax, it is a lesson early learned that a bibliophile must needs be in possession of certain patience. As you rummage among those copies of *Steamboat Gothic* (will sufficient homes ever be found for Frances Parkinson Keyes' multitudinous offspring?) take heart; you will one day find that unexpected jewel. I treasure a decadently dust-jacketed Elinor Wylie from the rambling caves of The Petersfield Bookshop (a must for anyone finding themselves in that part of Hampshire); and innumerable finds from Gilberts (est 1859) of Southampton and Winchester, the latter gloriously cloistered by the Cathedral Close.

In London, apart from the Sicilian Avenue offices of Skoob itself (which supplied the fix for an early Charles Bukowski habit I developed), Nigel Burwood's Charing Cross empire brought to light Tennantiana, including one fragment of a volume from Stephen's own library, its boards still boasting a pasted-in Cecil Beaton snap of the boy himself. It stands beside me as I write, embellished with the legend, "Stephen Tennant, Provence...for Virginia Bath and for Willa Cather with my love". Evidently, no Solomonic judgement was required to fulfill the gift to these esteemed ladies; I like to think it was Fate that brought it to his biographer's shelf, another example of the twisting, turning vicissitudes of the much-travelled, much-loved secondhand book. Their purveyors are a breed to be extolled and honoured, and this directory - begat by an exemplar of the type - shall, as their client's bible, do them fit homage.

Philip Hoare,
Shoreditch, 1996

GEORGE JEFFERY (1925-1994)

"A bookseller is a king, and a king cannot be a bookseller. But he was still too little to be a salesman"

Elias Canetti, *Auto Da Fe*

I first met George in 1974 when I was an Articled Clerk at the Bleeding Heart Yard. He was the only bookseller who knew of the book *Formosa*, a fictional account of an island of dragons. The main bulk of his stock then was Victorian publications which were soon replaced by books of the early twentieth century. Paperbacks were deemed to be minor items and scattered on the pavement amongst the periodicals. George's expertise excelled in pre-1800 publications, particularly plate-books which were reasonably priced. He was cheerful and encouraging. In the late Seventies, he was selling books at a 'dollar' (25 pence) a volume of minor books such as the Everyman Library. By 1979 when I opened Skoob Books, I had purchased over 10,000 volumes. He had a love and awe for the useful book and the knowledge between the boards, and viewed with contempt the ones who saw a book for its monetary value. Occasionally, I would offer to purchase the entire barrow during a downpour to save the books from the wet gutter when the mad scramble commenced. George understood my intention and had always acknowledged this via generous discounts. The groupies have never forgiven me.

George Jeffery III was born in Clerkenwell in the City of London. His grandfather had a secondhand bookshop in East Road, near Old Street in the 1880s. With the development of 'Bookseller's Row' which lined Farringdon Road with market barrows of books from Holborn Viaduct to Clerkenwell Road, George Jeffery I changed his method of bookselling to the barrows in 1909. By 1939, George Jeffery III had became an apprentice printer at Clerkenwell Green. He enlisted in 1942 and was dropped as a paratrooper at Arnheim and by 1945, he was a printer with the Army in Cairo. On a rare quiet Saturday afternoon, in the early Eighties, I mentioned that I was about to embark for Egypt again. George laughed, forewarned me of Abraham of El Hashish and reminisced of his motor-cycling escapades to Tripoli. In 1947, he returned to London to continue his printing career, married Mary in 1952 and took over his father's book barrows when George II fell ill. His father passed away in 1957 and he continued to operate five barrows between the Farringdon Road and his warehouse in Clerkenwell Close. George cleared the residue of libraries and collections after notable Auction Houses had selected their requirements. He also purchased a great deal at general furniture auctions in and around London. I had often bid against him without success and marvelled at the narrow profit margin he was achieving.

In 1980, the Commonwealth Institute sold a large quantity of books at Bonhams, Moscow Road, and I spent many days viewing the numerous tea chests of miscellaneous lots. Jumping down from a tower of tea-chests, I bumped into George who frowned at my energy. He peered into a sample of tea-chests and noted his valuation. At the sale, he managed to achieve more lots than myself.

The demise of Hodgson's Room at Chancery Lane, the book sale department of Sothebys, marked the end of an era. Whenever I made enquiries about lots of reading copies, Fred Snelling would refer me to George as the man. It was the only occasion my careful valuations got the better of George. Despite our competition, we remained friends and I have to admit, it was certainly cheaper to buy from him than from the source.

Saturday morning was the weekly opening day; the Jefferys would put out their recent acquisitions. It was as late as 1978 when all three generations were serving on Farringdon Road; Mrs. Jeffery, George's mother, Moya, his daughter, John, his son and himself. His son, George Jeffery IV, the present proprietor of the excellent bookshop at 106 St. John Street, was on sabbatical from the family business, developing his own enterprise. The books were displayed resting on their fore-edges, backstrip-up over six barrows, covered neatly with tarpaulin and tied. At the appointed time, which varied in the years of my attendance, George would reveal the first lot on the pavement and bark warnings to the enthusiasts not to peer beneath the canvas on the barrows. The initiated would chuckle and the wise had developed skills beyond the physical world to ascertain the quality of stock beneath. Others would run their fingers over the coarse material deciphering the required title as they stood shoulder to shoulder greedily. The clientele varied from convicted book-thieves to journalists from the Washington Post, Professors to suburban General Practitioners. The dedicated adopted various strategies to further their reach. Stiff elbows were a necessity; a constant dribble over another shoulder was soon to be imitated as an appreciation of the bargains available and the odour some bodies exuded failed to emanate from the individuals at other establishments on other occasions.

It has been claimed that half the supply of the Antiquarian book trade came from George who, as an amateur runner, linked the West End establishments as middlemen. How much of that profit the runners declared remains unknown. The escalating warehousing charge, market-stall rents and general expenses of the nineties made George's method of bookselling no longer commercially viable. The situation was not ameliorated by the harsh climatic conditions he had to endure.

At the conclusion of the first lot, priced at 25 pence a book and displayed on the pavement, the consumers would safely put aside their purchases by the wall of the railway. Often, there would be rows over the designation of a book, as certain titles would mysteriously relocate themselves to another stack and sometimes disappear totally, to the Jefferys' loss, as settlement is made at the grand finale. Then George would progress to the first barrow. This was referred to as the auction where the books had been priced individually and were of a quality that demanded his personal attention. An inspection preview was allowed prior to his opening time for the purposes of collation and to resolve any doubts the potential purchaser may have had about the item. Useful and often derogatory remarks were constantly dispensed voluntarily by the regular attendance. The general consensus was that someone had purchased a cheaper, better copy somewhere else and it must be worth a lot more. Bibliographical bullshit and useless information cut through the atmosphere of silent concentration. "That book is the one which established the time and date God created the world". On scrutinising the marked prices, one noticed comments like "Really, George, surely fifty quid is rather excessive for the key to the secret of the Universe!".

Prior to the era of the preview, George would mumble the title and price of a book and the quickest utterance of "Yes, George!" followed by the first hand to snatch it away, established ownership. Enthusiasm, auction fever and retribution were to George's advantage. Books were whisked away before he could complete reading the title, never mind the price. Many books suffered wear and tear in the procedure of sale. Boards and text rested with separate individuals, manuscripts became pamphlets and incunabula deteriorated beyond the skills of a bookbinder. On many occasions, the pricing was not to the purchaser's advantage, as it was a decision made relative to the cost. When it happened, the volume mysteriously found its way back to the 'unsold' box. Other items which suffered in condition *in transit* between George's hands and those of the prospective owner met a similar fate at George's expense. On the display of a notable title, everyone would anticipate an error of pricing on George's behalf, numerous hands would reach out surrounding the man as he picked up the book from the box. The unwritten rule was that one could only make an advance after the mention of the price. George would attempt to settle the restlessness by pushing the huddled bodies away and rattling the title and price. Hands grabbed for the book and the one which shot up from between his legs secured the tome to the disappointment of the others. Age caught up with him and how he managed to put up with such abuse for so long, one wonders.

There were times when two hands would grip a book at separate ends with George's fingers sandwiched between the boards and he would dispense equity by the toss of a coin. The more complicating situation of three hands on a book was settled in a similar fashion and the odd man out was the winner. In the early eighties, a part-time book-runner snapped up an unrecorded manuscript of Sir Thomas More's devotional treatise, *A Dialogue of Comfort* (1535) which the auction house failed to identify and George sold for less than £100. The manuscript was later sold at Sothebys for £43,000. Such was the highlight of the week for many and on the odd Saturdays when George was on holiday they would be found wandering lost around the Farringdon Road, in their anoraks, for want of things to do. In 1995, the National Lottery is drawn on Saturdays. There would be a dash from the wall to the space around the barrow and when there was not, the dedicated would hurl himself between two as George fought hard to retrieve his canvas sheet which had been interwoven between limbs. Insults and racist remarks would explode intermittently between handfuls of gems from first edition P.G. Woodhouses to Malinowskis. Elderly ladies with arms of iron, sturdy on their feet, would refuse to budge for the bargains before them. Often the enthusiasm would result in fisticuffs as the others went placidly collecting their jewels, oblivious to the tension beside them.

That was the Kingdom of George.

He leaves a wife, Mary, and five children: George IV, Charlotte, Eleanor, Moya and John.

Ike Ong
1995

SEAMUS HEANEY

NOBEL LECTURE 1995

Crediting Poetry

When I first encountered the name of the city of Stockholm, I little thought that I would ever visit it, never mind end up being welcomed to it as a guest of the Swedish Academy and the Nobel Foundation. At the time I am thinking of, such an outcome was not just beyond expectation: it was simply beyond conception. In the nineteen forties, when I was the eldest child of an ever-growing family in rural Co. Derry, we crowded together in the three rooms of a traditional thatched farmstead and lived a kind of den-life which was more or less emotionally and intellectually proofed against the outside world. It was an intimate, physical, creaturely existence in which the night sounds of the horse in the stable beyond one bedroom wall mingled with the sounds of adult conversation from the kitchen beyond the other. We took in everything that was going on, of course — rain in the trees, mice on the ceiling, a steam train rumbling along the railway line one field back from the house — but we took it in as if we were in the doze of hibernation. A historical, pre-sexual, in suspension between the archaic and the modern, we were as susceptible and impressionable as the drinking water that stood in a bucket in our scullery: every time a passing train made the earth shake, the surface of that water used to ripple delicately, concentrically, and in utter silence.

But it was not only the earth that shook for us: the air around and above us was alive and signalling too. When a wind stirred in the beeches, it also stirred an aerial wire attached to the topmost branch of the chestnut tree. Down it swept, in through a hole bored in the corner of the kitchen window, right on into the innards of our wireless set where a little pandemonium of burbles and squeaks would suddenly give way to the voice of a BBC newsreader speaking out of the unexpected like a *deus ex machina*. And that voice too we could hear in our bedroom, transmitting from beyond and behind the voices of the adults in the kitchen; just as we could often hear, behind and beyond every voice, the frantic, piercing signalling of morse code.

We could pick up the names of neighbours being spoken in the local accents of our parents, and in the resonant English tones of the newsreader the names of bombers and of cities bombed, of war fronts and army divisions, the numbers of planes lost and of prisoners taken, of casualties suffered and advances made; and always, of course, we would pick up too those other, solemn and oddly bracing words, “the enemy” and “the allies”. But even so, none of the news of these world-spasms entered me as terror. If there was something ominous in the newscaster’s tones, there was something torpid about our understanding of what was at stake; and if there was something culpable about such political ignorance in that time and place, there was something positive about the security I inhabited as a result of it.

The wartime, in other words, was a pre-reflective time for me. Pre-literate too.

Pre-historical in its way. Then as the years went on and my listening became more deliberate, I would climb up on an arm of our big sofa to get my ear closer to the wireless speaker. But it was still not the news that interested me; what I was after was the thrill of story, such as a detective serial about a British special agent called Dick Barton or perhaps a radio adaptation of one of Capt. W.E. Johns' adventure tales about an RAF flying ace called Biggles. Now that the other children were older and there was so much going on in the kitchen, I had to get close to the actual radio set in order to concentrate my hearing, and in that intent proximity to the dial I grew familiar with the names of foreign stations, with Leipzig and Oslo and Stuttgart and Warsaw and, of course, with Stockholm.

I also got used to hearing short bursts of foreign languages as the dial hand swept round them from BBC to Radio Eireann, from the intonations of London to those of Dublin, and even though I did not understand what was being said in those first encounters with the gutturals and sibilants of European speech, I had already begun a journey into the wideness of the world beyond. This in turn became a journey into the wideness of language, a journey where each point of arrival — whether in one's poetry or one's life — turned out to be a stepping stone rather than a destination, and it is that journey which has brought me now to this honoured spot. And yet the platform here feels more like a space station than a stepping stone, so that is why, for once in my life I am permitting myself the luxury of walking on air.

*

I credit poetry for making this space-walk possible. I credit it immediately because of a line I wrote fairly recently instructing myself (and whoever else might be listening) to "walk on air against your better judgement". But I credit it ultimately because poetry can make an order as true to the impact of external reality and as sensitive to the inner laws of the poet's being as the ripples that rippled in and rippled out across the water in that scullery bucket fifty years ago. An order where we can at last grow up to that which we stored up as we grew. An order which satisfies all that is appetitive in the intelligence and prehensile in the affections. I credit poetry, in other words, both for being itself and for being a help, for making possible a fluid and restorative relationship between the mind's centre and its circumference, between the child gazing at the word "Stockholm" on the face of the radio dial and the man facing the faces that he meets in Stockholm at this most privileged moment. I credit it because credit is due to it, in our time and in all time, for its truth to life, in every sense of that phrase.

*

To begin with, I wanted that truth to life to possess a concrete reliability, and rejoiced most when the poem seemed most direct, an upfront, representation of the world it stood in for or stood up for or stood its ground against. Even as a schoolboy, I loved John Keats's ode "To Autumn" for being an ark of the covenant between language and sensation; as an adolescent, I loved Gerard Manley Hopkins for the intensity of his exclamations which were also equations for a rapture and an ache I didn't fully know I knew until I read him; I loved Robert Frost for his farmer's accuracy and his wily down-to-earthness; and Chaucer too for much the same reasons. Later on I would find a different kind of accuracy, a moral down-to-earthness to which I responded deeply and always will, in the war poetry of Wilfred Owen, a poetry where a New Testament sensibility suffers and absorbs the shock of the new century's barbarism. Then later again, in the pure consequence of Elizabeth Bishop's style, in the sheer obduracy of Robert Lowell's and in the barefaced confrontation of Patrick Kavanagh's, I encountered further reasons for believing in poetry's ability — and responsibility — to say what happens, to "pity the planet," to be "not concerned with Poetry."

This temperamental disposition towards an art that was earnest and devoted to things as they are was corroborated by the experience of having been born and brought up in Northern Ireland and of having lived with that place even though I have lived out of it for the past quarter of a century. No place in the world prides itself more on its vigilance and realism, no place considers itself more qualified to censure any flourish of rhetoric or extravagance of aspiration. So, partly as a result of having internalized these attitudes through growing up with them, and partly as a result of growing a skin to protect myself against them, I went for years half-avoiding and half-resisting the opulence and extensiveness of poets as different as Wallace Stevens and Rainer Maria Rilke; crediting insufficiently the crystalline inwardness of Emily Dickinson, all those forked lightnings and fissures of association; and missing the visionary strangeness of Eliot. And these more or less costive attitudes were fortified by a refusal to grant the poet any more license than any other citizen; and they were further induced by having to conduct oneself as a poet in a situation of ongoing political violence and public expectation. A public expectation, it has to be said, not of poetry as such but of political positions variously approvable by mutually disapproving groups.

In such circumstances, the mind still longs to repose in what Samuel Johnson once called with superb confidence "the stability of truth", even as it recognizes the destabilizing nature of its own operations and enquiries. Without needing to be theoretically instructed, consciousness quickly realizes that it is the site of variously contending discourses. The child in the bedroom, listening simultaneously to the domestic idiom of his Irish home and the official idioms of the British broadcaster while picking up from behind both the signals of some other distress, that child was already being schooled for the complexi- ties of his adult predicament, a future where he would have to adjudicate among promptings variously ethical, aesthetical, moral, political, metrical, sceptical, cultural, topical, typical, post-colonial and, taken all together, simply impossible. So it was that I found myself in the mid-nineteen seventies in another small house, this time in Co. Wicklow south of Dublin, with a young family of my own and a slightly less imposing radio set, listening to the rain in the trees and to the news of bombings closer to home — not only those by the Provisional IRA in Belfast but equally atrocious assaults in Dublin by loyalist paramilitaries from the north. Feeling puny in my predicaments as I read about the tragic logic of Osip Mandelstam's fate in the 1930s, feeling challenged yet steadfast in my non-combatant status when I heard, for example, that one particularly sweet-natured school friend had been interned without trial because he was suspected of having been involved in a political killing. What I was longing for was not quite stability but an active escape from the quicksand of relativism, a way of crediting poetry without anxiety or apology. In a poem called "Exposure" I wrote then:

If I could come on meteorite!
Instead, I walk through damp leaves,
Husks, the spent flukes of autumn,

Imagining a hero
On some muddy compound,
His gift like a slingstone
Whirled for the desperate.

How did I end up like this?
I often think of my friends'
Beautiful prismatic counselling
And the anvil brains of some who hate me

As I sit weighing and weighing
My responsible *tristia*.
For what? For the ear? For the people?
For what is said behind-backs?

Rain comes down through the alders,
Its low conducive voices
Mutter about let-downs and erosions
And yet each drop recalls

The diamond absolutes.
I am neither internee nor informer;
An inner émigré, a grown long haired
And thoughtful; a wood-kerne

Escaped from the massacre,
Taking protective colouring
From bole and bark, feeling
Every wind that blows;

Who, blowing up these sparks
For their meagre heat, have missed
The once in a lifetime portent,
The comet's pulsing rose.

(from *North*)

In one of the poems best known to students in my generation, a poem which could be said to have taken the nutrients of the symbolist movement and made them available in capsule form, the American poet Archibald MacLeish affirmed that "Poetry should be equal to/not true." As a defiant statement of poetry's gift for telling truth but telling it slant, this is both cogent and corrective. Yet there are times when a deeper need enters, when we want the poem to be not only pleasurably right but compellingly wise, not only a surprising variation played upon the world, but a re-tuning of the world itself. We want the surprise to be transitive like the impatient thump which unexpectedly restores the picture to the television set, or the electric shock which sets the fibrillating heart back to its proper rhythm. We want what the woman wanted in the prison queue in Leningrad, standing there blue with cold and whispering for fear, enduring the terror of Stalin's regime and asking the poet Anna Akhmatova if she could describe it all, if her art could be equal to it. And this is the want I too was experiencing in those far more protected circumstances in Co. Wicklow when I wrote the lines I have just quoted, a need for poetry that would merit the definition of it I gave a few moments ago, as an order "true to the impact of external reality and ... sensitive to the inner laws of the poet's being".

*

The external reality and inner dynamic of happenings in Northern Ireland between 1968 and 1974 were symptomatic of change, violent change admittedly, but change nevertheless, and for the minority living there, change had been long overdue. It should have come early, as the result of the ferment of protest on the streets in the late sixties, but that was not to be and the eggs of danger which were always incubating got hatched out very quickly. While the Christian moralist in oneself was impelled to deplore the atrocious nature of the IRA's campaign of bombings and killings, and the "mere Irish" in oneself was appalled by the ruthlessness of the British Army on occasions like Bloody Sunday in Derry in 1972, the minority citizen in oneself, the one who had grown up conscious that his group was distrusted and discriminated against in all kinds of official and unofficial ways, this citizen's perception was at one with the poetic truth of the situation in recognizing that if life in Northern Ireland were ever really to flourish, change had to take place. But that citizen's perception was also at one with the truth in recognizing that the very brutality of the means by which the IRA were pursuing change was destructive of the trust upon which new possibilities would have to be based.

Nevertheless, until the British government caved in to the strong-arm tactics of the Ulster loyalist workers after the Sunningdale Conference in 1974, a well-disposed mind could still hope to make sense of the circumstances, to balance what was promising with what was destructive and do what W.B. Yeats had tried to do half a century before, namely, "to hold in a single thought reality and justice." After 1974, however, for the twenty long years between then and the ceasefires of August 1994, such a hope proved impossible. The violence from below was then productive of nothing but a retaliatory violence from above, the dream of justice became subsumed into the callousness of reality, and people settled in to a quarter century of life-waste and spirit-waste, of hardening attitudes and narrowing possibilities that were the natural result of political solidarity, traumatic suffering and sheer emotional self-protectiveness.

*

One of the most harrowing moments in the whole history of the harrowing of the heart in Northern Ireland came when a minibus full of workers being driven home one January evening in 1976 was held up by armed and masked men and the occupants of the van ordered at gunpoint to line up at the side of the road. Then one of the masked executioners said to them, "Any Catholics among you, step out here". As it happened, this particular group, with one exception, were all Protestants, so the presumption must have been that the masked men were Protestant paramilitaries about to carry out a tit-for-tat sectarian killing of the Catholic as the odd man out, the one who would have been presumed to be in sympathy with the IRA and all its actions. It was a terrible moment for him, caught between dread and witness, but he did make a motion to step forward. Then, the story goes, in that split second of decision, and in the relative cover of the winter evening darkness, he felt the hand of the Protestant worker next to him take his hand and squeeze it in a signal that said no, don't move, we'll not betray you, nobody need know what faith or party you belong to. All in vain, however, for the man stepped out of the line; but instead of finding a gun at his temple, he was thrown backward and away as the gunmen opened fire of those remaining in the line, for these were not Protestant terrorists, but members, presumably, of the Provisional IRA.

*

It is difficult at times to repress the thought that history is about as instructive as an abattoir; that Tacitus was right and that peace is merely the desolation left behind after the decisive operations of merciless power. I remember, for example, shocking myself with a thought I had about that friend who was imprisoned in the seventies upon suspicion of having been involved with a political murder: I shocked myself by thinking that even if he were guilty, he might still perhaps be helping the future to be born, breaking the repressive forms and liberating new potential in the only way that worked, that is to say the violent way — which therefore became, by extension, the right way. It was like a moment of exposure to interstellar cold, a reminder of the scary element, both inner and outer, in which human beings must envisage and conduct their lives. But it was only a moment. The birth of the future we desire is surely in the contraction which that terrified Catholic felt on the roadside when another hand gripped his hand, not in the gunfire that followed, so absolute and so desolate, if also so much a part of the music of what happens.

As writers and readers, as sinners and citizens, our realism and our aesthetic sense make us wary of crediting the positive note. The very gunfire braces us and the atrocious confers a worth upon the effort which it calls forth to confront it. We are rightly in awe of the torsions in the poetry of Paul Celan and rightly enamoured of the suspiring voice in Samuel Beckett because these are evidence that art can rise to the occasion and somehow be the corollary of Celan's stricken destiny as Holocaust survivor and Beckett's demure heroism as a member of the French Resistance. Likewise, we are rightly suspicious of that which gives too much consolation in these circumstances; the very extremity of our late twentieth century knowledge puts much of our cultural heritage to an extreme test. Only the very stupid or the very deprived can any longer help knowing that the documents of civilization have been written in blood and tears, blood and tears no less real for being very remote. And when this intellectual predisposition co-exists with the actualities of Ulster and Israel and Bosnia and Rwanda and a host of other wounded spots on the face of the earth, the inclination is not only not to credit human nature with much constructive potential but not to credit anything too positive in the work of art.

Which is why for years I was bowed to the desk like some monk bowed over his prie-dieu, some dutiful contemplative pivoting his understanding in an attempt to bear his portion of the weight of the world, knowing himself incapable of heroic virtue or redemptive effect, but constrained by his obedience to his rule to repeat the effort and the posture. Blowing up sparks for a meagre heat. Forgetting faith, straining towards good works. Attending insufficiently to the diamond absolute, among which must be counted the sufficiency of that which is absolutely imagined. Then finally and happily, and not in obedience to the dolorous circumstances of my native place but in despite of them, I straightened up. I began a few years ago to try to make space in my reckoning and imagining for the marvellous as well as for the murderous. And once again I shall try to represent the import of that changed orientation with a story out of Ireland.

*

This is a story about another monk holding himself up valiantly in the posture of endurance. It is said that once upon a time St. Kevin was kneeling with his arms stretched out in the form of a cross in Glendalough, a monastic site not too far from where we lived in Co. Wicklow, a place which to this day is one of the most wooded and watery retreats in the whole of the country. Anyhow, as Kevin knelt and prayed, a blackbird mistook his out-stretched hand for some kind of roost and swooped down upon it, laid a clutch of eggs in it and proceeded to nest in it as if it were the branch of a tree. Then, overcome with pity and constrained by his faith to love the life in all creatures great and small, Kevin stayed immobile for hours and days and nights and weeks, holding out his hand until the eggs hatched and the fledglings grew wings, true to life if subversive of common sense, at the intersection of natural process and the glimpsed ideal, at one and the same time a signpost and a reminder. Manifesting that order of poetry where we can at last grow up to that which we stored up as we grew.

*

St. Kevin's story is, as I say, a story out of Ireland. But it strikes me that it could equally well come out of India or Africa or the Arctic or the Americas. By which I do not mean merely to consign it to a typology of folktales, or to dispute its value by questioning its culturebound status within a multi-cultural context. On the contrary, its trustworthiness and its travel-worthiness have to do with its local setting. I can, of course, imagine it being deconstructed nowadays as a paradigm of colonialism, with Kevin figuring as the benign imperialist (or the missionary in the wake of the imperialist), the one who intervenes and appropriates the indigenous life and interferes with its pristine ecology. And I have to admit that there is indeed an irony that it was such a one who recorded and preserved this instance of the true beauty of the Irish heritage: Kevin's story, after all, appears in the writings of Giraldus Cambrensis, one of the people who invaded Ireland in the twelfth century, one whom the Irish-language annalist Geoffrey Keating would call, five hundred years later, "the bull of the herd of those who wrote the false history of Ireland." But even so, I still cannot persuade myself that this manifestation of early Christian civilization should be construed all that simply as a way into whatever is exploitative or barbaric in our history, past and present. The whole conception strikes me rather as being another example of the kind of work I saw a few weeks ago in the small museum in Sparta, on the morning before the news of this year's Nobel prize in literature was announced.

This was art which sprang from a cult very different from the faith espoused by St. Kevin. Yet in it there was a representation of a roosted bird and an entranced beast and a self-enrapturing man, except that this time the man was Orpheus and the rapture came from music rather than prayer. The work itself was a small carved relief and I could not help making a sketch of it; but neither could I help copying out the information typed on the card which accompanied and identified the exhibit. The image moved me because of its antiquity and durability, but the description on the card moved me also because it gave a name and credence to that which I see myself as having been engaged upon for the past three decades: "Votive panel", the identification card said, "possibly set up to Orpheus by local poet. Local work of the Hellenistic period."

*

Once again, I hope I am not being sentimental or simply fetishizing — as we have learnt to say — the local. I wish instead to suggest that images and stories of the kind I am invoking here do function as bearers of value. The century has witnessed the defeat of Nazism by force of arms; but the erosion of the Soviet regimes was caused, among other things, by the sheer persistence, beneath the imposed ideological conformity, of cultural values and psychic resistances of a kind that these stories and images enshrine. Even if we have learned to be rightly and deeply fearful of elevating the cultural forms and conservatisms of any nation into normative and exclusivist systems, even if we have terrible proof that pride in an ethnic and religious heritage can quickly degrade into the fascistic, our vigilance on that score should not displace our love and trust in the good of the indigenous *per se*. On the contrary, a trust in the staying power and travel-worthiness of such good should encourage us to credit the possibility of a world where respect for the validity of every tradition will issue in the creation and maintenance of a salubrious political space. In spite of devastating and repeated acts of massacre, assassination and extirpation, the huge acts of faith which have marked the new relations between Palestinians and Israelis, Africans and Afrikaners, and the way in which walls have come down in Europe and iron curtains have opened, all this inspires a hope that new possibility can still open up in Ireland as well. The crux of that problem involves an ongoing partition of the island between British and Irish jurisdictions, and an equally persistent partition of the affections in Northern Ireland between the British and Irish heritages; but surely every dweller in the country must hope that the governments involved in its governance can devise institutions which will allow that partition to become a bit more like the net on a tennis court, a demarcation allowing for agile give-and-take, for encounter and contending, prefiguring a future where the vitality that flowed in the beginning from those bracing words "enemy" and "allies" might finally derive from a less binary and altogether less binding vocabulary.

*

When the poet W.B. Yeats stood on this platform more than seventy years ago, Ireland was emerging from the throes of a traumatic civil war that had followed fast on the heels of a war of independence fought against the British. The struggle that ensued had been brief enough; it was over by May 1923, some seven months before Yeats sailed to Stockholm, but it was bloody, savage and intimate, and for generations to come it would dictate the terms of politics within the twenty-six independent counties of Ireland, that part of the island known first of all as the Irish Free State and then subsequently as the Republic of Ireland.

Yeats barely alluded to the civil war or the war of independence in his Nobel speech. Nobody understood better than he the connection between the construction or destruction of state institutions and the founding or foundering of cultural life, but on this occasion he chose to talk instead about the Irish Dramatic Movement. His story was about the creative purpose of that movement and its historic good fortune in having not only his own genius to sponsor it, but also the genius of his friends John Millington Synge and Lady Augusta Gregory. He came to Sweden to tell the world that the local work of poets and dramatists had been as important to the transformation of his native place and times as the ambushes of guerrilla armies; and his boast in that elevated prose was essentially the same as the one he would make in verse more than a decade later in his poem "The Municipal Gallery Revisited". There Yeats presents himself amongst the portraits and heroic narrative paintings which celebrate the events and personalities of recent history and all of a sudden realizes that something truly epoch-making has occurred: " 'This is not', I say,/'The dead Ireland of my youth, but an Ireland/The poets have imagined, terrible and gay.' " And the poem concludes with two of the most quoted lines of his entire oeuvre:

> Think where man's glory most begins and ends,
> And say my glory was I had such friends.

And yet, expansive and thrilling as these lines are, they are an instance of poetry flourishing itself rather than proving itself, they are the poet's lap of honour, and in this respect if in no other they resemble what I am doing in this lecture. In fact, I should quote here on my own behalf some other words from the poem: "You that would judge me, do not judge alone/This book or that." Instead, I ask you to do what Yeats asked his audience to do and think of the achievement of Irish poets and dramatists and novelists over the past forty years, among whom I am proud to count great friends. In literary matters, Ezra Pound advised against accepting the opinion of those "who haven't themselves produced notable work," and it is advice I have been privileged to follow, since it is the good opinion of notable workers — and not just those in my own country — that has fortified my endeavour since I began to write in Belfast more than thirty years ago. The Ireland I now inhabit is one that these Irish contemporaries have helped to imagine.

Yeats, however, was by no means all flourish. To the credit of poetry in our century there must surely be entered in any reckoning his two great sequences of poems entitled "Nineteen Hundred and Nineteen" and "Meditations in Time of Civil War", the latter of which contains the famous lyric about the bird's nest at his window, where a starling or stare that built in a crevice of the old wall. The poet was living then in a Norman tower which had been very much a part of the military history of the country in earlier and equally troubled times, and as his thoughts turned upon the irony of civilizations being consolidated by violent and powerful conquerors who end up commissioning the artists and the architects, he began to associate the sight of a mother bird feeding its young with the image of the honey-bee, an image deeply lodged in poetic tradition and always suggestive of the ideal of an industrious, harmonious, nurturing commonwealth:

The bees build in the crevices
Of loosening masonry, and there
The mother birds bring grubs and flies.
My wall is loosening; honey-bees,
Come build in the empty house of the stare.

We are closed in, and the key is turned
On our uncertainty; somewhere
A man is killed, or a house burned,
Yet no clear fact to be discerned:
Come build in the empty house of the stare.

A barricade of stone or of wood;
Some fourteen days of civil war;
Last night they trundled down the road
That dead young soldier in his blood:
Come build in the empty house of the stare.

We had fed the heart on fantasies,
The heart's grown brutal from the fare;
More substances in our enmities
Than in our love; O honey-bees,
Come build in the empty house of the stare.

I have heard this poem repeated often, in whole and in part, by people in Ireland over the past twenty-five years, and no wonder, for it is as tender-minded towards life itself as St. Kevin was and as tough-minded about what happens in and to life as Homer. It knows that the massacre will happen again on the roadside, that the workers in the minibus are going to be lined up and shot down just after quitting time; but it also credits as a reality the squeeze of the hand, the actuality of sympathy and protectiveness between living creatures. It satisfies the contradictory needs which consciousness experiences at times of extreme crisis, the need on the one hand for a truth-telling that will be hard and retributive, and on the other hand, the need not to harden the mind to a point where it denies its own yearnings for sweetness and trust. It is a proof that poetry can be equal to *and* true at the same time, an example of that completely adequate poetry which the Russian woman sought from Anna Akhmatova and which William Wordsworth produced at a corresponding moment of historical crisis and personal dismay almost exactly two hundred years ago.

*

When the bard Demodocus sings of the fall of Troy and of the slaughter that accompanied it, Odysseus weeps and Homer says that his tears were like the tears of a wife on a battlefield weeping for the death of a fallen husband. His epic simile continues:

A the sight of the man panting and dying there,
she slips down to enfold him, crying out;
then feels the spears, prodding her back and shoulders,
and goes bound into slavery and grief.
Piteous weeping wears away her cheeks:
but no more piteous than Odysseus' tears,
cloaked as they were, now, from the company.

Even today, three thousand years later, as we channel-surf over so much live coverage of contemporary savagery, highly informed but nevertheless in danger of growing immune, familiar to the point of overfamiliarity with old newsreels of the concentration camp and the gulag, Homer's image can still bring us to our senses. The callousness of those spear shafts on the woman's back and shoulders survives time and translation. The image has that documentary adequacy which answers all that we know about the intolerable.

But there is another kind of adequacy which is specific to lyric poetry. This has to do with the "temple inside our hearing" which the passage of the poem calls into being. It is an adequacy deriving from what Mandelstam called "the steadfastness of speech articulation," from the resolution and independence which the entirely realized poem sponsors. It has as much to do with the energy released by linguistic fission and fusion, with the buoyancy generated by cadence and tone and rhyme and stanza, as it has to do with the poem's concerns or the poet's truthfulness. In fact, in lyric poetry, truthfulness becomes recognizable as a ring of truth within the medium itself. And it is the unappeasable pursuit of this note, a note tuned to its most extreme in Emily Dickinson and Paul Celan and orchestrated to its most opulent in John Keats, it is this which keeps the poet's ear straining to hear the totally persuasive voice behind all the other informing voices.

Which is a way of saying that I have never quite climbed down from the arm of that sofa. I may have grown more attentive to the news and more alive to the world history and world-sorrow behind it. But the thing uttered by the speaker I strain towards is still not quite the story of what is going on; it is more reflexive than that, because as a poet I am in fact straining towards a strain, in the sense that the effort is to repose in the stability conferred by a musically satisfying order of sounds. As if the ripple at its widest desired to be verified by a reformation of itself, to be drawn in and drawn out through its point of origin.

I also strain towards this in the poetry I read. And I find it, for example, in the repetition of that refrain of Yeats's, "Come build in the empty house of the stare," with its tone of supplication, its pivots of strength in the words "build" and "house" and its acknowledgement of dissolution in the word "empty". I find it also in the triangle of forces held in equilibrium by the triple rhyme of "fantasies" and "enmities" and "honey-bees", and in the sheer in-placeness of the whole poem as a given form within the language. Poetic form is both the ship and the anchor. It is at once a buoyancy and a steadying, allowing for the simultaneous gratification of whatever is centrifugal and whatever is centripetal in mind and body. And it is by such means that Yeats's work does what the necessary poetry always does, which is to touch the base of our sympathetic nature while taking in at the same time the unsympathetic nature of the world to which that nature is constantly exposed. The form of the poem, in other words, is crucial to poetry's power to do the thing which always is and always will be to poetry's credit: the power to persuade that vulnerable part of our consciousness of its rightness in spite of the evidence of wrongness all around it, the power to remind us that we are hunters and gatherers of values, that our very solitudes and distresses are creditable, in so far as they, too, are an earnest of our veritable human being.

BIOGRAPHY

Seamus Heaney was born on 13 April 1939, the eldest of 9 children, on a farm in County Derry, Northern Ireland.

1951	Won a scholarship to St Columb's College
1957	Read English at Queen's University, Belfast and graduated in 1961
1961-65	Taught in Belfast schools and colleges
1965	Married Marie Devlin
1966	Published his first book of poems *Death of a Naturalist*
1966-72	Lecturer at Queen's University
1971	Guest lecturer at Berkeley and Harvard
1972	Became a full-time writer and moved to County Wicklow
1976	Returned to live in Dublin
1984	Appointed Boylston Professor of Rhetoric and Oratory at Harvard
1989	Professor of Poetry at Oxford

Digging the first poem in his first book expresses deep personal memories of a grandfather cutting turf, a father digging his spade into gravelly ground. This patient hard-working digging becomes a metaphor for the literary process itself:

> Between my fingers and my thumb
> The squat pen rests.
> I'll dig with it.

His early works show the influence of Ted Hughes and Patrick Kavanagh. At its freshest, it conveys a country-boy's first troubled encounters with sexuality, responsibility, and death; at its most pious, a merely sentimental affection for a disappearing, peasant-simple world. The language of his finest poems attends closely the traditional life of thatcher and farmer. He is a poet who meditates often on the depth and elemental force of the green world. Beyond the rustic homage can be glimpsed Heaney's anxiety about how he can best keep faith with the values of his tribe and ancestors while not lapsing into their grunting curtness and silence.

In the early 1970s Heaney searched for images and symbols adequate to our predicament while not wishing to become a mere propagandist. This established solidarity with his fellow Catholics during the height of the troubles.

In *Wintering Out*, the central symbol is the bog, the wide unfenced country of rural Ireland. In the bog, the "wet centre is everywhere". The difficult task is to find the archetypal centre of the Irish world as he uncovers the various layers of the Irish past, the cultural remains of an ancient race, the Norse and the Viking worlds. The two verse-form — narrow, two-stress, unrhymed quatrains which owe something to William Carlos Williams and becomes a means of drilling into the past.

North is Heaney's most politically overt book. *Field Work* contains his finest political poem 'Casualty'. *Station Island* is about Lough Derg, an ancient place of pilgrimage which includes a series of ghostly encounters including James Joyce.

Sweeney Astray is his version of the medieval Irish *Buile Suibhne*. *The Haw Lantern* has a moving solid sequence about his mother's death and *Seeing Things* contains poems about his dead father. "This last collection is Heaney at his most buoyant to date, discovering miracles at 50 and regaining some of the palpability and physicality of his first book — another twist in the development of a poet whose constant struggle is to honour his origins without surrendering to the restraints he fears they place on him." *Oxford Book of Twentieth Century Poetry*

BIBLIOGRAPHY:

Death of a Naturalist, London & New York, 1966
Door into the Dark, London & New York, 1969
Wintering Out, London 1972; New York 1973
North, London 1975; New York 1976
Field Work, London & New York, 1979
Poems: 1965-1975 (1980)
Preoccupations: Selected Prose 1968-1978, London & New York, 1980
Sweeney Astray, London & New York, 1984
Station Island, London 1984; New York 1985
The Haw Lantern, London & New York 1987
The Government of the Tongue, London & New York 1988
Seeing Things, London & New York 1991

Tony Curtis, ed: *The Art of Seamus Heaney* (1982)
Blake Morrison: *Seamus Heaney* (London, 1982)
Robert Buttel: *Seamus Heaney* (London, 1985)

1995: SEAMUS HEANEY
(Born on 13 April, 1939 in County Derry, Northern Ireland)
"his poems nostalgically recall the sights and smells of a country childhood, revealing in the recurring images of Irish potato-diggers and peat bog cutters"

1994: KENZABURO OE
(Born on 31 January, 1935 in Shikoku, Japan).
"his poetic force creates an imagined world, where life and myth condense to form a disconcerting picture of the human predicament"

Bibliography:
A Strange Job 1957
The Catch 1958 (trans.: *Prize Stock*, 1994 London)
Plucking Buds and Shooting Lambs (1958) (trans.:*Nip the Buds, Shoot the Kids*, London, 1995)
A Personal Matter (1963)
Hiroshima Notes (1965)
The Silent Cry (1967)
Our Time (1959)
The Complete Works (1966-67)
Imagination In The Atomic Age (1970)
Rouse Up, O Young Men Of The New Age! (1970)
The Flood Has Come in unto My Soul (1973)
Contemporary Games (1979)
The Clever Rain Tree (1980)
Women who Listen To The Rain Tree (1982)
ed. *Fire From The Ashes* (1983)
The Treatment Tower (1990)
Teach Us To Outgrow Our Madness (London, 1994)
Aghwee The Sky Monster (London, 1994)
The Day He Himself Shall Wipe My Tears Away (London, 1994)

1993: TONI MORRISON
(Born Chloe Anthony Wofford in 1931)

Bibliography:
The Bluest Eyes, N.Y.: Holt, Rinehart & Winston, 1970
Sula, N.Y.: Knopf, 1977
Tar Baby, N.Y.: Knopf, 1981
Beloved, N.Y.: Knopf, 1987
Jazz, N.Y.: Knopf, 1992
Playing in the Dark: Whiteness and the Literary Imagination. Cambridge, Mass & London: Harvard U P, 1992
ed. *Race-ing Justice, En-gendering Power: Essays on Anita Hill, Clarence Thomas, and the Construction of Social Reality*, N.Y.: Pantheon, 1992

1992: DEREK WALCOTT
(Born in 1930 on the island of St. Lucia, West Indies)

Bibliography:
Another Life (1973)
The Muse of History (1974)
What the Twilight Says: An Overture (1980)
Midsummer (1984)
Collected Poems, 1948-84 (1991)
Omeros (1991)

1991: NADINE GORDIMER
(Born on 20 November, 1923 in Springs, South Africa)

Bibliography:
A Guest of Honour
The Conservationist
Burger's Daughter
July's People
A Sport of Nature
My Son's Story
Jump (1991)
The Essential Gesture
On The Mines
The Black Interpreters

1990: OCTAVIO PAZ
(Born in 1914 in Mexico City)
"for impassioned writing with wide horizons, characterized by sensuous intelligence and humanistic integrity"

Bibliography:

Poetry
Lloyd Mallan, "A little Anthology of Young Mexican Poets," in *New Directions 9, 1947*
Sun Stone, trans. Muriel Rukeyser. London & N.Y.: New Directions, 1962.
Sun-Stone, trans. Peter Miller. Toronto: Contact Press, 1963.
Selected Poems, trans. Muriel Rukeysert. Bloomington: Indiana Univ. Press, 1963.
Piedra de Sol: The Sun Stone, trans. Donald Gardner. York, England: Cosmos Publications, 1969.
¿Aguila o sol? Eagle or Sun?, trans. Eliot Weinberger. N.Y.: October House, 1970.
Configurations, various trans. N.Y.: New Directions, London: Cape, 1971.
Renga: A Chain of Poems, trans. Charles Tomlinson. N.Y.: George Braziller, 1972 (collaborative poem written with Tomlinson, Jacques Roubaud, & Edoardo Sanguineti).
Early Poems: 1935-1955, various trans. N.Y.: New Directions, 1973, & Bloomington: Indiana Univ. Press, 1974.
3 Notations / Rotations. Cambridge, Mass.: Carpenter Center for the Visual Arts, Harvard Univ., 1974 (limited edition with graphic designs by Toshihiro Katayama).
Blanco, trans. Eliot Weinberger. N.Y.: The Press, 1974 (limited edition with "illuminations" by Adja Yunkers).
Eagle or Sun?, trans. Eliot Weinberger, N.Y.: New Directions, 1976 (new version).
A Draft of Shadows and Other Poems, ed. & trans. Eliot Weinberger, N.Y.: New Directions, 1979 (additional translations by Mark Strand & Elizabeth Bishop).
Selected Poems, ed. Charles Tomlinson, Middlesex, England: Penguin Books, 1979 (various translators).
Airborn / Hijos del Aire, trans. Charles Tomlinson. London: Anvil Press, 1981 (collaborative poem written with Tomlinson).
The Monkey Grammarian, trans. Helen Lane. N.Y.: Seaver Books, 1981.
Obsidian Butterfly, trans. Eliot Weinberger. Barcelona: Ediciones Poligrafa, 1983 (limited edition), with artwork by Brian Nissen).
Selected Poems, ed. Eliot Weinberger. N.Y.: New Directions, 1984 (various translators).
The Four Poplars, trans. Eliot Weinberger. N.Y.: The Red Ozier Press, 1985 (limited edition with woodblock by Antonio Frasconi).
Homage and Desecrations, trans. Eliot Weinberger. N.Y.: The Red Ozier Press, 1987 (limited edition with artwork by Richard Mock).

Prose
The Labyrinth of Solitude, trans. Lysander Kemp. N.Y.: Grove Press, 1961.
Marcel Duchamp, or the Castle of Purity, trans. Donald Gardner. London: Cape Goliard, & N.Y.: Grossman, 1970.
Claude Lévi-Strauss: An Introduction, trans. J.S. Bernstein & M. Bernstein. Ithaca: Cornell Univ. Press, 1970.
The Other Mexico: Critique of the Pyramid, trans. Lysander Kemp. N.Y.: Grove Press, 1972.
Alternating Current, trans. Helen Lane. N.Y.: Viking Press, 1973.
The Bow and the Lyre, trans. Ruth L.C. Simms. Austin: Univ. of Texas Press, 1973.
Children of the Mire: Poetry from Romanticism to the Avant-Garde, trans. Rachel Phillips. Cambridge, Mass.: Harvard Univ. Press, 1974.
Conjunctions and Disjunctions, trans. Helen Lane. N.Y.: Viking Press, 1974.
The Siren and the Seashell, and Other Essays on Poets and Poetry, trans. Lysander Kemp & Margaret Seyers Peden. Austin: Univ. of Texas Press, 1976.
Marcel Duchamp: Appearance Stripped Bare, trans. Rachel Phillips & Donald Gardner. N.Y.: Viking Press, 1978.
The Labyrinth of Solitude, trans.

Lysander Kemp, Yara Milos & Rachel Phillips Belash. N.Y.: Grove Press, 1985 (expanded edition containing other works).
One Earth, Four or Five Worlds: Reflections on Contemporary History, trans. Helen Lane. N.Y.: Harcourt Brace Jovanovich, 1985.
On Poets and Others, trans. Michael Schmidt. N.Y.: Seaver Books, 1986.
Convergences: Selected Essays on Art and Literature, trans. Helen Lane. N.Y.: Harcourt Brace Jovanovich, 1987.

Anthologies, critical studies, interviews
An Anthology of Mexican Poetry, ed. Octavio Paz, trans. Samuel Beckett. Bloomington: Indiana Univ. Press, 1958.
New Poetry of Mexico, selected by Paz, Ali Chumacero, José Emilio Pacheco & Homero Aridjis, bilingual edition edited by Mark Strand. N.Y.: E.P. Dutton, 1970 (various trans.).
Rachel Phillips, *The Poetic Modes of Octavio Paz*. London: Oxford Univ. Press, 1972.
Rita Guibert, *Seven Voices*, trans. Frances Partridge. N.Y.: Alfred Knopf, 1973 (contains most extensive interview with Paz available in English).
The Perpetual Present: The Poetry and Prose of Octavio Paz, ed. Ivar Ivask, Norman. Univ. of Oklahoma Press, 1973.
Jason Wilson, *Octavio Paz: A study of His Poetics*. Cambridge, England: Cambridge University Press, 1979.
Octavio Paz: Homage to the Poet, ed. Kosrof Chantikian. San Francisco: Kosmos Editions, 1980 (contains a complete translation by Harry Haskell of the Play *Rappaccini's Daughter*).
John M. Fein, *Toward Octavio Paz: A Reading of His Major Poems, 1957-1976*. Lexington: The University Press of Kentucky, 1986.

1989: CAMILO JOSÉ CELA
(Born on 11 May, 1916 in Iria Flavia, district of Padrón, province of la Coruña)
"for a rich and intensive prose, which with restrained compassion forms a challenging vision of man's vulnerability"

1988: NAGUIB MAHFOUZ
(Born in 1911 in Cairo)
"who, through works rich in nuance — now clear-sightedly realistic, now evocatively ambiguous — has formed an Arabian narrative art that applies to all mankind"

Bibliography:
Novels in English Translation
Midaq Alley (Trevor Le Gassick), Beirut: Khayat, 1966; London: Heinemann, 1975; American Univ. Press in Cairo, 1984; London: Doubleday, 1992.
Mirrors (Roger Allen), Minneapolis: Bibliotheca Islamica, 1977.
Miramar (Fatma Moussa-Mahmoud), London: Heinemann, 1978; American Univ. Press in Cairo, 1985 (?).
'Al-Karnak', in Saad El-Gabalawy, trans. with introduction, *Three Contemporary Egyptian Novels*, Fredericton, N.B.: York Press, 1979.
Children of Gebelawi (Philip Stewart), London: Heinemann, 1981.
The Thief and the Dogs (Trevor Le Gassick & M.M. Badawi), American Univ. in Cairo Press, 1984; London: Doubleday, 1990.
Wedding Song (Olive E. Kenny), American Univ. in Cairo Press, 1984; London: Doubleday, 1990.
Autumn Quail (Roger Allen), American Univ. in Cairo Press, 1985; London: Doubleday, 1990.
The Beginning and the End (Ramses Awad), American Univ. in Cairo Press, 1985; London: Doubleday, 1990.
The Beggar (Kristin Walker Henry & Nariman Khales Naili al-Warraki), American Univ. in Cairo Press, 1986; London: Doubleday, 1990.
Respected Sir (Rasheed El-Enany), London: Quartet Books, 1986; American Univ. in Cairo Press, 1987; New York: Doubleday, 1990.
The Search (Mohamed Islam), American Univ. in Cairo Press, 1987; London: Doubleday, 1991.
Fountain and Tomb (Soad Sobhi, Essam Fattouh and James Kenneson), Washington, D.C.: Three Continents Press, 1988.

The Day the Leader was Killed (Malak Hashed), Cairo: General Egyptian Book Organization, 1989.
The Cairo Trilogy:
Palace Walk (William M. Hutchins & Olive E. Kenny), London: Doubleday, 1990.
Palace of Desire (William Maynard Hutchins, Lorne M. Kenny & Olive E. Kenny), London: Doubleday, 1991.
Sugar Street (William Maynard Hutchins & Angele Botros Samaan), London: Doubleday, 1992.
The Journey of Ibn Fattouma (Denys Johnson-Davies), London: Doubleday, 1992.

Collections of Short Stories & Plays in English Translation
God's World (Akef Abadir & Roger Allen), Minneapolis: Bibliotheca Islamica, 1973.
The Time and the Place and Other Stories (Denys Johnson-Davies), New York: Doubleday, 1991.
One-Act Plays 1 (Nehad Selaiha), Cairo: General Egyptian Book Organization, 1989 (contains four out of Mahfouz's eight one-act plays).

1987: JOSEPH BRODSKY

(Born in 1940 in Leningrad, presently residing in the United States)

"for an all-embracing authorship, imbued with clarity of thought and poetic intensity"

Bibliography:
Joseph Brodsky: Selected Poems, trans. George L. Kline, London: Penguin Books, 1973, New York: Harper & Row, 1974.
A Part of Speech, Farrar, Straus, & Giroux, 1980.
Less Than One, Farrar, Straus, & Giroux, 1986.
To Urania, Farrar, Straus, & Giroux, 1988.
Watermark, Farrar, Straus & Giroux, 1992.

1986: WOLE SOYINKA

(Born on 13 July 1934 in Abeokuta, western Nigeria)

"who in a wide cultural perspective and with poetic overtones fashions the drama of existence"

Bibliography:

Plays
The Swamp Dwellers (1963)
The Lion and the Jewel (1963)
The Trial of Brother Jero (1963)
A Dance of the Forests (1963)
The Strong Breed (1963)
The Road (1965)
Kongi's Harvest (1967)
Madmen and Specialists (1971)
Jero's Metamorphosis (1973)
The Bacchae of Euripides (1973)
Death and the King's Horseman (1975)
Opera Wonyosi (1981)
A Play of Giants (1984)
Requiem for a Futurologist (1985)

Novels, Autobiographies, Essays and Poems
The Interpreters (1965)
Season of Anomy (1973)
The Man Died: Prison Notes (1972)
Aké (1981)
Isara. A Voyage Around "Essay" (1990)
Myth, Literature and the African World (1975)
Art, Dialogue & Outrage (1988)
Idanre, and Other Poems (1967)
Poems from Prison (1969)
A Shuttle in the Crypt (1972)
Ogun Abibiman (1976)
Mandela's Earth & Other Poems (1988)

1985: CLAUDE SIMON

(Born in Tananarive, Madagascar, presently residing in Paris and Salses.)

"who in his novel combines the poet's and the painter's creativeness with a deepened awareness of time in the depiction of the human condition"

1984: JAROSLAV SEIFERT

(Born on 23 September, 1901 in Zizkov, Prague. Died in 1986)

"for his poetry which endowed with freshness, sensuality and rich inventiveness provides a liberating image of the indomitable spirit and versatility of man"

1983: WILLIAM GOLDING

(Born in 1911 in Cornwall. Died in 1993).

"for his novels which, with the perspicuity of realistic narrative art and the diversity and universality of myth, illuminate the human condition in the world of today"

Bibliography:
The Inheritors (novel) 1955
Pincher Martin (novel) 1965
The Brass Butterfly (play) 1958
Free Fall (novel) 1959
The Spire (novel) 1964
The Hot Gates (essays) 1965
The Pyramid (novel) 1967
The Scorpion God (three short novels) 1971
Darkness Visible (novel) 1979
Rites of Passage (novel) 1980
A Moving Target (essays & autobiographical pieces) 1982
The Paper Men (novel) 1984
An Egyptian Journal 1985
Close Quarters (novel) 1987
Fire Down Below (novel) 1989

1982: GABRIEL GARCÍA MÁRQUEZ

(Born in 1928 in Aracataca, northern Colombia)

"for his novels and short stories, in which the fantastic and the realistic are combined in a richly composed world of imagination, reflecting a continent's life and conflicts"

Bibliography:
Leaf Storm, and Other Stories. Trans. G. Rabassa. London: Cape, 1972; New York: Harper & Row, 1972, 1979; Pan Books, 1979.
No One Writes to the Colonel. Trans. J.S. Bernstein. London: Cape, 1971; New [illegible]rk: Harper & Row, 1979.
[illegible]*Evil Hour*. Trans. G. Rabassa. New [illegible] Harper & Row, 1979.
[illegible]*ma's Funeral*. (Published with: *No One Writes to the Colonel*. See above.)
One Hundred Years of Solitude. Trans. G. Rabassa. New York: Harper & Row, 1970; Pan Books, 1980.
Innocent Eréndira, and Other Stories. Trans. G. Rabassa. New York: Harper & Row, 1978, 1979; Pan Books, 1981.
The Autumn of the Patriarch. Trans. G. Rabassa. New York: Harper & Row, 1976; Pan Books, 1978.
Chronicle of a Death Foretold. Trans. G. Rabassa. London: Cape, 1982.
Collected Stories. N.Y.: Harper, 1984; revised edition, London: Cape, 1991.
Love in the Time of Cholera. Trans. E. Grossman. New York: Knopf & London: Cape, 1988.
Diatribe of Love Against a Seated Man (play produced in Buenos Aires, 1988).
Collected Novellas. New York: Harper Collins, 1990.
The General in his Labyrinth. Trans. E. Grossman. New York: Knopf, 1990 & London: Cape, 1991.

1981: ELIAS CANETTI

(Born on 25 July, 1905 in Ruse, Bulgaria.

"for writings marked by a broad outlook, a wealth of ideas and artistic power"

Bibliography:
Auto-da-Fé. 1946 Trans. C.V. Wedgwood. (Appeared in the US in 1947 as *The Tower of Babel*)
Crowds and Power. Trans. 1962. Published in Hamburg.
Kafka's Other Trial. Trans. 1974
The Voices of Marrakesh. Trans. 1978. Published by Hanser in Munich.
The Human Province. Trans. 1978.
Ear Witness: Fifty Characters. Trans. 1979.
The Tongue Set Free. Trans. 1979.
The Torch in My Ear. Trans. 1982.
The Secret Heart of the Clock. Trans. 1989.
The Play of the Eyes. Trans. 1990.

1980: CZESLAW MILOSZ
(Born on 30 June, 1911 in Seteiniai, Lithuania)
"who with uncompromising clear-sightedness voices man's exposed condition in a world of severe conflicts"

1979: ODYSSEUS ELYTIS
(Born on 2 November, 1911 in Heraclion, Crete)
"for his poetry, which, against the background of Greek tradition, depicts with sensuous strength and intellectual clear-sightedness modern man's struggle for freedom and creativeness"

Bibliography:

Literature
Orientations 1940
Sun — The First 1943
An Heroic And Funeral Chant For The Lieutenant Lost In Albania 1946
To Axion Esti 1959
Six Plus One Remorses For The Sky 1960
The Light Tree And The Fourteenth Beauty 1972
The Sovereign Sun 1972
The Trills Of Love 1973
The Monogram 1973
Step-Poems 1974
(Offering) My Cards To Sight 1974
The Painter Theophilos 1973
Second Writing 1976
The Magic Of Papadiamantis 1976
Signalbook 1977
Maria Nefeli 1978
Selected poems Ed. E. Keeley & Ph. Sherrard 1981
Three Poems under a Flag of Convenience 1986
Krinagoras 1987
The Elegies of Oxopetras 1991

1978: ISAAC BASHEVIS SINGER
(Born in Radzymin near Warsaw, emigrated to USA in 1935. Died in 1991)
"for his impassioned narrative art which, with roots in a Polish-Jewish cultural tradition, brings universal human conditions to life"

Bibliography:

Novels
The Slave, trans. by the author & Cecil Hemley. New York: Farrar-Straus, 1962; London: Secker and Warburg, 1963.
Enemies: A Love Story, trans. Alizah Shevrin & Elizabeth Shub. N.Y.: Farrar Straus, 1972.
Shosha. N.Y.: Farrar Straus, 1978.
Reaches of Heaven. N.Y.: Farrar Straus, 1980.
The Golem. London: Deutsch, 1983.
The Penitent. N.Y.: Farrar Straus, 1983.
Yentl the Yeshiva Boy, trans. from the Yiddish by Marion Magid & Elisabeth Pollet. N.Y.: Farrar Straus, 1983.
The King of the Fields. N.Y.: Farrar Straus, 1988.
Scum, trans. by Rosaline Dukalsky Schwartz. N.Y.: Farrar Straus, 1991.

Collections of Short Stories
Short Friday, trans. Ruth Whitman & others. N.Y.: Farrar Straus, 1964; London: Secker and Warburg, 1967.
The Séance, trans. Ruth Whitman & others. N.Y.: Farrar Straus, 1968; London: Cape, 1970.
Passions, trans. by the author in collab. with others. N.Y.: Farrar Straus, 1975; London: Cape, 1976.
Old Love. N.Y.: Farrar Straus, 1979.
The Power of Light. N.Y.: Farrar Straus, 1980.
The Image and Other Stories. N.Y.: Farrar Straus, 1985.
The Death of Methuselah and Other Stories. London: Cape, 1988.

Memoirs
A Little Boy in Search of God: Mysticism in a Personal Light. N.Y.: Doubleday, 1976.
A Young Man in Search of Love, trans. Joseph Singer. N.Y.: Doubleday, 1978.
Lost in America. N.Y.: Doubleday, 1981.

For Children
Zlateh the Goat and Other Stories, trans. by the author & Elizabeth Shub. N.Y.: Harper, 1966; London: Secker and Warburg, 1967.
When Schlemiel Went to Warsaw and Other Stories, trans. by the author & Elizabeth Shub. N.Y.: Farrar Straus, 1968.
A Day of Pleasure: Stories of a Boy Growing Up in Warsaw, trans. by the author & Elizabeth Shub. N.Y.: Farrar Straus, 1969.

The Fools of Chelm and Their History, trans. by the author & Elizabeth Shub. N.Y.: Farrar Straus, 1973.
Why Noah Chose the Dove, trans. Elizabeth Shub. N.Y.: Farrar Straus, 1974.
Stories for Children. N.Y.: Farrar Straus, 1986.

1977: VICENTE ALEIXANDRE
(Born on 26 April, 1898 in Sevilla, Spain. Died in 1984)
"for a creative poetic writing which illuminates man's condition in the cosmos and in present-day society, at the same time representing the great renewal of the traditions of Spanish poetry between the wars"

1976: SAUL BELLOW
(Born in 1915 in Lachine, Quebec)
"for the human understanding and subtle analysis of contemporary culture that are combined in his work"

Bibliography:

Novels
Dangling Man 1944
The Victim 1947
The Adventures of Augie March 1954
Seize The Day 1956
Henderson The Rain King 1979
Herzog 1964
Mosby's Memoirs and Other Stories 1968
Mr. Sammler's Planet 1970
Humboldt's Gift 1975
Him with His Foot in his Mouth and Other Stories 1984
More Die of Heartbreak 1984
The Bellarosa Connection a novella 1989
A Theft a novella 1989
Something to Remember Me By three tales 1992

Non-fiction
To Jerusalem and Back: A Personal Account 1976

ays
er the Weather Produced on
way in 1966

1975: EUGENIO MONTALE
(Born in 1896 in Genoa. Died in 1981)
"for his distinctive poetry which, with great artistic sensitivity, has interpreted human values under the sign of an outlook on life with no illusions"

Bibliography:
It Depends. A Poet's Notebook, tr. (poetry), 1977
Collected Poems (poetry), 1980

1974: EYVIND JOHNSON
(Born in 1900 in Svartbjörsbyn, north of Sweden. Died in 1976)
"for a narrative art, far-seeing in lands and ages, in the service of freedom"

1974: HARRY MARTINSON
(Born in 1904 in Jämshög. Died in 1978)
"for writings that catch the dewdrop and reflect the cosmos"

1973: PATRICK WHITE
(Born on 28 May, 1912 in Knightsbridge, London. Died in 1990)
"for an epic and psychological narrative art which has introduced a new continent into literature"

Bibliography:
Happy Valley
The Living and the Dead
The Aunt's Story
The Tree of Man
Riders in the Chariot
The Solid Mandala
The Vivisector
The Eye of the Storm
The Cockatoos

1972: HEINRICH BÖLL
(Born on 21 December, 1917 in Cologne. Died in 1985)
"for his writing which through its combination of a broad perspective on his time and a sensitive skill in characterization has contributed to a renewal of German literature"

1971: PABLO NERUDA
(Born on 12 July, 1904 in Parral, Chile. Died in 1973)
"for a poetry that with the action of an elemental force brings alive a continent's destiny and dreams"

Bibliography:
The Sea and the Bells, tr. (poetry) 1973
A Call for the Destruction of Nixon and Praise for the Chilean Revolution, tr. (poetry) 1974
Memoirs tr. (prose)
Passions and Impressions tr. (prose) 1978

1970: ALEXANDER SOLZHENITSYN
(Born on 11 December, 1918 in Kislovodsk)
"for the ethical force with which he has pursued the indispensable traditions of Russian literature"

Bibliography:
August 1914
The Tenderfoot and the Tramp
The First Circle
One Day in the Life of Ivan Denisovich
The Cancer Ward
Matryona's Farm

1969: SAMUEL BECKETT
(Born in 1906 in Dublin. Died in 1989 in Paris)
"for his writing, which — in new forms for the novel and drama — in the destitution of modern man acquires its elevation"

Bibliography:

Works in English
Ends and Odds: Plays & Sketches 1977
All Strange Gone Away (short prose) 1979
Company (short prose) 1980
The Expelled and other Novellas 1980
Rockaby and Other Pieces (plays and prose) 1981
Three Occasional Pieces (plays) 1982
Worstward Ho (short prose) 1983
Disjecta: Miscellaneous Writing and a Dramatic Fragment 1983
Collected Shorter Prose 1945-1980 1984
Collected Poems 1930-1979 1986
Nohow On (short stories) 1989
As the Story Was Told: Uncollected and Late Prose 1990

Works in English translated from French by the author
The Lost Ones (short prose) 1972
First Love (short prose) 1973
Mercier and Camier (novel) 1974
Malone Dies (novel) 1975
The Unnamable (novel) 1975
For to End Yet Again and Other Fizzles (short prose) 1976
Six Residua (short prose) 1978
Ill Seen, Ill Said 1982

1968: YASUNARI KAWABATA
(Born in 1899 in Osaka. Died in 1972)
"for his narrative mastery, which with great sensibility expresses the essence of the Japanese mind"

Bibliography:
Izu Dancer
Snow Country
Thousand Cranes
Sound of Mountains
The Lake
The Sleeping Beauty
Kyoto

1967: MIGUEL ANGEL ASTURIAS
(Born in 1899 in Guatemala. Died in 1974)
"for the vividness of his literary work, rooted in national traits and Indian traditions"

1966: SHMUEL YOSEF AGNON
(Born in 1888 in Buczacz, Eastern Galicia. Died in 1970. Except for an extended stay in Germany from 1913 to 1924, Agnon has lived in Palestine since 1907)
"for his profoundly distinctive narrative art with motifs from the life of the Jewish people"

1966: LEONIE NELLY SACHS
(Born on 10 December, 1891 in Berlin and lived in Sweden since 1940)
"for her outstanding lyrical and dramatic writings, which interpret Israel's destiny with touching strength"

1965: MIKHAIL ALEKSANDROVICH SHOLOKHOV
(Born in 1905 in the land of the Cossacks)
"for the artistic power and integrity with which, in his epic of the Don, he has given expression to a historic phase in the life of the Russian people"

1964: JEAN-PAUL SARTRE
(Born in 1905 in Paris. Died in 1979) Refusal of Prize.
"for his work which, rich in ideas and filled with the spirit of freedom and the quest for truth, has exerted a far-reaching influence on our age"

1963: GIORGOS SEFERIS
(Born in 1900 in Smyrna, Asia Minor. Died in 1971)
"for his eminent lyrical writing, inspired by a deep feeling for the Hellenic world of cultures"

1962: JOHN STEINBECK
(Born in 1902 in Salinas, California. Died in 1968)
"for his realistic as well as imaginative writings, distinguished by a sympathetic humour and a keen social perception"

Bibliography:
Tortilla Flat 1935
In Dubious Battle 1936
Of Mice and Men 1937
The Long Valley 1938
The Grapes of Wrath 1939
East of Eden 1952
The Winter of Our Discontent 1961
Travels with Charley 1962

1961: IVO ANDRIC
(Born in Dolac, Travnik in 1892)
"for the epic force with which he has traced themes and depicted human destinies from his country's history"

1960: SAINT-JOHN PERSE
(Born in 1887 in France. Settled in the United States)
"for the soaring flight and the evocative imagery of his poetry, which in a vi[illegible]ionary fashion reflects the conditions [illegible]r times"

1959: SALVATORE QUASIMODO
(Born in 1901 in Syracuse. Died in 1968)
"for his lyrical poetry, which with classical fire expresses the tragic experience of life in our own times"

Bibliography:
The Selected Writings of Salvatore Quasimodo (1960)
Selected Poems (1965)

1958: BORIS LEONIDOVICH PASTERNAK
(Born in 1890 in Moscow. Died in 1960) Refusal of Prize.
"for his important achievement both in contemporary lyrical poetry and in the field of the great Russian epic tradition"

1957: ALBERT CAMUS
(Born in 1913 in Algeria. Died in 1960. Went to France at the age of twenty-five)
"for his important literary production, which with clearsighted earnestness illuminates the problems of the human conscience in our times"

1956: JUAN RAMÓN JIMÉNEZ
(Born in 1881 in Moguer. Died in 1958. Settled in Puerto Rico in 1951)
"for his lyrical poetry, which in the Spanish language constitutes an example of high spirit and artistic purity"

1955: HALLDÓR KILJAN LAXNESS
(Born in 1902 in Reykjavik, Iceland. Travelled and lived abroad, mainly in Europe)
"for his vivid epic power, which has renewed the great narrative art of Iceland"

1954: ERNEST HEMINGWAY
(Born in 1898 in Oak Park, Illinois. Died in 1961)
"for his powerful mastery of the art of storytelling, most recently displayed in The Old Man and the Sea, and for his influence on contemporary style"

Bibliography:
The Sun Also Rises 1926
Men Without Women 1927
A Farewell to Arms 1929
The Fifth Column and the First Forty-Nine Stories 1938
For Whom the Bell Tolls 1940
In Our Time 1942
The Old Man and the Sea 1952

1953: SIR WINSTON LEONARD SPENCER CHURCHILL
(Born in 1874 in Britain. Died in 1965)
"for his mastery of historical and biographical description as well as for brilliant oratory in defending exalted human values"

Bibliography:
The Story of the Malakand Field Force 1898 (Campaign report)
The River War 1899 (Campaign report)
Savrola 1900 (novel)
Lord Randolph Churchill 1906 (biography of his father)
The World Crisis 1923-29
My Early Life 1930
Biography of the Duke of Marlborough 1933-38
Great Contemporaries 1937
The Unrelenting Struggle 1942 (Speech)
The Dawn of Liberation 1945 (Speech)
Victory 1946 (Speech)
Painting as Pastime 1948
Memoirs of the Second World War 1948-1953/54
A History of the English-speaking Peoples 1956-58

1952: FRANÇOIS MAURIAC
(Born in 1885 in Bordeaux. Died in 1970)
"for the deep spiritual insight and the artistic intensity with which he has in his novels penetrated the drama of human life"

1951: PÄR FABIAN LAGERKVIST
(Born in 1891 in Sweden. Died in 1974). Lived mainly in France and Italy.
"for the artistic vigour and true independence of mind with which he endeavours in his poetry to find answers to the eternal questions confronting mankind"

1950: BERTRAND ARTHUR WILLIAM RUSSELL
(Born in 1872 in Trelleck, Wales. Died in 1970)
"in recognition of his varied and significant writings, in which he champions humanitarian ideals and freedom of thought"

Bibliography:
The Principles of Mathematics 1903
Introduction to Mathematical Philosophy 1919
History of Western Philosophy 1946
Autobiography 1872-1944 (2 volumes) 1968 and 1968

1949: WILLIAM FAULKNER
(Born in 1897 in USA. Died in 1962)
"for his powerful and artistically unique contribution to the modern American novel"

Bibliography:
The Sound and the Fury 1929
Sanctuary 1931
Requiem For A Nun 1951
Light in August 1932
Absalom, Absalom! 1936
Intruder In the Dust 1948
The Hamlet 1940
The Town 1957
The Mansion 1959
The Reivers 1962

1948: THOMAS STEARNS ELIOT
(Born in 1888 in St. Louis, Missouri. Settled in England and became a British citizen. Died in 1965)
"for his outstanding, pioneer contribution to present-day poetry"

Bibliography:
Prufrock 1917
The Waste Land 1922
Ash Wednesday 1930
Murder in the Cathedral 1935
The Family Reunion 1939
Four Quartets 1943
Notes towards the Definition of Culture 1948
The Cocktail Party 1949
The Confidential Clerk 1954
The Elder Statesman 1959
Collected Poems 1909-62 1963

1947: ANDRÉ GIDE
(Born in 1869. Died in 1951)
"for his comprehensive and artistically significant writings, in which human problems and conditions have been presented with a fearless love of truth and keen psychological insight"

1946: HERMANN HESSE
(Born on 2 July, 1877 in Calw, Black Forest. Settled in Switzerland in 1912. Died in 1962)
"for his inspired writings which, while growing in boldness and penetration, exemplify the classical humanitarian ideals and high qualities of style"

Bibliography:
Peter Camenzind 1904
Knulp 1915
Demian 1919
Siddhartha 1922
Steppenwolf 1927
The Journey to the East 1932
Reminiscences 1937
Magister Ludi 1943
War and Peace 1946

1945: GABRIELA MISTRAL
(Born in 1889 in Vicuña, Chile. Died in 1957)
"for her lyric poetry which, inspired by powerful emotions, has made her name a symbol of the idealistic aspirations of the entire Latin American world"

1944: JOHANNES V. JENSEN
(Born on 20 January,1873 in North Jutland. Died in 1950)
"for the rare strength and fertility of his poetic imagination, with which is combined an intellectual curiosity of wide scope and a bold, freshly creative style"

1940-1943: Second World War. Prizes not awarded.

1939: FRANS EEMIL SILLANPÄÄ
(Born on 16 September, 1888 in the Hämeenkyrö Parish of Finland. Died in 1964)
"for his deep comprehension and exquisite art in painting the nature of his country and the life of its peasants in their mutual relations"

1938: PEARL S. BUCK
(Born in 1892 in Hillsboro, West Virginia. Died in 1973)
"for her rich and truly epic descriptions of peasant life in China and for her biographical masterpieces"

Bibliography:
East Wind, West Wind 1930
Good Earth 1931
Sons 1932
The First Wife and Other Stories 1933
All Men are Brothers 1933
The Mother 1934
A House Divided 1935
The Exile and Fighting Angel 1936
This Proud Heart 1938
The Spirit and the Flesh 1944
The Child Who Never Grew 1950
The Time Is Now 1967

1937: ROGER MARTIN DU GARD
(Born in 1881 in Neuilly-sur-Seine. Died in 1958)
"for the artistic vigour and truthfulness with which he has pictured human contrasts as well as some fundamental aspects of contemporary life in the series of novels entitled Les Thibault"

1936: EUGENE GLADSTONE O'NEILL
(Born on 16 October, 1888 in New York City. Died in 1953.)
"for the power, honesty, and deep-felt emotions of his dramatic works, which embody an original concept of tragedy"

Bibliography:
Bound East for Cardiff 1914
Before Breakfast 1916
The Long Voyage Home 1917
In the Zone 1917
The Moon of the Caribbees 1917
Ile 1917
The Rope 1918
Beyond the Horizon 1918
The Dreamy Kid 1918
Where the Cross is Made 1918
The Straw 1919
Gold 1920
Anna Christie 1920
The Emperor Jones 1920
Diff'rent 1920
The First Man 1921
The Fountain 1921-22
The Hairy Ape 1921
Welded 1922
All God's Chillun Got Wings 1923
Desire Under the Elms 1924
Marco Millions 1923-25
The Great God Brown 1925
Lazarus Laughed 1926
Strange Interlude 1926-27
Dynamo 1928

Mourning Becomes Electra 1929-31
Ah, Wilderness 1932
Days Without End 1932-33
The Iceman Cometh 1946
A Moon for the Misbegotten 1952
Long Day's Journey into Night (posth. 1956)
Hughie (posth. 1959)
A Touch of the Poet (posth. 1958)
More Stately Mansions (posth. 1962)

1935: Prize not awarded.

1934: LUIGI PIRANDELLO
(Born in 1867 in Girgenti, Sicily. Died in 1936)
"for his bold and ingenious revival of dramatic and scenic art"

1933: IVAN ALEKSEEVICH BUNIN
(Born in 1870 in Vorónezh. Emigrated to France in 1920. Died in 1953)
"for the strict artistry with which he has carried on the classical Russian traditions in prose writing"

1932: JOHN GALSWORTHY
(Born in 1867 in Britain. Died in 1933)
"for his distinguished art of narration, which takes its highest form in The Forsyte Saga"

Bibliography:
The Island Pharisees 1904
The Forsyte Saga 1906
The Silver Box 1906
Strife 1909
Justice 1910
The Mob 1914
The Skin Game 1920
The Man of Property
In Chancery 1920
To Let 1921
A Modern Comedy, The White Monkey 1924
The Silver Spoon 1926
Swan Song 1928
A Silent Wooing 1927
Passersby 1927
On Forsyte Change 1930

1931: ERIK AXEL KARLFELDT
(Born in 1864 in Karlbo. Died in 1931)
"the poetry of Erik Axel Karlfeldt"

1930: SINCLAIR LEWIS
(Born in 1885 in Minnesota. Since 1942, he has lived mainly in Europe. Died in 1951)
"for his vigorous and graphic art of description and his ability to create, with wit and humour, new types of characters"

Bibliography:
Our Mr. Wrenn
The Trail of the Hawk
The Job
The Innocents and
Free Air
} Published between 1914 and 1919
Main Street 1920
Babbitt 1922
Arrowsmith 1925
Mantrap 1926
Elmer Gantry 1927
The Man Who Knew Coolidge 1928
Dodsworth 1929
Ann Vickers 1933
It Can't Happen Here 1935
The Prodigal Parents 1938
Gideon Planish 1943
Cass Timberlane 1945
Kingsblood Royal 1947
The God-Seeker 1949
World So Wide 1951
From Main Street to Stockholm: Letters of Sinclair Lewis 1919-1930 1952

1929: THOMAS MANN
(Born on 6 June, 1875 in Lübeck. Died in 1955).
"principally for his great novel, Buddenbrooks, which has won steadily increased recognition as one of the classic works of contemporary literature"

1928: SIGRID UNDSET
(Born in 1882 in Kallundborg. Lived in Lillehammer since 1919. Died in 1949)
"principally for her powerful descriptions of Northern life during the Middle Ages"

1927: HENRI BERGSON
(Born in 1859. Died in 1941)
"in recognition of his rich and vitalizing ideas and the brilliant skill with which they have been presented"

1926: GRAZIA DELEDDA
(Born in 1875 in Nuoro, Sardinia. Died in 1936)
"for her idealistically inspired writings which with plastic clarity picture the life on her native island and with depth and sympathy deal with human problems in general"

1925: GEORGE BERNARD SHAW
(Born in 1856 in Dublin. Died in 1950)
"for his work which is marked by both idealism and humanity, its stimulating satire often being infused with a singular poetic beauty"

Bibliography:
Plays Pleasant and Unpleasant 1898
Candida 1898
Caesar and Cleopatra 1901
Man and Superman 1903
Major Barbara 1905
The Doctor's Dilemma 1906
Androcles and the Lion 1912
Pygmalion 1912
Back to Methuselah 1921
Saint Joan 1923

1924: WLADYSLAW STANISLAW REYMONT
(Born on 6 May, 1868 in Kobielo, Poland. Died in 1925)
"for his great national epic, The Peasants"

1923: WILLIAM BUTLER YEATS
(Born in 1865 in Dublin. Died in 1939).
"for his always inspired poetry, which in a highly artistic form gives expression to the spirit of a whole nation"

Bibliography:
The Countess Cathleen 1892
The Land of Heart's Desire 1894
Cathleen ni Houlihan 1902
The King's Threshold 1904
Deirdre 1907
The Wild Swans at Coole 1919
Michael Robartes and the Dancer 1921
The Tower 1928
The Winding Stair and Other Poems 1933
Last Poems and Plays 1940

1922: JACINTO BENAVENTE
(Born in 1866 in Madrid. Died in 1954)
"for the happy manner in which he has continued the illustrious traditions of the Spanish drama"

1921: ANATOLE FRANCE
(Born in 1844. Died in 1924)
"in recognition of his brilliant literary achievements, which are characterized by nobility of style, magnanimous human sympathy, charm, and a true French temper"

1920: KNUT PEDERSEN HAMSUN
(Born in 1860 in Lom, Norway. Died in 1952)
"for his monumental work, Growth of the Soil"

1919: CARL FRIEDRICH GEORG SPITTELER
(Born on 24 April, 1845 in Liestal, Canton of Baselland. Died in 1924)
"in special appreciation of his epic, Olympischer Frühling"

1918: Prize not awarded.

1917: KARL ADOLPH GJELLERUP
(Born on 2 June, 1857 in Roholte, Praestö. Died in 1919)
"for his varied and rich poetry, which is inspired by lofty ideals"

1917: HENRIK PONTOPPIDAN
(Born on 24 July, 1857 in Fredericia. Died in 1943)
"for his authentic descriptions of present-day life in Denmark"

1916: CARL GUSTAF VERNER VON HEIDENSTAM
(Born in 1859. Died in 1940)
"in recognition of his significance as the leading representative of a new era in our literature"

1915: ROMAIN ROLLAND
(Born on 29 January, 1866 in Nièvre. Died in 1945)
"as a tribute to the lofty idealism of his literary production and to the sympathy and love of truth with which he has described different types of human beings"

1914: Prize not awarded.

1913: RABINDRANATH TAGORE
(Born in 1861. Died in 1941)
"because of his profoundly sensitive, fresh, and beautiful verse, by which, with consummate skill, he has made his poetic thought, expressed in his own English words, a part of the literature of the West"

Bibliography:
Manasi (The Ideal One) 1890
Sonar Tari (The Golden Boat) 1894
Gitanjali (Song Offerings) 1910
Gitimalya (Wreath of Songs) 1914
Balaka (The Flight of Cranes) 1916
The Gardner 1913
Fruit-Fathering 1916
The Fugitive 1921
Gitanjali: Song Offerings 1912
Raja (The King of the Dark Chamber) 1910
Dakghar (The Post Office) 1912
Achalayatan (The Immovable) 1912
Muktadhara (The Waterfall) 1922
Raktakaravi (Red Oleandes) 1926
Gora 1910
Ghare-Baire (The Home and the World) 1916
Yogayog (Crosscurrents) 1929

1912: GERHART JOHANN ROBERT HAUPTMANN
(Born on 15 November, 1862 in Bad Obersalzbrunn. Died in 1946)
"primarily in recognition of his fruitful, varied, and outstanding production in the realm of dramatic art"

1911: MAURICE POLYDORE MARIE BERNHARD MAETERLINCK
(Born in 1862 in Ghent, Belgium. Died in 1949)
"in appreciation of his many-sided literary activities and especially of his dramatic works, which are distinguished by a wealth of imagination and by a poetic fancy which reveal, sometimes in the guise of a fairy tale, a deep inspiration, while in a mysterious way they appeal to the readers' own feelings and stimulate their imaginations"

1910: PAUL JOHANN LUDWIG HEYSE
(Born on 15 March, 1830 in Berlin. Died in 1914)
"as a tribute to the consummate artistry, permeated with idealism, which he has demonstrated during his long productive career as a lyric poet, dramatist, novelist, and writer of world-renowned short stories"

1909: SELMA OTTILIANA LOVISA LAGERLÖF
(Born in 1858 in Östra Emterwik, Värmland, Sweden. Died in 1940)
"in appreciation of the lofty idealism, vivid imagination, and spiritual perception that characterize her writings"

1908: RUDOLF CHRISTOPH EUCKEN
(Born in 1846 in Aurich, Germany. Died in 1926)
"in recognition of his earnest search for truth, his penetrating power of thought, his wide range of vision, and the warmth and strength of presentation with which in his numerous works he has vindicated and developed an idealistic philosophy of life"

1907: RUDYARD KIPLING
(Born in 1865 in Bombay. Died in 1936)
"in consideration of the power of observation, originality of imagination, virility of ideas, and remarkable talent for narration which characterize the creations of this world-famous author"

Bibliography:
Departmental Ditties 1886
Plain Tales from the Hills 1888
Soldiers Three 1888
Barrack Room Ballads 1892
Jungle Book 1894
The Second Jungle Book 1895
The Seven Seas 1896
Captains Courageous 1897
The Day's Work 1898
Stalky and Co. 1899
Kim 1901
Just So Stories 1902
Trafficks and Discoveries 1904
Puck of Pook's Hill 1906

Actions and Reactions 1909
Debits and Credits 1926
Thy Servant a Dog 1930
Limits and Renewals 1932

1906: GIOSUÈ CARDUCCI
(Born in 1835 in Val di Castello, near Pisa. Died in 1907)
"not only in consideration of his deep learning and critical research, but above all as a tribute to the creative energy, freshness of style, and lyrical force which characterize his poetic masterpieces"

1905: HENRYK SIENKIEWICZ
(Born in 1846 in Wola Okrzejska, Poland. Died in 1916)
"because of his outstanding merits as an epic writer"

1904: FRÉDÉRIC MISTRAL
(Born in 1830 in Provence. Died in 1914)
"in recognition of the fresh originality and true inspiration of his poetic production, which faithfully reflects the natural scenery and native spirit of his people, and, in addition, his significant work as a Provençal philologist"

1904: JOSÉ DE ECHEGARAY YEIZAGUIRRE
(Born in 1833 in Madrid. Died in 1916)
"in recognition of the numerous and brilliant compositions which, in an individual and original manner, have revived the great traditions of the Spanish drama"

1903: BJØRNSTJERNE MARTINUS BJØRNSON
(Born in 1832. Died in 1910)
"as a tribute to his noble, magnificent, and versatile work as a poet, which has always been distinguished by both the freshness of its inspiration and the rare purity of its spirits"

1902: CHRISTIAN MATTHIAS THEODOR MOMMSEN
(Born in 1817 in Garding, Schleswig. Died in 1903)
"the greatest living master of the art of historical writing, with special reference to his monumental work, History of Rome"

1901: SULLY PRUDHOMME
(Born in 1839. Died in 1907)
"in special recognition of his poetic composition, which gives evidence of lofty idealism, artistic perfection, and a rare combination of the qualities of both heart and intellect"

AN ABC OF BOOK AUCTION TERMS

as generally used in their catalogues by Bloomsbury Book Auctions

by Frank Herrmann FSA

author of *The English as Collectors: a Documentary Crestomathy; Sotheby's: Portrait of an Auction House;* the children's classic, *The Giant Alexander* (over 500,000 copies sold worldwide since its first publication in 1964).
FH has spent most of his life in book publishing and was the founder-director of Bloomsbury Book Auctions in 1983.

ABBREVIATIONS:

T.E.G.	Top edge gilt
N.D./nd	No date printed in the book
N.P.	No place
v.s.	Various sizes
A.L.s.	Autograph letter signed
T.L.s	Typed letter signed
pp	Pages
N.Y.	New York
(6)	i.e. there are six books in this lot (qv)
T.S.	Typescript
MS/S	Manuscript/s

ASSOCIATION COPY: One which belonged to someone of fame or distinction, recognisable because of a signature, or textual notes, or a bookplate.

BIBLIOGRAPHY: A list of standard bibliographies often referred to in abbreviated form (e.g. Wing, STC) is given at the end.

BID/BIDDING: Signal to the auctioneer that you are taking part in buying a lot (qv).

BINDING MATERIALS: (and styles) Can be roughly divided into leathers, cloths and papers. Among leathers there are:

Calf, made from the hide of a calf; comes plain, speckled, sprinkled, mottled or 'tree', i.e. patterned.

Vellum, parchment-like substance made from specially treated calf hide.

Niger, goatskin.

Morocco, leather made of Moroccan goat hide.

Sheep (contemporary), a soft sheepskin often used in the seventeenth-century.

Parchment, split sheepskin.

Roan, a soft form of sheepskin of poor lasting quality.

Japan Vellum, a strong paper made in Japan that looks like vellum.

Cloth (Binders) ('original'), covers a multitude of different grade textile materials used both in hand and machine-binding.

Buckram, tough linen cloth with a pleasant finish (much used by the earlier private presses).

Half Cloth, when spine and corners are cloth and the rest of the binding is paper glued onto boards.

Quarter Cloth, only the spine in cloth.

Pictorial cloth, one onto which an illustration has been printed, usually by lithography.

Blind Stamped, blocked (qv) without gold foil or ink, simply leaving an impressed pattern.

BLOCKING: Term used for stamping of the book title, author's name, publisher's name and decorative elements onto spine (or front board) of a book in gold, coloured foil or ink.

BOOK JACKET/ DUST JACKET: The protective covering over the binding devised and supplied by the publisher. Increasingly book jackets have become a selling tool for new books when publishers' representatives are "subscribing" new titles to the book trade, before publication. They are also intended to attract the putative buyer in a bookshop and make readily available for him a synopsis of the book or 'blurb' (on the front flap), to tell the buyer what the price of the book is and to give him biographical details about the author (on the back flap) and possibly a list of other related titles brought out by the same publisher (on the back board).

The front board (i.e. the bit you see when the book is lying on a table) is an area for unlimited ingenuity in terms of graphic design by artists and typographers.

Since they came into use in the earlier part of the nineteenth century, book jackets were more often than not taken off and thrown away by librarians and book collectors: hence their relative rarity and their particular appeal to collectors of modern first editions.

BOOK SIZES AND/OR FORMATS: Book sizes are dictated by the area of the printed sheet and the number of times (and the way) in which it has been folded. Thus, if one folds a 30in x 40in sheet (called a Quad Crown sheet) four times, one finishes up with a section/signature (qv) of sixteen pages resulting in a Crown 8vo format (5in x 7½in). If one folds the same size of sheet three times only, the end product is an eight page section twice the size (10in x 7½in) Crown Quarto; and folding it only twice produces an even larger format, 15in x 10in, Crown Folio.

Additional folding results in smaller sizes, i.e. 16mos. Unusual folding produces duodecimos, or 24mos, or oblong rectangles ("landscape" formats). Other conventional British sizes (used before the introduction of metrication and the Continental 'A' sizes) in order of increasing page size are: Large Crown, Demy, Royal, Imperial.

The subject is vast and where "impositions" are concerned, i.e. how the text pages are placed on the printed sheet so that they come up in the right numerical sequence when folded in a particular way (the choice of folds is virtually unlimited) - would require an entire explanatory tcxtbook (and one is, indeed, available).

BOUGHT IN: Did not reach its reserve (qv), therefore unsold.

CASE: The trade name for the combined front board (qv), spine (qv) and back board glued onto cloth which goes round the book block (i.e. the trimmed text and illustrations) before it becomes the binding in the mechanical process of edition binding.

CATALOGUE: A detailed list prepared by experts of what will be sold at an auction.

COMMISSION: The percentage the auctioneer keeps for his effort in selling a lot.

COMMISSION BID: One received by the auctioneer from an absentee bidder.

CONDITION: If a book is still in the perfect state in which a publisher issued it, it is said to be in mint condition. This is not often the case after reading, or handling, or even long storage. The nearer to mint, i.e. the better the condition, the happier the book collector seeking perfection. However, condition dictates price.

The same title in good condition will be much more expensive than one with torn pages, a broken binding, foxing (qv) or some missing illustrations. Variations in condition are one of the things that make antiquarian bookselling fun.

CONTEMPORARY: A term that may confuse. It can be used in the context (see also LATER) either of the time when a book first saw the light of day or as of now, today.

CONTINENTAL: Foreign, i.e. not in English; probably more difficult to sell both for you and for us.

DEFECTS: Book auction catalogues are frequently read and used by purchasers who do not have the opportunity to inspect the books for themselves. Much of the catalogue description is therefore given over to listing the defects. In the case of bindings they are mostly self-explanatory and include such phrases as:

a) *Bindings:* Hinges weak, spine broken, joints split, covers detached, worn, broken, back strip lacking, brittle, rubbed, faded, corners bumped, mouse-nibbled (occurs more often than you might think!), clasps defective, spine faded, frayed at edges.

b) *Textual:* Phrases that frequently need to be used are: Cropped, water stained, spotted, foxed (qv), offsetting (qv has occurred, text leaf perforated, lacking blank, or title, or advertisements, or some plates, perforated library stamps, etc., etc.

DISBOUND: The binding case has dropped off or been removed and only the book block (see Case) remains.

DOUBLURE: A French binder's term used to describe the front board of a book, covered in leather inside (as well as out), i.e. in place of the paste-down of an end paper (qv).

END PAPERS: Usually blank (sometimes decorated or marbled) double leaves at the beginning and end of books included by the book binder to give additional strength.

ETC: A note from the cataloguer to say "I cannot go on; you know what I mean".

FOLDING PLATE: One which is bigger than the page size of a book and thus has to be folded several times (by the binder) to include it without overlap.

FOLIO: Page number, or large size of book (double quarto).

FORMAT: (See BOOK SIZES AND/OR FORMATS)

FRONT BOARD: The part of the binding you see when a hard bound book is lying on a table. Also known as upper cover.

FOXING: Chemical action in the paper resulting in brown spots and discoloration. Can be treated. "Browning", also used, involves discoloration of larger areas.

FRONTISPIECE: A full page illustration tipped in to face the title page.

GUTTER: The two inner margins of a book seen when it is opened flat.

HAMMER PRICE: The price at which the auctioneer brought down his hammer to conclude the sale of an item. You now have to pay a 15% premium additionally (so that the auctioneer can pay his staff, his telephone bill and his rates).

INCUNABULA: Books produced soon after the invention of printing by moveable types, before 1500. Learned bibliographers also invented "Post-incunabula" for an early 16th Century book.

LATER:	Used in the sense that some part of the book has been replaced since its first publication, e.g. many seventeenth-century books are found in later bindings.
LEAF/LEAVES:	A descriptive term for pieces of paper of which a book is composed and consisting of a front side ('recto') and a back ('verso').
LOT:	Numbered item in a sale. See also "Multiple Lot".
MANUSCRIPT:	(MS) Not printed: it can be a letter, a musical score, the work of a scribe before printing was invented. Prices are much less predictable than for printed books, because by its very nature the item is likely to be unique.
MARGIN:	The white space between the text and the edges of the page or the gutter (qv). Margins are often referred to as 'cropped', i.e. they have been reduced by a second trim of the binder's guillotine when a book is rebound, often shaving off headlines or folios (page numbers).
MARGINALIA:	Literally, hand-written comments made in the margins of a book.
MULTIPLE LOT:	One containing more than one book. Can be a short-cut for lazy book auctioneers. BBA uses the device to sell an assortment of books, usually on one general subject, of interest to booksellers where no single title is of substantial value.
OFFSETTING:	The (unintended) transfer of ink from one page on to the page facing it. Often occurs from a page containing an engraving to one of text, and vice versa.
ORIGINAL CLOTH/ BOARDS, ETC.	Still in the binding in which the book was published.
PASSED:	Nobody wanted the lot so the auctioneer withdrew it from the sale. Happens rarely nowadays.
PREMIUM:	A percentage charge (generally 15% up to £20,000 or £30,000) paid by the vendor on top of the hammer price (qv), introduced into the UK in the early seventies by the major auction houses because of increasing overheads.
PRESENTATION COPY:	Usually one which the author gave to a friend or acquaintance having signed it, and generally after having penned a personal and relevant message into it first.
PRIVATE TREATY SALE:	A sale arranged by the auctioneer direct to a buyer, i.e. not through an auction.

QUANTITY:	(QTY) A bundle of books, pamphlets, catalogues or other printed matter where it is not worth the auctioneer's while to catalogue more than a few items.
RE-BACKED:	Used to describe a new spine (qv) that has been made to replace the original one because that fell off or came to pieces.
RECTO:	The front of a leaf (qv).
RESERVE:	The price below which the owner will not sell.
SIGNATURE:	In the bookish sense, a section of the book resulting from folding the printed sheet a number of times; thus a book of 256 pages can consist of 16 signatures of 16 pages, or 8 signatures of 32 pages. The word is derived from the letter used in the lower margin of a first leaf, to assist the binder in assembling (or "gathering", or collating) the book in the right sequence. (See also BOOK SIZES AND/OR FORMATS)
SLEEPER:	A valuable item tucked into a multiple lot which the auctioneer has not noticed or catalogued; or slipped in craftily in order to create competition among several bidders, each one of whom thinks only he has spotted it.
SOLD AS A PERIODICAL NOT SUBJECT TO RETURN:	i.e. its sale may not be rescinded, unlike other books whose deficiencies have not been included in the catalogue description (see also above).
SLIPCASE:	Open board case, usually supplied by the original publisher, to protect the book and its jacket; alternatively, made by a binder, often covered in a decorated paper, for a valuable book with a delicate binding.
SOLD NOT SUBJECT TO RETURN:	The auctioneer realises that a lot (qv) described thus is in a pretty ropey state. You cannot take it back to him afterwards and say it is not complete (which you can do, within a given time, if the auctioneer has catalogued an item inaccurately).
SPINE:	The back of the book: i.e. it is the part of the binding that most often has blocked on it the author's name, the title of the book, and the publisher's name at the foot. It is also the part that becomes detached most easily with over-use or brittle old age and is the Achilles' heel of a book in good condition.
STACK:	A pile of books not individually described included in a lot; implies a large number.

t.e.g.:	Top edge gilt; i.e. the top of the book is trimmed smooth and then covered with very thin gold foil by the binder. This is an expensive device much used in the late nineteenth century, but now much more rarely because of cost. But it makes books much easier to dust!
UNCUT:	The pages not having been trimmed by the binder (or subsequent owner).
VENDOR:	The person that is selling the property.
VERSO:	The back of a leaf (qv), i.e. the verso of the title page nowadays contains the publishing details of a book.
w.a.f.:	With all faults. Alternative to 'Sold Not Subject to Return' (qv).
WARRANTY/TITLE:	The auctioneer has to be sure that he is selling something genuinely owned by the vendor (i.e. that it is not stolen property). So he asks for a warranty as to title.
WITHDRAWN:	A lot (qv) is withdrawn if the vendor (qv) changes his mind about selling it. The auctioneer announces withdrawn lots at the beginning of a sale. Sometimes it means that he has lost the book since the catalogue was printed!

BIBLIOGRAPHIES, STANDARD

Catalogue descriptions often contain abbreviated references to standard works of bibliography, e.g. 'Wing, STC, Nissen'. The following are some of the major titles frequently referred to. There are, of course, many others:

ABBEY	Abbey (Major John R.)	Life in England in Aquatint & Lithography
		Scenery of Great Britain and Ireland in Aquatint & Lithography
		Travel in Aquatint & Lithography
ADAMS	Adams (H.M.)	Catalogue of Books Printed on the Continent of Europe, 1501-1600, in Cambridge Libraries
BMC	BMC	British Museum General Catalogue of Printed Books, or specifically B.M. Catalogue of 15th Century Books
BOHATTA	Bohatta (H.)	Bibliographie des Livres d'Heures horae B.M.V. . . . officia . . . des XV und XVI Jahrhunderts

BRUNET	Brunet (J.C.)	Manuel du libraire et de l'amateur de livres
CIORANESCU	Cioranescu (A.A.)	Bibliographie de la Littérature Française du dixhuitième siècle
COLAS	Colas (R.)	Bibliographie Générale du Costume et de la Mode
DARLOW & MOULE	Darlow & Moule	Historical Catalogue of the Printed Editions of the Holy Scripture
DE RICCI/ COHEN	Cohen de Ricci	Guide de l'amateur de livres à (ed. Seymour de Ricci) vignettes du XVIIIe siècle
		Guide de l'amateur de livres à gravures du XVIIIe siècle
ESTC		Eighteenth Century Short Title Catalogue
FERGUSON	Ferguson (J.A.)	Bibliography of Australia
GOFF	Goff (F.R.)	Incunabula in American Libraries
GREG	Greg (W.)	Bibliography of the English Printed Drama to the Restoration
HAZEN	Hazen	Bibliography of the Strawberry Hill Press
KLEBS	Klebs (A.C.)	Incunabula scientifica et medica
MENDELSOHN	Mendelsohn	South African Bibliography
NISSEN	Nissen (Claus)	Die Botanische Buchillustration Die Illustrierten Vogelbücher Die Zoologische Buchillustration
RENOUARD	Renouard (A.A.)	Annales de l'Imprimèrie des Alde
ROSCOE	Roscoe (S.)	Thomas Bewick: A Bibliography Raisonné of the editions of the General History of Quadrupeds, The History of British Birds and the Fables of Aesop issued in his lifetime
ROTHSCHILD	Rothschild Library	A Catalogue of the Eighteenth Century Printed Books and Manuscripts
SABIN	Sabin (J.)	A Dictionary of Books relating to America

SADLEIR	Sadleir (M.)	XIX Century Fiction: A Bibliographical Record
STC	STC	A Short-Title Catalogue of Books Printed in England, Scotland, and Ireland . . . 1475-1640
TEERINK	Teerink (M.)	A Bibliography of the Writings of Jonathan Swift
UPCOTT	Upcott (W.)	A Bibliographical Account of the Principal Works relating to English Topography
WILLEMS	WILLEMS (A.)	Les Elzevier - Histoire et Annales Typographiques
WING	Wing (Donald)	Short Title Catalogue of Books Printed in England - 1641-1700

GLOSSARY OF BOOKSELLING TERMS

ANTIQUARIAN:	Though disputed, usually refers to books printed before 1800.
BACKSTRIP:	The middle section of the binding joining the front boards to the rear, on which the names of author and title are usually displayed. See diagram.
BINDING COPY:	A book which needs rebinding.
BLEED:	The part of an illustration which extends outside the normal printed area and thus obliterates the margin.
BLIND STAMPING/ BLIND TOOLING:	Blank designs stamped by the binder's tools on binding not yet inked or gilded.
BOLTS:	Sheets printed in octavo (eight pages on a sheet) etc., and bound, result in folds (bolts) on the edges until they are trimmed. See diagram.
BOOK:	U.N.E.S.C.O. definition: 'a non-periodical literary publication containing 49 or more pages, not counting the covers'.
BROADSHEET OR BROADSIDE:	Where only one page is printed on a sheet of standard paper size e.g. crown, demy etc., and does not require folding.
BROWNED/FOXED SPOTTED:	Stained or discoloured.
CHAPBOOK:	Pamphlets sold by 'chapmen' or hawkers - the comics of the 18th and early 19th centuries. Some depicted abbreviated old romances and fairy tales; other were of morality, usually illustrated by crude woodcuts.
COLOPHON:	In books printed before 1600, refers to the IMPRINT of a book when it appears on the title page; in modern times to the design or trademark of the publisher.
CROPPED:	When the edges of a book are trimmed excessively and the margins cut so that part of the text or an illustration is lost.
EDITION:	All the copies of a book printed without alteration of text or type-setting. When the same type or plates are reprinted, the later copies are of the same edition, but of a new IMPRESSION.
ELECTROTYPE:	A printing process whereby a duplicate is made by copper electrolysis on a wax mould of the original printing block. The copper shell is reinforced with lead to make a letterpress block.
END MATTER:	The last pages of the book which do not form part of the main text e.g. Index, Bibliography, Appendix, etc.

END PAPERS:	The four pages at the beginning and end of the book. The first and last pages are pasted to the boards. The second and third are the FLY LEAVES see diagram.
ET INFRA	(Latin - 'and below'): used to describe a collection of books of various sizes e.g. 12 vols. 4vp et infra.
FLY-LEAF:	Blank leaf at beginning or end of book. See ENDPAPERS.
FLY-TITLE:	An extra title-page, usually illustrated, preceding the main title page; or an additional title page denoting a new section of a book.
FORE-EDGE:	The edge of a book furthest from its SPINE. See diagram.
FORE-EDGE PAINTING:	A painting on the fore-edge, usually gilded over, which only becomes legible on realigning the fore-edge.
FRENCH FOLD:	A sheet of four pages folded twice without cutting the HEAD and bound. The pages inside the folds are blank.
FRONT MATTER:	See PRELIMS.
FUNKY:	A book which is unsaleable for various reasons e.g. obsolescence, change in reading trends etc. Originated from the ethnic jazz phrase 'That's kinda funky.'
GATHERING:	Where one or more sheets are folded and arranged in sequence ready to be sewn and assembled into a book.
GAUFFERED (GOFFERED) EDGES:	Gilt edges stamped with a pattern.
GUTTER:	The area made by the back-margins in the middle of two pages, divided by the spine.
HALF-TITLE (BASTARD-TITLE):	The right side page preceding the title page, normally displaying the title only.
HEAD:	The top edge of a page. See diagram.
HEADBAND:	A cord attached to the SPINE and sometimes extended for use as a bookmark. See diagram.
HEAD MARGIN:	The blank space at the top of a page.
HISTORIATED:	Decorated letters at the beginning of chapters, or decorations used to stress the different parts of a book.
HORN BOOK:	A common aid for children between the 16th and 18th centuries, containing the alphabet, the ten digits, some elementary spelling and the Lord's Prayer: In the form of a wooden tablet with a handle, the paper is covered by a transparent piece of horn.

IMPENSIS:	(Latin - 'at the expense of'): in early books precedes the name of whoever undertook financial responsibility for publication.
IMPRESSION:	See EDITION.
IMPRINT:	Information as to publisher, printer, date, copyright etc., usually printed on the reverse of the title page.
INCUNABULUM (plural INCUNABULA):	Commonly known as INCUNABLE, refers to a book printed before 1500 A.D. by movable type. From the Latin 'cunae' meaning cradle (of printing).
INDIA PAPER:	First made by the Oxford University Press, in imitation of paper from the East; a thin, strong, opaque paper used in books of numerous pages to reduce the bulk. (India Paper Editions are very collectable).
INLAID:	Where a piece of paper or leather is placed on another piece of the same material so that the two pieces are flush e.g. in renewing all four margins of a page.
LIMP:	Any form of binding in which boards are not used and which are therefore flexible e.g. paperbacks.
PLATE-MARK:	An impression left on the margin of an engraving by pressure of the metal plate used for printing.
PRELIMINARY PAGES (PRELIMS):	The introductory part of a book preceding the main text, consisting of the half-title, frontispiece, title-page, imprint dedication, contents, list of illustration, preface and acknowledgements, foreword, introduction etc.
RAISED BANDS:	The ridges on the backstrip made for decorative purpose or caused by the accumulation of cords in the gathering.
RECTO:	The page on the right-hand side. The reverse is the VERSO.
SHAVED:	When edges of a book are shaved, and some of the text is lost.
STEREOTYPE:	A duplicate is made from a papier-mache or plastic mould of the original printing block. The reproduction is less fine than from blocks made by ELECTROTYPE.
STUB:	A strip of paper on the inner margin caused by the insertion or extraction of an extra page.
THREE-DECKER:	A novel in three volumes.
TIP-IN:	To insert a page, usually an illustration, by pasting into a bound book.

TRIMMED (CUT) EDGES: The edges of a book are cut so that so that the pages are smooth and of an uniform size, as most modern books are. Some older books have only the top edge trimmed or none at all; these are known as UNTRIMMED.

UNCUT: When the pages of a book are still in their folded origin and have to be cut open. Also known as UNOPENED.

UNLETTERED: Where the name of author and title do not appear on the binding.

UNTRIMMED: See TRIMMED.

VERSO: The page on the left-hand side. The reverse or the RECTO.

VIGNETTE: Little decorative illustration on blank spaces on a page, usually at the beginning or end of a chapter.

WATERMARK: A distinguishing mark or device impressed in a sheet of paper during manufacture, usually barely noticeable unless the sheet is held against strong light.

XYLOGRAPHICA: Block books where each page is printed from a single engraved block of wood. Earlier block books were printed in brownish ink on one side of the page only. Later ones were printed in black ink and on both sides e.g. Biblia Pauperum, Apocalypse and Ars Moriendi.

BOOK ILLUSTRATION PRINTING PROCESSES

AQUATINT: A technique of INTAGLIO printing. First devised by J.B. Ieprince in 1787. Resin is applied to a heated copper plate. The illustration is then scratched on and acid applied. The acid corrodes the scratched parts of the plate, making an illustration characterised by a texture of fine dots.

COLLOTYPE: A PLANOGRAPHIC printing process where the photographic image is projected onto a glass metal plate coated with gelatine. The gelatine hardens in proportion to the intensity of light exposure forming a natural screen. When the plate is moistened, the water is absorbed according to the hardness of the gelatine. As ink and water do not mix, the photographic image is reproduced in varying fine tone due to the uneven distribution of ink. Collotype colour printing requires separate colour plates and each plate has a limitation of only two thousand impressions. It is therefore very expensive to produce. E.g. Muirhead and Gertrude Bone's "Old Spain" (1936, Published Price 100 guineas) and other Art Books.

COPPER-ENGRAVING: An illustration is traced onto the surface of the copper-plate. The outline and details are engraved with a ta burin, a needle-like tool.

Variations of tone and fine detail can be achieved by the different depth and width of the incisions, and errors can be corrected by beating, smoothing and re-engraving. Unlike WOODCUTS, it is an INTAGLIO process where the ink is wiped off the surface, leaving the ink in the recessed lines to be impressed onto damp paper.

DRY-POINT: Unlike COPPER-ENGRAVING, a tool called DRY-POINT is used to cut into the plate without scratching out any metal. Thus the plate is more delicate and only capable of very few impressions. The lines are finer and more regular.

ETCHING: (Engraving by Acid): A metal plate is coated with acid-resistant varnish. The illustration is scratched through the varnish and the plate is immersed in sulphuric acid. Thus the acid etches the illustration. The varnish is removed and the plate is ready to print from.

INTAGLIO: (Italian - engraving): where the engraved illustration is beneath the surface of the plate which retains the ink, and excess ink on the surface is wiped off.

LITHOGRAPHY: (Drawing on Stone): invented by Alois Senefelder. The drawing in crayon (called 'chalk') or greasy ink is laid down on a specially prepared stone or other PLANOGRAPHIC surface. The surface of the stone without illustrations gets wet. The inking roller is then applied and only the drawing which is not charged with water becomes inked. A sheet of paper is pressed onto the surface and thus the drawing is transferred by auto-lithography. Offset photo-lithography involves the transfer of the inked photographic image onto a clean roller from which it is printed. Chromolithography uses the same process to print colour illustrations, with various surfaces of different colours.

MEZZOTINT: A copper or steel plate is roughened by a semi-circular tool making numerous fine dents throughout the surface. The illustration is composed by smoothing the surface to various depths to achieve different tones. The rough parts absorb ink and print as black. The tonal range achieved with this INTAGLIO method surpasses that of etching or line-engraving.

NATURE PRINTING: This technique consists in impressing objects e.g. plants, insects, feathers etc., to engrave themselves. A steel roller is used to squeezed the object onto a lead plate on which it makes an impression. The first example of this process is Von Heufler's "Mosses of Arpasch" in Transylvania. The second is Dr Lindley's "Ferns of Great Britain and Ireland".

PLANOGRAPHIC: (Flat Surface) Where the surface printed from is flat, e.g. LITHOGRAPHY, COLLOTYPE, etc.

PHOTOGRAVURE: An INTAGLIO process where the photographic image is printed onto a copper plate through a screen, which breaks up the tones into dots of equal density but varying size. The plate is etched with acid and is then ready to print from.

STEEL-ENGRAVING: Involves the same process as COPPER-ENGRAVING, but uses steel plate which is more durable.

STIPPLE-ENGRAVING: (The English Manner): an INTAGLIO process where the engraved lines are replaced by fine dots, whose density controls the variation in tone suitable for copying oil paintings.

WOODCUT: An illustration is drawn along the soft grain of a block of wood. The wood surrounding the illustration is cut away and the relief is ready to print from. Its main characteristics are its greater blank areas, and its lack of fine detail.

WOOD-ENGRAVING: The illustration is drawn and cut across the grain on the hard surface. WOOD ENGRAVINGS are capable of producing fine lines and cross hatching, which result in variation of tone as well as control of perspective. E.g. Works of Thomas Berwick. Confusingly, wood engravings are often referred to as woodcuts.

BOOK BINDING

BUCKRAM: A strong, coarse fabric of linen or cotton stiffened with glue and other substances, with a prominent weave.

CALF: Leather made from the skin of a young cow, naturally light brown in colour but often dyed.

DIVINITY CALF: A smooth, brownish calf, commonly used for binding religious books in the nineteenth century.

OLD CALF: A very darkened version of CALF, usually natural.

CLOTH: Loosely used to describe (any) binding material which is not leather. It can be woven, non-woven (artificial), p.v.c. or a paper-based material with an impregnated surface.

FORREL (FOREL): Produced by dividing the split sheepskin from which PARCHMENT is made. It is thus thinner than PARCHMENT and off-white in colour.

MOROCCO: A high-grade leather, originally made in Morocco, of goat-skin tanned with sumach; characterised by its pronounced grain.

PARCHMENT: Produced from the inner layer of sheepskin, untanned but de-greased. It is thin, hard and stiff and liable to rub and tear. It is thus unsuitable for binding and is often used for writing material, e.g. Deeds, Covenants, etc.

QUARTER, HALF, THREE QUARTER BINDING:	Where the spine and corners are covered in a different material, usually leather, from the rest of the book, usually cloth.
ROAN:	A soft sheepskin treated to resemble MOROCCO.
RUSSIA:	A hard-wearing, attractive leather made by tanning cow-hide with the barks of birch, willow or oak and then soaking it in birch-tar oil as an insect repellent to give it a smooth finish.
SHEEPSKIN:	Used in binding early books. It is similar to leather but coarser in grain.
SKIVER:	A poor, thin, soft, dressed leather, from the grain side (underside) of a sheepskin, tanned in sumach and dyed. Often mistaken for ROAN.
VELLUM:	Made from the underside of specially treated calfskin, de-greased but not tanned. It is yellow or off-white in colour, extremely tough and resistant to scratching.

ENGLISH ABBREVIATIONS

A

*A.D.	Autographed document.
A.D.S.	Autographed document, signed.
A.E.G.	All edges gilt.
A.L.	Autographed letter.
A.L.S.	Autographed letter, signed.
a.v.	Authorized version.
abr.	Abridged.
annot.	Annotations, annotated, annotator.
anon.	Anonymous.
Aqua.	Aquatint illustration(s).

B

b.l.	Black letter.
bd.	Bound.
bdg.	Binding.
bds.	Boards.

C

C. & P.	Collated and perfect.
c. or ca.	Circa. About.
c.p.	China paper. (India paper).
cf.	Calf.
cl., clo.	Cloth.
col., cold.	Coloured.
cont.	Contemporary (e.g. cont. cl., contemporary cloth).

D

d.e.	Deckle edges.
Dec.	Decorated.
D.W. or D/W	Dust Wrapper .
(D.J. or D/J)	(Dust Jacket)
Demy 8v0.	Demy octavo, 5.5" by 8.75".

E

E.	Edges.
e.d.l.	Edition de luxe.
e.i.	Extra-illustrated.
e.p.c.	Editor's presentation copy.
ed., edit.	Edited, edition, editor.
edn.	Edition.
el. fo.	Elephant folio. (About 14" by 23").
emb.	Embossed.
Engs., engr.	Engraving(s).
etch.	Etching(s), etcher.
Ex-lib	Ex-library.

F

F.	Fine. (almost like new).
f.	Folio (sheet).
F., fo., fol.	Folio (12" and over).
f.e.p.	Fore-edges painted.
F.P.	Fine paper.
fac.(s), fac.-sim.(s)	Facsimile(s).
Fe.	48mo. (3" to 4")
front.	Frontispiece.

G

G.	Good (showing some signs of use).
Gt., glt., gt., g.	Gilt.
g.l.	Gothic (black) letter.
g.m.e.	Gilt marbled edges.

H

hb., hbk.	Hardback.
h.c.	Half calf.
hf.	Half (e.g. hf. cf., half calf).
hm.	Half Morocco.
h.m.p., h.p.	Handmade paper.

I

i.j.p.	Imperial Japanese paper.
illum.	Illuminated.
i.p.	India paper.
impft., imp.	Imperfect, imperial, imported.
inscr.	Inscribed, inscription.

J

j.p.	Japan paper.
juv.	Juvenile.

L

lea.	Leather.
lf.	Lettering faded.
l.g.	Gothic letter (litterae gothicae).
l.p.	Large paper.
l.s.	Letter signed.

M

M.	Mint.
m.e.	Marbled edges.
m.o.p.	Manuscript on paper.
mor.	Morocco.
mut.	Mutilated.

N

n.d.	No date.
n. ed.	New edition.
n.p.	No place (of publication).
n.u.	Name unknown.

O

o.p.	Out of print.

P

P.	Poor (text complete, otherwise defective; a reading copy only).
pb., pbk.	Paperback.
p.l.	Preliminary leaf or leaves.
p.o.a.s.	Printed on asses' skin (shagreen).
p.o.f.	Printed on fore-edge.
p.o.r.p.	Printed on rice paper.
p.o.s.	Printed on silk or satin.
pm., pph.,pam.	Pamphlet.

Q

q.v.	Quod vide (which see).

R

r.e.	Red edges.
R.e.	Royal edition.
Rebkd	Rebacked.
rect., ro.	Recto (right-hand page).
rev.	Revised, revision.
rn., ro.	Roan.
Rxb., Rxbgh.	Roxburghe binding.

S

s.a., l., et n.	Sine anno (without date of publication).
s.d.	Sans date (without date).
s.e.	Special edition.
seq.	Sequentes, sequentia (the following; the next).
s.l.	Sine loco (without place of publication).
s.n.	Sine nomine (without name of printer).
s.v.	Sub voce / verbo (under the word or title).

T

tabby.	Watered (moire) silk.
tall copy	Copy on large paper.
T.E.G.	Top edge gilt.
T.L.S.	Typed letter, signed.
t.p.m.	Title page mutilated.
t.p.w.	Title page wanting.
tr., trans.	Translated, translation(s), translator(s).
typog.	Typographical, typography.

U

unb., unbd.	Unbound.
unc., unct.	Uncut (pages not trimmed in rebinding).
und.	Undated.

V

v.d.	Various dates.
vel., vell.	Vellum.
V.G.	Very good.
vign.	Vignette.
vig. t.	Vignette title.
vo., vers.	Verso (left-hand page), back of printed page.

W

w.	Waterstained.
w.a.f.	With all faults.

X

xylog.	Xylographic. Engraved on wood. Relating to"block books".

LATIN ABBREVIATIONS

A

a capite ad calcem — Completely.

a.n. — Absque nota. No particulars of publication.

apud. — From the publishing house of -.

B

beatus — Blessed, of blessed memory.

C

catera desunt — The rest lacking, or missing.

c.f. — Cum figuris. With illustrations.

cum — With.

cum barbis — Rough (deckle) edges.

cum iconibus — With figures.

cum notis variorum — With variorum notes.

D

del. (deli., delin.) — Delineavit. He (she) drew it.

dir. — Direxit. (He) arranged, edited.

E

editio — Edition.

editio princeps — First edition.

editus — Published, edited.

F

f., fe., fec., ft. — Fecit. (He) made it. (Usually of illustrations.)(e.g. X fecit aqua forti, X etched it).

H

hoc titulo — In, or under, this title.

I

ib. (ibid.) — Ibidem. In the same place.

icones. — Figures, diagrams.

ign. — Ignotus. Unknown.

impressus — Printed. Used also to indicate the colophon.

imprimatur — Let it be printed. Official sign of approval.

inedita — Unpublished works.

inf. infra. — Below, see below.

interpres. — Translator.

inv. — Invenit. (He) designed it.

ipse — Himself. (e.g. Se ipse del., drawn by himself.)

L

lib. (libb.) — Liber(-bri). Book(s).

N

n.v. — Ne varietur. Definitive; editio ne varietur, definitive edition.

O

ob. — Obiit. He (she) died.

P

pingebat, pinx. — He (she) painted it. pinxit.

princeps — First, original; editio princeps, first edition.

Q

q.v. — Quode vide (which see)

S

sc. (sculp., sculps) — sculpebat, sculpsit. (He) engraved it.

sine — Without.

sine anno — Without year of publication.

sine anno, loco et nomine — Without year or place of publication or name of printer.

sine dato — Without date of publication.

sine impressore — Without name of printer.

sine loco — Without place of publication.

sine loco, anno vel nomine — Without place, year, or name of printer.

sine nomine — Without name of printer.

sumpt. — sumptibus. At the cost of, published by (or for).

T

titulus — Title.

titulus secundarius — Half title, bastard title.

traductum — Translated.

typographia — Printing House.

typographus — Printer.

V

variorum — Of many writers. (e.g. editio variorum, edition including versions, notes, etc., of different people.)

THE PARTS OF A BOOK

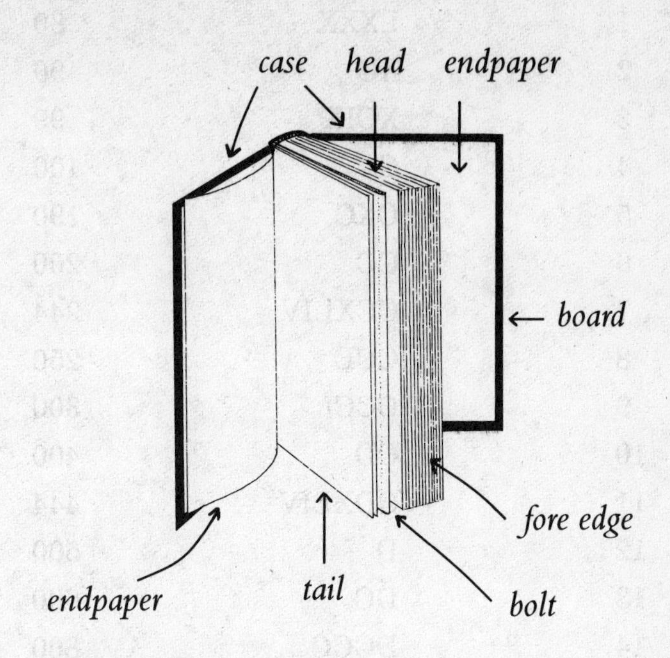

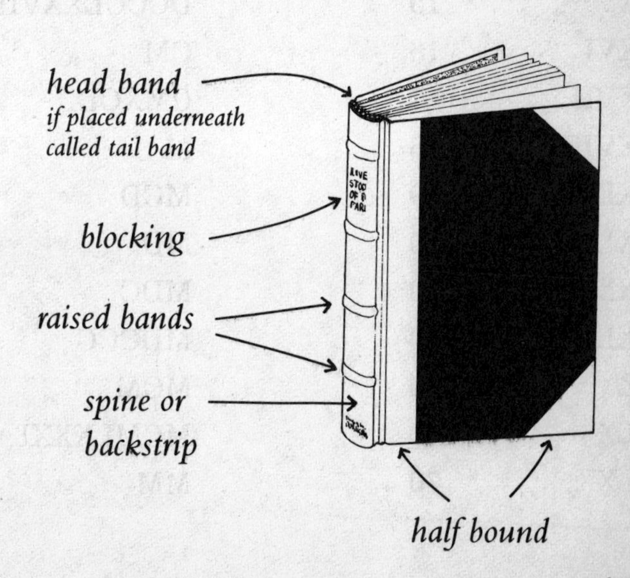

ROMAN NUMERALS

I	1
II	2
III	3
IV	4
V	5
VI	6
VII	7
VIII	8
IX	9
X	10
XI	11
XII	12
XIII	13
XIV	14
XV	15
XVI	16
XVII	17
XVIII	18
XIX	19
XX	20
XXX	30
XL	40
L	50
LX	60
LXX	70
LXXX	80
XC	90
XCIX	99
C	100
CXC	190
CC	200
CCXLIV	244
CCL	250
CCC	300
CD	400
CDXLIV	444
D	500
DC	600
DCCC	800
DCCCLXXVIII	878
CM	900
CMXCIX	999
M	1000
MCD	1400
MD	1500
MDC	1600
MDCCC	1800
MCM	1900
MCMLXXXI	1981
MM	2000

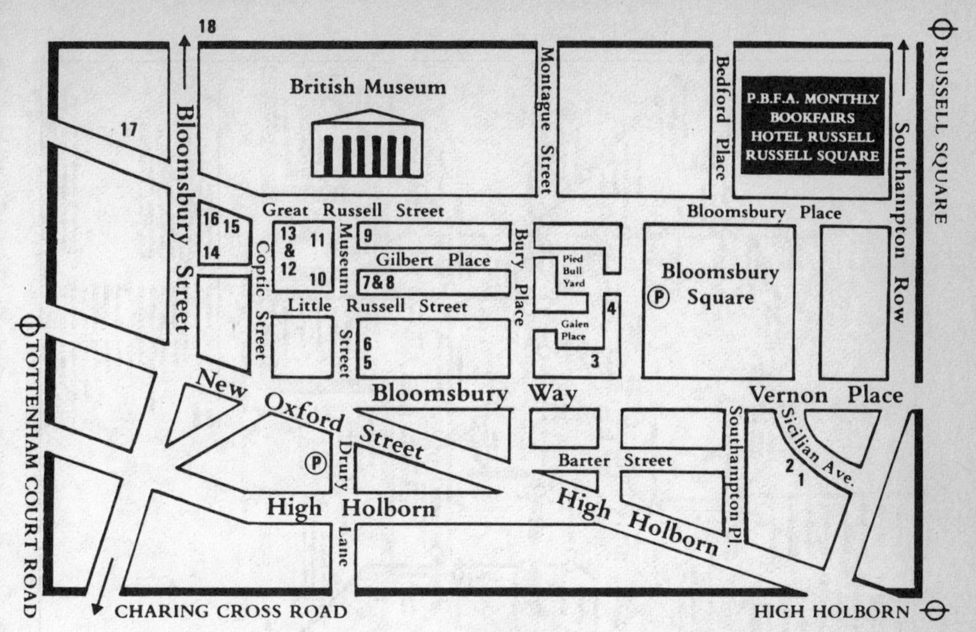

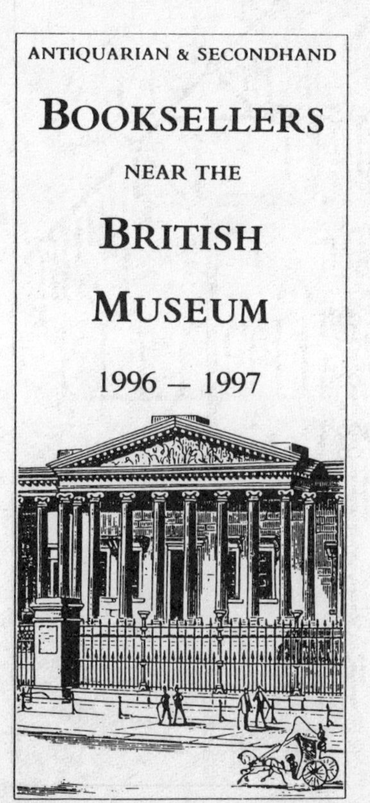

KEY

1. Skoob Books
2. Skoob Two
3. Bloomsbury Workshop
4. Gekoski
5. Atlantis Bookshop
6. Jack Duncan Basement Bookshop
7. Grenville Books
8. Ulysses - Modern Firsts, illustrated
9. Ballantyne & Date
10. Roe & Moore
11. Ulysses - General, Travel, Art
12. Jarndyce Antiquarian Books
13. Fine Books Oriental
14. Unsworths Booksellers
15. London Antiquarian Book Arcade
16. Museum Bookshop
17. Robert Frew
18. Dillons Bookstore

Nearest Underground stations are: Holborn, Tottenham Court Road and Russell Square.

There are NCP car parks in Drury Lane and Bloomsbury Square

LONDON BOOKFAIRS 1996 — 1997

Every month at the
HOTEL RUSSELL, RUSSELL SQUARE, WC1.
Sunday 2.00 — 7.00; Monday 11.00 — 7.00.

1996		1997	
April	14th — 15th	January	12th — 13th
May	12th — 13th	February	9th — 10th
June	21st — 24th	March	9th — 10th
June/July	30th — 1st	April	13th — 14th
August	11th — 12th	May	11th — 12th
September	8th — 9th	June & July	see below
October	13th — 14th	August	10th — 11th
November	3rd — 4th	September	14th — 15th
December	8th — 9th	October	12th — 13th

P.B.F.A. June & July Fairs 1997, dates to be announced.
For times & further information on P.B.F.A. fairs,
telephone 01763 248400.

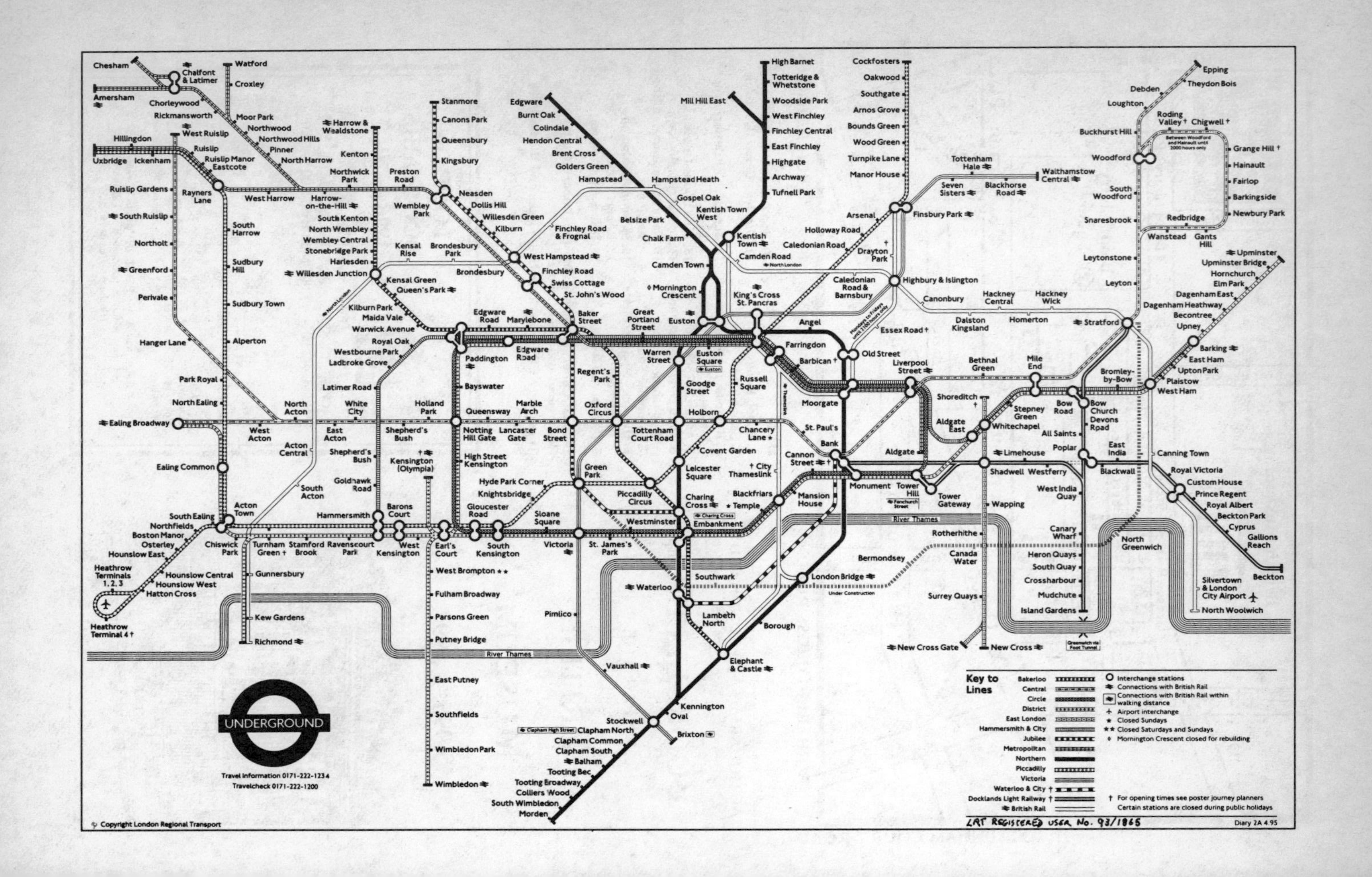

UNDERGROUND
Travel Information 0171-222-1234
Travelcheck 0171-222-1200
Copyright London Regional Transport
Key to Lines
Bakerloo
Central
Circle
District
East London
Hammersmith & City
Jubilee
Metropolitan
Northern
Piccadilly
Victoria
Waterloo & City †
Docklands Light Railway †
British Rail
Interchange stations
Connections with British Rail
Connections with British Rail within walking distance
Airport interchange
Closed Sundays
Closed Saturdays and Sundays
Mornington Crescent closed for rebuilding
† For opening times see poster journey planners
Certain stations are closed during public holidays
LRT REGISTERED USER No. 93/1865
Diary 2A 4.95
River Thames
Chesham
Chalfont & Latimer
Amersham
Chorleywood
Rickmansworth
Watford
Croxley
Moor Park
Northwood
Northwood Hills
Pinner
North Harrow
Harrow & Wealdstone
Kenton
Hillingdon
West Ruislip
Ruislip
Ruislip Manor
Eastcote
Uxbridge
Ickenham
Ruislip Gardens
Rayners Lane
West Harrow
Harrow-on-the-Hill
South Ruislip
South Harrow
Northolt
Sudbury Hill
Greenford
Perivale
Sudbury Town
Hanger Lane
Alperton
Park Royal
North Ealing
Ealing Broadway
Ealing Common
South Ealing
Northfields
Boston Manor
Osterley
Hounslow East
Hounslow Central
Hounslow West
Hatton Cross
Heathrow Terminals 1, 2, 3
Heathrow Terminal 4 †
Acton Town
Chiswick Park
Turnham Green †
Stamford Brook
Ravenscourt Park
Gunnersbury
Kew Gardens
Richmond
Stanmore
Canons Park
Queensbury
Kingsbury
Northwick Park
Preston Road
Wembley Park
Neasden
Dollis Hill
Willesden Green
Kilburn
South Kenton
North Wembley
Wembley Central
Stonebridge Park
Harlesden
Willesden Junction
Kensal Rise
Brondesbury Park
Brondesbury
Kensal Green
Queen's Park
Kilburn Park
Maida Vale
Warwick Avenue
Royal Oak
Westbourne Park
Ladbroke Grove
Latimer Road
North Acton
West Acton
East Acton
Acton Central
South Acton
White City
Shepherd's Bush
Goldhawk Road
Kensington (Olympia)
Holland Park
Hammersmith
Barons Court
West Kensington
Earl's Court
West Brompton ★★
Fulham Broadway
Parsons Green
Putney Bridge
East Putney
Southfields
Wimbledon Park
Wimbledon
Edgware
Burnt Oak
Colindale
Hendon Central
Brent Cross
Golders Green
Hampstead
Belsize Park
Chalk Farm
Hampstead Heath
Gospel Oak
Finchley Road & Frognal
West Hampstead
Finchley Road
Swiss Cottage
St. John's Wood
Kentish Town West
Kentish Town
Camden Road
Camden Town
Mornington Crescent
High Barnet
Totteridge & Whetstone
Woodside Park
West Finchley
Finchley Central
East Finchley
Highgate
Archway
Tufnell Park
Mill Hill East
North London
Edgware Road
Marylebone
Baker Street
Paddington
Great Portland Street
Euston
King's Cross St. Pancras
Warren Street
Euston Square
Regent's Park
Goodge Street
Russell Square
Bayswater
Queensway
Notting Hill Gate
Lancaster Gate
Marble Arch
Bond Street
Oxford Circus
Tottenham Court Road
Holborn
Chancery Lane ★
High Street Kensington
Hyde Park Corner
Knightsbridge
Green Park
Piccadilly Circus
Leicester Square
Covent Garden
Gloucester Road
South Kensington
Sloane Square
Victoria
St. James's Park
Westminster
Charing Cross
Embankment
Temple ★
Blackfriars
City Thameslink †
Thameslink
Waterloo
Southwark
Lambeth North
Pimlico
Vauxhall
Elephant & Castle
Borough
Kennington
Oval
Stockwell
Brixton
Clapham High Street
Clapham North
Clapham Common
Clapham South
Balham
Tooting Bec
Tooting Broadway
Colliers Wood
South Wimbledon
Morden
Angel
Farringdon
Barbican †
Old Street
Moorgate
St. Paul's
Bank
Cannon Street ★ †
Mansion House
Monument
Tower Hill
Fenchurch Street
Tower Gateway
Aldgate
Aldgate East
Liverpool Street
Essex Road †
Mondays to Fridays until 2100 hours only
London Bridge
Under Construction
Bermondsey
Cockfosters
Oakwood
Southgate
Arnos Grove
Bounds Green
Wood Green
Turnpike Lane
Manor House
Arsenal
Holloway Road
Caledonian Road
Drayton Park †
Caledonian Road & Barnsbury
Highbury & Islington
Finsbury Park
Seven Sisters
Tottenham Hale
Blackhorse Road
Walthamstow Central
Canonbury
Dalston Kingsland
Hackney Central
Hackney Wick
Homerton
Stratford
Bethnal Green
Mile End
Shoreditch †
Whitechapel
Stepney Green
Bow Road
Bow Church
Devons Road
All Saints
Poplar
Limehouse
Shadwell
Westferry
Wapping
Rotherhithe
Canada Water
Surrey Quays
New Cross Gate
New Cross
West India Quay
Canary Wharf
Heron Quays
South Quay
Crossharbour
Mudchute
Island Gardens
Greenwich via Foot Tunnel
East India
Blackwall
Bromley-by-Bow
West Ham
Plaistow
Upton Park
East Ham
Barking
Upney
Becontree
Dagenham Heathway
Dagenham East
Elm Park
Hornchurch
Upminster Bridge
Upminster
Leyton
Leytonstone
Snaresbrook
South Woodford
Woodford
Buckhurst Hill
Loughton
Debden
Theydon Bois
Epping
Roding Valley †
Chigwell †
Grange Hill †
Hainault
Fairlop
Barkingside
Newbury Park
Gants Hill
Redbridge
Wanstead
Between Woodford and Hainault until 2000 hours only
Canning Town
Royal Victoria
Custom House
Prince Regent
Royal Albert
Beckton Park
Cyprus
Gallions Reach
Beckton
North Greenwich
Silvertown & London City Airport
North Woolwich

ANY AMOUNT OF BOOKS
62 Charing Cross Road
London WC2H 0BB
(0171) 240 8140
Mon-Sun 10:30-9:30
Est. 1985. Medium. Gen Stock and Mod 1sts. Cat: 3 pa: Lit, Art. Buys: Ring first. cc: AV. Tube: Leicester Sq. "A good varied stock. High turnover. Large bargain basement."
Owner: Nigel Burwood

ASH RARE BOOKS
25 Royal Exchange
Threadneedle Street
London EC3V 3LP
(0171) 626 2665
Fax (0171) 623 9052
Mon-Fri 10-5:30
Est. 1946. Small. Spec: 1sts, Lit: also Gen Stock and Mod 1sts, London, Atqn. Cat: 4-5 pa: Mod 1sts, Atqn, Lit, Trav. cc: AVAm. Tube: Bank. "Small select stock - Atqn, rare and fine books. Also antique maps and prints."
Owner: Laurence Worms

ATLANTIS BOOKSHOP
49A Museum Street
London WC1A 1LY
(0171) 405 2120
Mon-Fri 10:30-6, Sat 11-5
Est. 1922. Large. Spec: Occult, Rel: also Healing, Eso, Myth. Buys: Ring first. cc: AV. Tube: Holborn. "New and s'hand on all occult subjects - Crowley, Magick, Earth Mysteries, Palmistry, Tarot, UFO's, Spiritualism, Astrology."
Manager: Caroline Wise

BALLANTYNE & DATE
38 Museum Street
Bloomsbury
London WC1A 1LP
(0171) 242 4249
Fax (0171) 430 0684
Mon-Sat 10:30-6, Sun 12-6
Small. Spec: Illus: also C20th Art & Des, C20th Trans, C20th Photo. Buys: Anytime. Book search. cc: AVAm. Tube: Holborn. "We also have prints, drawings, & posters inc. artists' ceramics. Contemporary art gallery on 1st floor."
Owners: R. Ballantyne-Way & R. Date

BELL BOOK & RADMALL LTD
4 Cecil Court
London WC2N 4HE
(0171) 240 2161
Fax (0171) 379 1062
Mon-Fri 10-5:30, Sat 10-4:30
Est. 1974. Medium. Spec: 1sts, US 1sts: also CR, SF, Fant. Cat: 2 pa: Gen. Buys: Ring first. Book search. cc: AVAmD. Tube: Leicester Sq.
Owners: Joan Bell & A.J. Sillem

THE BLOOMSBURY WORKSHOP
12 Galen Place
off Bury Place
London WC1A 2JR
(0171) 405 0632
Mon-Fri 10-5:30
Est. 1986. Small. Spec: Bloomsbury Lit: also Hogarth Press. Cat: 10 pa. Buys: Ring first. cc: AV. Tube: Tottenham Ct. Rd. "Extensive range of Bloomsbury lit, rare Woolf and Strachey 1sts. Also paintings and drawings by Duncan Grant, Vanessa Bell and other Bloomsbury artists."
Owners: T. Bradshaw & Rosemary Evison

THE BOOKING HALL
7 Charlotte Place
London W1P 1AQ
(0171) 255 2123
Mon-Fri 11-3, 4-7, Sat 11-5
Est. 1987. Small. Spec: Railway: also BR Buses, Trams. Buys: Anytime. Book search. cc: AV. Tube: Goodge Street. "Also new books, videos, and s'hand model railway items."
Owner: N. Downend

BOOKS FROM INDIA U.K., LTD
45 Museum Street
London WC1A 1LR
(0171) 405 7226
Fax (0171) 831 4517
Mon-Fri 10-5:30, Sat 10-5
Est. 1970. Large. Spec: Arts, Fict, Eso, Humanities, India: also Gen Stock and Langs, Dictionaries, References. Cat: 50 pa: various. Buys: Ring first. Book search. cc: AVAmDEJS. Tube: Tottenham Ct. Rd. or Holborn/BR: Charing Cross. "About 200 yards from either tube station, Museum St. is off New Oxford St. Carry about 20,000 assorted titles in 12 languages, drawn from over 600 publishers of India."
Owners: Mrs and Mr S. Vidyarthi

BOUTLE AND KING
23 Arlington Way
London EC1R 1UY
(0171) 278 4497
Mon-Sat 10:30-7
Est. 1990. Medium. Spec: Surrealism, Atec: also Gen Stock. Buys: Anytime. cc: AV. Tube: Angel. "Near to Sadlers Wells Theatre. Particular interest in expressionism, experimental writing, Atlas Press."
Owners: Clive Boutle & Steve King

ALAN BRETT LIMITED
24 Cecil Court
Charing Cross Road
London WC2N 4HE
(0171) 836 8222
Mon-Fri 9:30-5, Sat 9-5, Sun 10-4
Est. 1977. Small. Spec: Vanity Fair, Topog: also Gen Stock and Illus. Cat: 1 pa: Vanity Fair. Buys: Anytime. cc: AVAmDJ. Tube: Leicester Sq. "Vast stock of flower prints; many illustrated London news volumes. Also Gillraw, Rowlandson, Rackham, and other prints. Gallery of film star memorabilia downstairs."
Mng. Dir.: Alan Brett

BURY PLACE RARE BOOKS & PRINTS
14 Bury Place
London WC1
(0171) 404 6869
Mon-Sat 11-6, Sun 1-7
Large. Spec: Trav, Atqn: also Gen Stock and Fine and Rare. Cat: 12 pa: Spec subjs. Buys: Ring first. Tube: Holborn. "Opposite British Museum. Over 2000 sq. ft. of rare, s'hand & collectors books and maps. 20,000 books in basement. Largest s'hand bookshop in London. We're authorised to clear large stocks of ref. library material from mason institutions. Print & map gallery adjacent."
Owner: Library Collections Association

CHARING CROSS ROAD BOOKSHOP
56 Charing Cross Road
London WC2H 0BB
(0171) 836 3697
Fax (0171) 240 1769
Mon-Sun 10:30-9:30
Est. 1988. Medium. Spec: Lit, Art: also Mod 1sts. Cat: 3 pa: Mod 1sts, Art. Buys: Ring first. cc: AV. Tube: Leicester Sq. "Bargains in basement. Books by the yard."
Owner: Nigel Burwood

T.A. CHERRINGTON
1-11 Hay Hill
Mayfair
London W1X 7LF
(0171) 493 1343
Fax (0171) 499 2983
Mon-Fri 10-5:30
Est. 1993. Medium. Spec: Atlases, Nat Hist: also Platebooks, Topog. Buys: Ring first. cc: AVAm. Tube: Green Park. "Also has a stall at W. Jones & Son Arcade, Westbourne Grove (Sat 8-2)."
Owner: T.A. Cherrington

CINEMA BOOKSHOP
13 Great Russell Street
London WC1B 3NH
(0171) 637 0206
Fax (0171) 436 9979
Mon-Sat 10:30-5:30
Est. 1969. Medium. Spec: Cinema. Buys: Ring first. cc: AV. Tube: Tottenham Ct. Rd. "All cinema-related material. Posters, prints, books, magazines specialising in out-of-print cinema material."
Owner: Fred Zenner

J. CLARKE-HALL LTD
5 Bride Lane
London EC4Y 8DX
(0171) 353 4116
Mon-Fri 10:30-6
Est. 1934. Medium. Spec: Mod 1sts, Printing: also Gen Stock and Samuel Johnson, Lewis Carroll. Cat: 4 pa: S. Johnson, L. Carroll, Mod 1sts, Illus. Buys: Ring first. Tube: Blackfriars. "Also selling maps, prints, and ephemera: Print Shop (Mon-Fri 12-4), at 22 Bride Lane."
Owner: S.M. Edgecombe

COLLINGE & CLARK
13 Leigh Street
London WC1H 9EW
(0171) 387 7105
Fax (0171) 833 0335
Mon-Fri 11-6:30, Sat 11-3:30
Est. 1989. Medium. Spec: Priv Press, Illus, C18th & C19th, Pol & Soc Hist: also Gen Stock and Art, Topog. Cat: 2-3 pa: Spec subjs. Buys: Anytime. cc: AV. Tube: Russell Sq.
Owners: J. Collinge & O. Clark

DANCE BOOKS LTD
15 Cecil Court
Charing Cross Road
London WC2N 4EZ
(0171) 836 2314
Fax (0171) 497 0473
Mon-Sat 11-7
Est. 1968. Small. Spec: All forms of Dance: also Ballet. Cat: 1 pa. Buys: Ring first. cc: AV. Tube: Leicester Sq. "Also posters, videos, and CD's."
Directors: J. O'Brien & D. Leonard

DAUNT BOOKS
83 Marylebone High Street
London W1M 3DE
(0171) 224 2295
Fax (0171) 224 6893
Mon-Sat 9-7:30
Est. 1990. Small. Spec: Trav. Buys: Anytime. cc: AV. Tube: Baker St. "Mainly new books with emphasis related to travel."
Owner: James Daunt

LEWIS DAVENPORT
7 Charing Cross Underground Concourse
The Strand
London WC2N 4HZ
(0171) 836 0408
Mon-Fri 10-5:30, Sat 10-4:30
Est. 1898. Small. Spec: Conjuring. Buys: Anytime. BR/Tube: Charing Cross.
Owner: Mrs B. Davenport

DILLONS (THE BOOKSTORE)
82 Gower Street
London WC1E 6EQ
(0171) 636 1577 ext.244
Mon-Fri 9-7, Tue 9:30-7, Sat 9:30-6
Est. 1936. Large. Spec: Humanities, Acad: also Gen Stock. Cat: 2 pa: Acad. Buys: Ring first. Tube: Goodge Street. "Mainly acad books but currently building up atqn books."
Manager: Philip Youren

DAVID DRUMMOND AT PLEASURES OF PAST TIMES
11 Cecil Court
Charing Cross Road
London WC2N 4EZ
(0171) 836 1142
Mon-Fri 11-2:30, 3:30-5:45 (Sat, occ & by appt)
Est. 1967. Small. Spec: Perf Arts, Chld: also Gen Stock. Buys: Anytime. Tube: Leicester Sq. "Internationally famous bookselling precinct between St. Martin's Lane and Charing Cross Road. Pre 1940's Chld books, Ephemera relating to Performing Arts, Victoriana (inc. Valentines) & classified postcards."
Owner: David Drummond

JACK DUNCAN BASEMENT BOOKSHOP
44 Museum Street
London WC1A 1LY
(0171) 242 5335
Fax (0171) 242 2978
Mon-Sat 12-4 (or by appt)
Spec: Fine sets, Lit: also Medieval Hist, Art, Phil.
Owner: Jack Duncan

JACK DUNCAN CARTOONS & BOOKS
44 Museum Street
London WC1A 1LY
(0171) 242 5335
Fax (0171) 242 2978
Mon-Fri 10-6, Sat 10-5
Spec: Cartoon/Caricature Books, Folio Society: "Large stock of books plus regular monthly exhibitions of orig, signed cartoons and caricatures."
Owner: Jack Duncan

THE ECONOMISTS' BOOKSHOP
(Secondhand Dept.)
Clare Market, Portugal Street
London WC2A 2AB
(0171) 405 5531
Fax (0171) 403 1584
Mon-Fri 9.30-6, Wed 10-6 (Term time Sat. 10-4)
Est. 1937. Large. Spec: Econ: also Pol, Hist. Cat: 2 pa. Buys: Ring first. Book search. cc: AVAm. Tube: Holborn. "We specialize in Soc. Sci, Atqn, s'hand and remainders."
Manager: Mr J. Peters

FRANCIS EDWARDS
13 Great Newport Street
Charing Cross Road
London WC2H 7JA
(0171) 379 7669
Fax (0171) 836 5977
Mon-Sat 9:30-6:30
Small. Spec: Naval, Avia: also Mil Hist. Cat: 4 pa: Naval, Mil Hist. Buys: Anytime. cc: AVAmDS. Tube: Leicester Sq.
Manager: Mr Mitchell

EUROBOOKS LTD
2 Woodstock Street
London W1
(0171) 491 0223 (tel/fax)
Mon-Fri 10-6, Sat 10-4
Est. 1992. Large. Spec: Atqn, Humanities, Plate books, Victorian Trav: also Gen Stock and Masonic, Occult, Atqn prints & maps. Cat: 4 pa: various. Buys: Anytime. Book search. cc: AVAmES. Tube: Bond St. "Opposite Phillips Auction, Bond St. Booksearch, collection development, antiquarian/print and map search, unusual books and sets."
Owner: A. O'Leary

FERRINGTON
The Bookshop
31-35 Great Ormond Street
London WC1N 3HZ
(0171) 430 1394
Mon-Fri 12-6 (or ring)
Est. 1994. Spec: London, Chld. Buys: Ring first. Book search. cc: AV. Tube: Holborn/Russell Sq.
Owner: Mark Rogers

SIMON FINCH RARE BOOKS
10 New Bond Street
London W1Y 0SJ
(0171) 499 0974
Mon-Fri 10-6
Est. 1981. Small. Spec: Lit: Cat: 3-4 pa. Buys: Ring first. cc: AVAm. Tube: Green Park. "Good stock of 1600-1850's Eng Lit. Also bound sets."
Owner: Simon Finch

FINE BOOKS ORIENTAL LTD
46 Great Russell Street
London WC1B 3PA
(0171) 636 6068
Fax (0171) 436 6544
Mon-Fri 9:30-5
Est. 1978. Medium. Spec: Japan: also Mid E, Oriental. Buys: Anytime. cc: AVAmD. Tube: Tottenham Ct. Rd.
Owner: Jeffrey Somers

SAM FOGG RARE BOOKS AND MANUSCRIPTS
35 St. George Street
London W1R 9FA
(0171) 495 2333 (tel/fax)
Mon-Fri 10-6
Est. 1981. Small. Spec: Illuminated Mss: also Art. Cat: occ. Buys: Ring first. Tube: Green Park.
Owner: Mr S. Fogg

FOOD FOR THOUGHT
27 Cecil Court
London WC2N 4EZ
(0171) 379 8171
Fax (0171) 379 1994
Mon-Sat 10:30-8
Medium. Gen Stock. Buys: Anytime. cc: AVAm. Tube: Leicester Sq. "Books in fine condition on any subject."
Owners: Dr James Fought & Simon Gough

ROBERT FREW LTD
106 Great Russell Street
London WC1B 3NA
(0171) 580 2311
Fax (0171) 580 2313
Mon-Fri 10-6, Sat 10-2
Est. 1985. Small. Spec: Atqn Trav, Atqn Lit: also Atqn Illus. Cat: occ: Gen. Buys: Ring first. cc: AVAm. Tube: Tottenham Ct. Rd. "Also maps and prints. Atqn books and early printing, fine bindings, sets, and illus."
Owners: R. Frew & P. Chantziaras

GAY'S THE WORD
66 Marchmont Street
London WC1N 1AB
(0171) 278 7654
Mon-Sat 10-6, Thur 10-7, Sun 2-6 (also public holidays)
Est. 1979. Spec: Gay. Buys: Ring first. cc: AVAmD. Tube: Russell Sq. "The largest Eng Lang Gay, Lesbian, Feminist bookshop in Europe. Tea and coffee available."
Manager: Paul Hegarty

GEKOSKI
Pied Bull Yard
15A Bloomsbury Square
London WC1A 2LP
(0171) 404 6676
Fax (0171) 404 6595
Mon-Fri 10-5:30
Est. 1982. Small. Spec: Mod 1st edns: also Letters and Manuscripts. Cat: 1 pa: Mod Lit. Buys: Anytime. cc: AVS. Tube: Holborn.
Owner: R.A. Gekoski

GOLDEN SQUARE BOOKS
16 Golden Square
London W1
(0171) 434 3337
Fax (0171) 434 3835
Mon-Fri 10:30-7, Sat 10:30-6
Est. 1994. Large. Spec: W & E Phil, Rel: also Psy, Classics. Buys: Ring first. cc: AVS. Tube: Piccadilly Circus. "Quality texts in specialist areas."
Owner: Peter Harrison

GOLFIANA
Grays-in-the-Mews
Davies Mews
London W1
(0171) 408 1239/ (01223) 357958 (office)
Fax (0171) 493 9344
Mon-Fri 10-6
Small. Spec: Golf, Motoring. Cat: 1 pa: Golf. Buys: Ring first. cc: AVAm. Tube: Bond St. "All golf subjects covered - books, ephemera, silver pictures, clubs, postcards, etc.; motoring books, ephemera, and tin and diecast toys. Office P.O. Box 178, Cambridge, CB4 3UF."
Owner: Sarah Fabian Baddiel

GRANT & CUTLER
55-57 Gt. Marlborough Street
London W1V 2AY
(0171) 734 2012
Fax (0171) 734 9272
Mon-Sat 9-5:30, Thur 9-7
Est. 1936. Large. Spec: For. Lang. Cat: 6 pa: For. Lang. Buys: Ring first. cc: AV. Tube: Oxford Circus. "Over 100,000 books, mainly new - some s'hand. Also cassettes, videos. UK's largest For Lang booksellers."

GRENVILLE BOOKS
40A Museum Street
London WC1A 1LT
(0171) 404 2872 (tel/fax)
Mon-Fri 10:30-6:30, Sat-Sun 11-5
Spec: Trav, Soc Hist of Women: also Gen Stock and Spain, Portugal & Latin America, Mod 1sts. Buys: Ring first. Tube: Holborn/Tottenham Ct. Rd.
Owner: Peter Brewer

HANDSWORTH BOOKS
148 Charing Cross Road
London WC2H 0EE
(0171) 836 1931
Mon-Sat 10-8, Sun 11:30-5:30
Est. 1992. Medium. Spec: Art, Mil, Hist, and Lit: also Gen Stock and Acad (Humanities). Cat: 1 pa: History. Buys: Ring first. cc: AVE. Tube: Tottenham Ct. Rd. "Next to Centre Point. In the basement of Bookpedlar."
Owner: Stephen Glover

HARRISON'S BOOKS
Stand J20/21 Gray's Mews Antiques Market
1-7 Davies Mews
London W1Y 1AR
(0171) 629 1374
Mon-Fri 10-6
Est. 1967. Large. Spec: Angling, Old German: also Gen Stock. Cat: 4 pa: 2 Gen, 1 Angling, 1 Ephemera. Buys: Anytime. Tube: Bond Street. "Jubilee and Central Lines. An interesting display of the scarce and unusual modern and classical. Maps and prints, interesting ephemera."
Partners: Bernard & Leo Harrison

G. HEYWOOD HILL LTD
10 Curzon Street
London W1Y 7FJ
(0171) 629 0647
Fax (0171) 408 0286
Mon-Fri 9-5:30, Sat 9-12:30
Est. 1936. Medium. Gen Stock and Lit, Atqn, Chld. Buys: Ring first. Book search. Tube: Green Park. "Stocks old and new books."
Manager: John Saumarez-Smith

P.J. HILTON
12-14 Cecil Court
London WC2N 4HE
(0171) 379 9825
Mon-Sat 9:30-7:30
Est. 1991. Medium. Spec: Eng Lit: also Gen Stock and Fr Lit, Rel, Hist. Buys: Ring first. Book search. Tube: Leicester Sq. "Gen atqn and s'hand books particularly Eng Lit including Fict, Po, C16th - C19th. Also C20th Lit inc. Mod 1sts and popular novelists."
Owner: Paul Hilton

HOSAINS BOOKS
25 Connaught Street
London W2 2AY
(0171) 262 7900
Fax (0171) 794 7127
Tue-Fri 11-5
Small. Spec: Cent Asia, Mid E: also Indian Subcontinent. Cat: 3-4 pa: Spec subj. Buys: Ring first. cc: AVAm. Tube: Marble Arch. "Also stock lithographs, miniatures, and manuscripts relating to our specialist subjects."
Owners: K.S. Hosain & Mrs Y. Hosain

INDEX BOOKCENTRE
28 Charlotte Street
London W1P 1JH
(0171) 636 3532
Mon-Fri 9-7, Sat 11-5
Small. Spec: Pol, Phil. Tube: Goodge St. "Very small selection of politics and philosophy."
Manager: G. Thurley

JARNDYCE ANTIQUARIAN BOOK-SELLERS
46 Great Russell Street
London WC1B 3PA
(0171) 631 4220
Fax (0171) 436 6544
Mon-Fri 9:30-5 (pref. by appt)
Spec: C18th and C19th English books, Pre 1900 1sts: also Dickensiana, Hist, Lit. Cat: 6 pa: Dickens, Plays & Theatre, C19th, Romantics, etc. Buys: Ring first. Tube: Tottenham Ct. Rd. "ABA, PBFA."
Owners: Brian Lake & Janet Nassau

JUDD STREET BOOKS
102 Judd Street
London WC1H 9MT
(0171) 833 1900
Est. 1993. Medium. Spec: Hist, Phil, Econ: also Psy, Pol, Educ. Cat: 3 pa. Buys: Ring first. cc: AVES. Tube: King's Cross & Euston.
Owner: Nigel Kemp

JUDD TWO BOOKS
82 Marchmont Street
London WC1N 1AG
(0171) 387 5333
Mon-Sat 11-7, Sun 11-6
Est. 1993. Medium. Spec: Lit, Atec, Film: also Women's Stud, Gay, Culture, Media, Photog, Art. Buys: Ring first. Book search. cc: AVES. Tube: Russell Sq. "Marchmont Street is straight across pedestrian crossing outside tube station. Arts and literature branch, used and bargain books, 10% student discount."
Manager: A. Donaldson

LONDON ANTIQUARIAN BOOK ARCADE LTD
37 Great Russell Street
London WC1B 3PP
(0171) 436 2054
Fax (0171) 436 2057
Mon-Sat 10-6, Sun 12-5
Est. 1995. Medium. Spec: Mod 1sts, Fine Art: also Gen Stock and Antiquarian (C18th). Buys: Anytime. Book search. cc: AVES. BR: Tottenham Ct. Rd. "Diagonal/across British Museum nr. Bloomsbury St. Consortium of 30+ dealers (and growing)."
Directors: Myrna Adolph-Morris & Dr Ronald L. Morris

MAGGS BROS. LTD
50 Berkeley Square
London W1X 6EL
(0171) 493 7160
Fax (0171) 499 2007
Mon-Fri 9:30-5
Est. 1853. Large. Spec: Rare, 1sts: also Gen Stock and Atqn, Mil, Continental. Cat: 15 pa: Spec subj. Buys: Anytime. cc: AV. Tube: Green Park. "Market leaders in autographs and manuscripts. Huge back up of reference books."
Mng. Dir.: John F. Maggs

THE MAGHREB BOOKSHOP/ LIBRAIRE DU MAGHREB
45 Burton Street
London WC1H 9AL
(0171) 388 1840
Mon-Sat 9:30-6 (or by appt)
Est. 1984. Medium. Spec: Maghreb from 600: also Islamic Studies. Cat: 2 pa. Buys: Anytime. Book search. Tube: Russell Sq. "A highly specialised bookseller on Maghreb-Algeria, Libya, Mauritania, Morocco, and Tunisia. Also very good stock on the Arab world, Africa, and Islam with foreign lang books on those subjects."
Owner: Mohamed ben Madani

THE MARCHMONT BOOKSHOP
39 Burton Street
London WC1H 9AL
(0171) 387 7989
Mon-Fri 11-6:30, Sat 12-3
Est. 1977. Medium. Spec: Lit: also Gen Stock. Cat: occ. Buys: Ring first. Tube: Euston/Russell Sq. "Good stock of lit, especially mod poetry."
Owner: Don Holder

MARCHPANE
16 Cecil Court
London WC2N 4HE
(0171) 836 8661
Fax (0171) 497 0567
Mon-Sat 10:30-6:30
Est. 1989. Medium. Spec: Chld: also Illus. Cat: 2 pa: Gen, Lewis Carroll. Buys: Anytime. cc: AV. Tube: Leicester Sq. "Also prints."
Mng. Dir.: K.R. Fuller

MARLBOROUGH RARE BOOKS LTD
144-146 New Bond Street
London W1Y 9FD
(0171) 493 6993
Fax (0171) 499 2479
Mon-Fri 9:30-5:30
Est. 1955. Small. Spec: Atqn, Illus: also Eng Lit, Atec, Bindings. Cat: 4-5 pa: as above. Buys: Ring first. Book search. cc: V. Tube: Bond St./Green Park. "Office on 4th floor above Sotheby's."
Owner: J. Gestetner

MURDER ONE
71-73 Charing Cross Road
London WC2H 0AA
(0171) 734 3483
Mon-Wed 10-7, Thur-Sat 10-8
Est. 1988. Small. Spec: Crime: also Romance, Mystery, SF, Horror. Cat: 3 pa: Mystery, SF. Buys: Anytime. cc: AVAm. Tube: Leicester Sq. "Mainly new books."
Owners: M. Jakubowski & N. Landau

MUSEUM BOOKSHOP LTD
36 Great Russell Street
London WC1B 3PP
(0171) 580 4086
Mon-Fri 10-5:30, Sat 10:30-5:30
Est. 1979. Medium. Spec: Egyptology: also Classics, Conservation. Cat: 3 pa: Egyptology, Mid E, Conservation. Buys: Anytime. Book search. cc: AVAmDJ. Tube: Tottenham Ct. Rd./Holborn. "Small scholars' bookshop."
Owners: Ashley Jones & David Mezzetti

AVRIL NOBLE
2 Southampton Street
London WC2E 7HA
(0171) 240 1970
Mon-Fri 10-6, Sat 10-4
Small. Spec: Cartog, Atqn. Buys: Anytime. cc: AVAm. Tube: Charing Cross/Covent Garden. "Maps and prints. Fine selection of atqn maps of all areas of the world, David Roberts, botanical prints."
Owner: Avril Noble

HENRY PORDES BOOKS LTD
58-60 Charing Cross Road
London WC2H 0BB
(0171) 836 9031
Fax (0181) 886 2201
Mon-Sat 10-7
Est. 1983. Medium. Spec: Cinema: also Gen Stock and Atqn, Lit. Buys: Anytime. cc: AV. Tube: Leicester Sq. "Fast changing stock of interesting and reasonably priced books. Remainders as well."
Directors: Henry Pordes & N. Pordes

JONATHAN POTTER LTD
125 New Bond Street
London W1Y 9AF
(0171) 491 3520
Fax (0171) 491 9754
Mon-Fri 10-6 (Sat by appt)
Medium. Spec: Cartog: Cat: occ. Buys: Ring first. cc: AVAmD. Tube: Bond St. "Retail shop with large stock of fine decorative and rare maps and atlases."
Owner: Jonathan Potter

ARTHUR PROBSTHAIN
41 Great Russell Street
London WC1B 3PH
(0171) 636 1096
Mon-Fri 9-5:30, Sat 11-4
Medium. Spec: Oriental, African: Cat: reg. cc: AVAmD. Tube: Tottenham Ct. Rd. "A very thorough coverage of all things Oriental: Lang, Art, Hist from Mid E through India to Far East."
Owner: Walter Sheringham

BERNARD QUATRICH LTD
5-8 Lower John Street
Golden Square
London W1R 4AU
(0171) 734 2983
Mon-Fri 9:30-1, 2-5:30
Est. 1847. Large. Spec: Trav, Sci & Med: also Human Sci, Cont Lit, Near and Mid E. Cat: 10 pa: all subjects. Buys: Ring first. Tube: Piccadilly Circus. "Also Mss, Biblio, Econ, Art, Maths."
Mng. Dir.: Nicholas Poole-Wilson

QUINTO OF CHARING CROSS ROAD
48A Charing Cross Road
London WC2H 0BB
(0171) 379 7669
Fax (0171) 836 5977
Mon-Sat 9-9, Sun 12-8
Medium. Gen Stock and Hist. Buys: Ring first. cc: AVAmD. Tube: Leicester Sq.
Manager: Mr Mitchell

RARE BOOKS
237 Shaftesbury Avenue
London WC2H 8GH
(0171) 240 8715 (tel/fax)
Mon-Sat 11-6
Est. 1996. Large. Spec: Trav, Atqn: also Fine & Rare books. Cat: 10-12 pa: Spec subjs. Buys: Ring first. Tube: Tottenham Court Road. "Also antique prints & maps. Proprietors of Bury Place Rare Books."
Owner: David Fairbairn

REG & PHILIP REMINGTON
18 Cecil Court
Charing Cross Road
London WC2N 4HE
(0171) 836 9771
Fax (0171) 497 2526
Mon-Fri 10-5
Est. 1979. Small. Spec: Trav: also Voyages. Buys: Ring first. Tube: Leicester Sq.
Owners: R. & P. Remington

ROE & MOORE
29 Museum Street
London WC1A 1LH
(0171) 636 4787
Fax (0171) 636 6110
Est. 1988. Medium. Spec: Art, Illus: also Fr, Chld, Fine Bindings. Cat: 4 pa: Art. Buys: Anytime. cc: AV. Tube: Holborn.
Owners: A. Roe & D. Moore

BERTRAM ROTA LTD
1st Floor, 31 Long Acre
Covent Garden
London WC2E 9LT
(0171) 836 0723
Mon-Fri 9:30-5:30
Est. 1923. Medium. Spec: 1sts: also Priv Press, Atqn. Cat: 4 pa: Mod 1sts, Priv Press, Atqn. Buys: Ring first. Book search. cc: AV. Tube: Covent Garden/Leicester Sq.
Owner: Anthony Rota

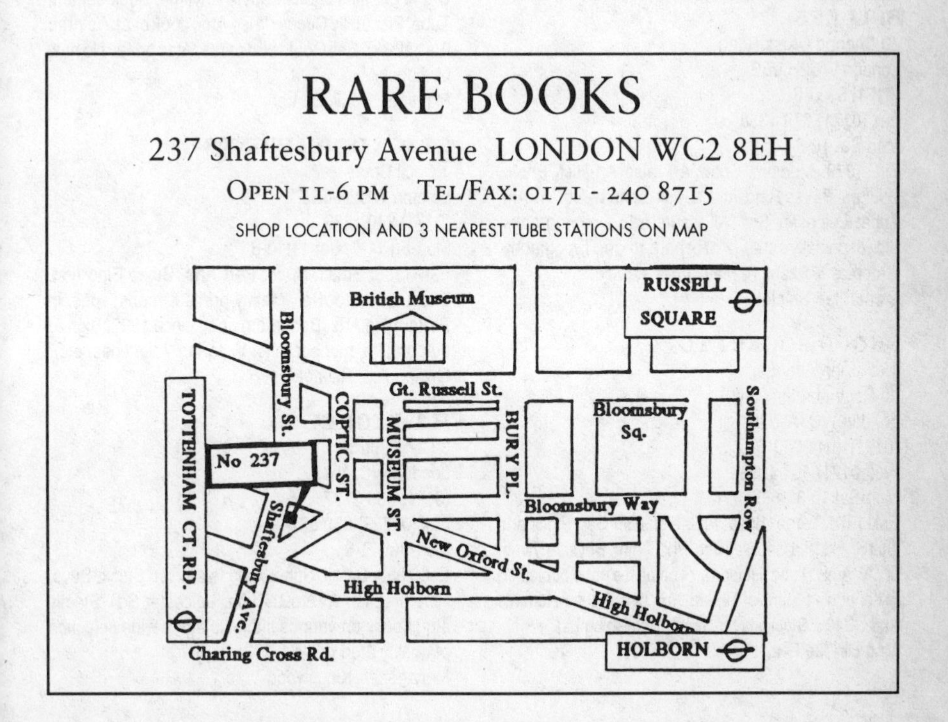

RUSSELL RARE BOOKS
1-11 Hay Hill
Mayfair
London W1X 7LF
(0171) 629 0532
Fax (0171) 499 2983
Mon-Fri 10-5:30
Est. 1978. Medium. Spec: Atqn: also Illus, Bound sets. Cat: occ. Buys: Anytime. cc: AVAm. Tube: Green Park.
Owner: Charles Russell

SCHUSTER GALLERY
14 Maddox Street
London W1R 9PL
(0171) 491 2208
Mon-Fri 10-5:30 (Sat by appt)
Est. 1973. Small. Spec: Nat Hist: also Atlases. Buys: Ring first. cc: AVAm. Tube: Oxford Circus. "Off Regent Street. Mostly atqn prints, Books of Hours, Maps, Illus. Mss."
Owner: Mr Schuster

SHIPLEY (SPECIALIST ART BOOK-SELLERS)
70 Charing Cross Road
London WC2H 0BB
(0171) 836 4872
Fax (0171) 379 4358
Mon-Sat 10-6
Est. 1979. Medium. Spec: Art: also Art Hist, Photo, Design. Buys: Ring first. Book search. cc: AVAm. Tube: Leicester Sq. "All visual arts - monographs, etc., especially out-of-print or hard-to-get. Typography, Graphics & Fashion. Mail Order service."
Owner: Ian Shipley

SKOOB BOOKS LTD
15 Sicilian Avenue
off Southampton Row
London WC1A 2QH
(0171) 404 3063
Fax (0171) 404 4398
Mon-Sat 10:30-6:30
Est. 1978. Large. Spec: Phil, Fict: also Gen Stock and Cult St, Hist, Lit Crit. Cat: occ: Phil, Anthr. Buys: Anytime. cc: AVAmS. Tube: Holborn. "'The best s'hand bookshop in London' - Financial Times. 10% discount for students and UB40s. Stockists for Skoob Publishing Ltd."
Mng Dir: Ike Ong

SKOOB TWO
17 Sicilian Avenue
off Southampton Row
London WC1A 2QH
(0171) 405 0030
Fax (0171) 404 4398
Mon-Sat 10:30-6:30
Est. 1986. Medium. Spec: Classics, Eso: also Gen Stock and Anthrop, Arch, SF. Buys: Anytime. cc: AVAmS. Tube: Holborn. "Stockists of Skoob Esoterica. Also Psy, Medicine, Science and Maths books. Large music section and CDs. Students and UB40s 10% discount."
Owner: Ike Ong

HENRY SOTHERAN LTD
2-5 Sackville Street
London W1X 2DP
(0171) 439 6151
Fax (0171) 434 2019
Mon-Fri 9:30-6, Sat 10-4
Est. 1761. Large. Spec: Atqn: also Trav, Chld, Art. Cat: 4 pa: all subjects. Buys: Anytime. Book search. Tube: Piccadilly Circus. "Also Atec (took over Weinreb Atec stock). Sell Gould bird prints, Atec prints. No new bird books."
Manager: Rosie Barker

STAGE DOOR PRINTS
1 Cecil Court
London WC2N 4EZ
(0171) 240 1683
Mon-Fri 11-6, Sat 11:30-6
Est. 1983. Small. Spec: Perf Arts. Buys: Ring first. Tube: Leicester Sq. "Mainly prints & maps, spec. in Performing Arts. Bookroom open since 1992. Signed autographs, monographs, Victorian Valentines, etc."
Owner: A.L. Reynold

H.T. STOREY
3 Cecil Court
London WC2N 4EZ
(0171) 836 3777
Fax (01689) 850 0274
Mon-Sat 10-6
Est. 1933. Small. Spec: Atqn: also Gen Stock. Buys: Ring first. cc: AVAmD. Tube: Leicester Sq. "Strictly atqn books on various subjects and a wide selection of quality atqn prints."
Manager: T. Kingswood

TOOLEY ADAMS & CO. LTD
13 Cecil Court
London WC2N 4EZ
(0171) 240 4406
Fax (0171) 240 8058
Mon-Fri 9-5
Est. 1989. Medium. Spec: Atlases, Cartobibliographies. Buys: Anytime. cc: AVAm. Tube: Leicester Sq. "Specialist atqn atlases & maps. Some topographical views."
Owners: D. Adams & S. Luck

THE TRAVELLER'S BOOKSHOP
25 Cecil Court
London WC2N 4EZ
(0171) 836 9132
Fax (0171) 379 4928
Mon-Fri 11-7, Sat 11-6:30
Est. 1989. Medium. Spec: Trav, Guides, Atqn. Buys: Ring first. Book search. cc: AVAmD. Tube: Leicester Sq. "We stock new books, Baedeckers & other guides & maps."
Manageress: Lucinda Boyle

TRAVIS & EMERY (MUSIC & MUSICAL LITERATURE)
17 Cecil Court
Charing Cross Road
London WC2N 4EZ
(0171) 240 2129
Fax (0171) 497 0473
Mon-Fri 10-6, Sat 10-1
Est. 1960. Medium. Spec: Mus: Cat: 3 pa: Mus, Vocal, Opera. Buys: Ring first. cc: AV. Tube: Leicester Sq. "We believe we are the only s'hand bookshop in London dealing exclusively in Music."
Owner: Mrs V. Emery

ULYSSES
40 Museum Street
London WC1A 1LH
(0171) 831 1600 (tel/fax)
Mon-Sat 10:30-6, Sun 12-6
Est. 1991. Medium. Spec: Mod 1sts, C20th Illus: Cat: 5 pa: Spec subjs. Buys: Anytime. Book search. cc: AVAmDJ. Tube:Holborn/Tottenham Ct. Rd.
Owners: Peter Ellis & Peter Jolliffe

ULYSSES
31 Museum Street
London WC1A 1LH
(0171) 637 5862
Fax (0171) 831 1600
Mon-Sat 10:30-6, Sun 12-6
Est. 1987. Medium. Spec: For & Br Topog, Post-1850 Arts: also Gen Stock. Cat: 5 pa: Spec subjs. Buys: Anytime. Book search. cc: AVAmDJ. Tube: Holborn/ Tottenham Ct. Rd.
Owners: Gabriel Beaumont & Joanna Herald

UNSWORTH, RICE & COE
12 Bloomsbury Street
London WC1B 3QA
(0171) 436 9836
Fax (0171) 637 7334
Mon-Fri 10-8, Sat 10-7, Sun 12-7
Est. 1992. Large. Spec: Hist, Classics: also Gen Stock and Atqn, Arts, Soc Sci. Buys: Anytime. Book search. cc: AVAmDJS. Tube: Holborn & Tottenham Ct. Rd. "Shop situated between Gt. Russell St. and New Oxford St. Offers the best value in the area (bookshops of London). Atqn in the basement."
Owners: C. Unsworth, T. Rice & S. Coe

VINTAGE MAGAZINE SHOP LTD
39-41 Brewer Street
London W1R 3FD
(0171) 439 8525
Mon-Sat 10-7, Sun 12-8
Est. 1975. Small. Spec: Magazines: also Comics. Buys: Ring first. Tube: Piccadilly Circus. "The biggest magazine stock in Europe. Also annuals, film magazines, posters, cards."

ROWLAND WARD'S (AT HOLLAND & HOLLAND LTD)
31-33 Bruton Street
London W1X 8JS
(0171) 499 4411
Fax (0171) 499 4544
Mon-Fri 9:30-5:30, Sat 10-4
Est. 1870. Small. Spec: Big game hunting, Guns: also Trav, Africana. Cat: 1 pa. Buys: Ring first. Book search. cc: AVAmD. Tube: Green Park/Bond St. "Small specialists bookshop. Visitors always welcome."
Manageress: Sally King-Brain

WATKINS BOOKS LTD
19-21 Cecil Court
Charing Cross Road
London WC2N 4EZ
(0171) 836 2182
Fax (0171) 836 6700
Mon-Sat 10-6, Wed 10-8, Thur 10:30-6
Est. 1900. Small. Spec: Occult: also Astrol, Myth, Myst. Buys: Ring first. cc: AV. Tube: Leicester Sq. "Mainly new books, but substantial atqn Occult & Mystical section. We offer a wide selection on the theme of mind-body-spirit."
Owners: V. Chris, H. Suzuki & D. Weiser

THE WELLSPRING BOOKSHOP (RUDOLF STEINER BOOKS)
5 New Oxford Street
London WC1A 1BA
(0171) 405 6101
Mon-Fri 10-5:30, Sat 11-5
Est. 1989. Small. Spec: Rudolf Steiner Books, Anthroposophy: also Gen Stock and Med, Agri, Educ, Eso, Christian. Cat: Newsltrs: 4 pa: Gen w/new titles. Buys: Ring first. Book search. cc: AVE. Tube: Holborn & Tottenham Court. "We are at the beg of New Oxford St. where it comes off High Holborn. We are a charity - an educational trust to make more widely available the work of Rudolf Steiner."
Owner/Mng. Dir: N. Willby

WILDY & SONS LTD
Lincoln's Inn Archway
Carey Street
London WC2A 2JD
(0171) 242 5778
Fax (0171) 430 0897
Mon-Fri 8:45-5:15
Est. 1830. Large. Spec: Law. Buys: Ring first. cc: AVAmD. Tube: Chancery Lane/Holborn. "The largest s'hand bookshop in England dealing only in Law. Also legal prints & caricatures."
Manager: John Simkins

NIGEL WILLIAMS RARE BOOKS
22 Cecil Court
London WC2N 4HE
(0171) 836 7757
Fax (0171) 379 5918
Mon-Sat 10:30-5:30
Est. 1995. Medium. Spec: C19th and C20th Lit 1st edns: also Books about books, Chld, PG Wodehouse, Sherlock Holmes. Cat: 6 pa: Mod 1sts, 4 pa: PG Wodehouse. Buys: Anytime. cc: AVAmDEJS. Tube: Leicester Sq. "1 min from Leicester Sq. underground. One of the finest selections of 1st edns and detective fiction in the UK."
Owner: Nigel Williams

THE WOBURN BOOKSHOP
10 Woburn Walk
London WC1H 0JL
(0171) 388 7278
Mon-Fri 11-7, Sat 11-5
Small. Spec: Cult Stud, Soc Hist: also Phil, Jud, Art. Buys: Anytime. Tube/BR: Euston. "Good s'hand and Atqn stock. Also Atec and Cinema."
Owners: Philip Walden & Andrew Burgin

ZENO (BOOKSELLERS & PUBLISHERS)
The Greek Bookshop
6 Denmark Street
London WC2H 8LP
(0171) 240 1968/836 2522 (tel/fax)
Mon-Fri 9:30-6, Sat 9:30-5
Est. 1944. Medium. Spec: Greece: Cat: 3 pa. Buys: Anytime. Book search. cc: AV. Tube: Tottenham Ct. Rd. "Books in Greek & Eng Lang books on Greece, Cyprus, Balkans, Mid E, Trav, Hist, all subjects. Also Byzantium & methods of learning Greek."
Owner: Mr M.P. Zographos

A. ZWEMMER LTD
24 Litchfield Street
London WC2H 9NJ
(0171) 240 4158
Fax (0171) 836 4079
Mon-Fri 9:30-7, Sat 10-6
Est. 1920. Large. Spec: Out-of-Print Contemporary Art, Art Hist: also Atec, Dec Art, Oriental & Oceanic. Buys: Ring first. cc: AVAmD. Tube: Leicester Sq. "Large s'hand out-of-print stock within new bookshop. Out-of-print books in Art Ref & Art Hist. Artists' Catalogues Raisonnes. Out-of-Print Buyer: Charles Vernon Hunt."
Manager: Michelle Hinchelwood

ANTIQUE CITY BOOKSHOP
Antique City Market
Units 2 & 3, 98 Wood Street
London E17 3HX
(0181) 520 8300
Mon-Sat 9:30-5, Thur close
Est. 1995. Small. Gen Stock and Mil, Collectables. Buys: Ring first. Book search. BR: Walthamstow Wood St.
Owner: Alan Stone

CENTERPRISE BOOKSHOP
136/138 Kingsland High Street
London E8 2NS
(0171) 254 9632
Fax (0171) 923 1951
Mon-Sat 10:30-5:30
Est. 1971. Small. Spec: Black writing, Indian, Gay: also Gen Stock and Chld, Local Interest, Feminist. Buys: Ring first. Book search. cc: AVS. BR: Dalston Kingsland. "Near Dalston Junction. Buses: 6, 76, 149, 243 pass door. Friendly shop with cafe/gallery attached."
Manageress: Judith Skinner

MAGPIE BOOKSHOP
53 Brushfield Street
Spitalfields
London E1 6AA
(0171) 247 4263
Mon-Sat 11-4, Sun 10-5
Est. 1994. Small. Spec: SF, Eso: also Gen Stock and Gen Fict, East London Hist, Chld,. Cat: Intermittent: SF. Buys: Anytime. Book search. cc: AVE. BR/Tube: Liverpool St. "In old Spitalfields Market. Bookstalls in market on Sunday, sometimes weekdays. Some stock on WWW at Virtual. Bookshop Com. E-mail: Groberts@cix.compulink.co.uk."
Owners: David Keew & Graeme Roberts

SPORTING BOOKSHOP
Antique City Bookshop
Units 4,5 & 6, 98 Wood Street
London E17 3HX
(0181) 521 9803
Mon-Sat 9:30-5
Est. 1986. Small. Spec: Cricket, Football: also Boxing, Sport. BR: Walthamstow Wood St.
Owner: David Ellis

THE ALEXANDRA BOOKSHOP
209 Park Road
London N8 8JG
(0181) 889 1674
Tue-Sat 10-6, Mon & Wed close
Est. 1992. Small. Spec: Contemporary Fict, Hist: also Gen Stock and Cookery, Gardening, Trav. Buys: Anytime. "Situated between Crouch End & Muswell Hill. At foot of Muswell Hill close to Alexandra Palace entrance."
Owner: L. Freeman

THE AVIATION BOOKSHOP
656 Holloway Road
London N19 3PD
(0171) 272 3630
Mon-Sat 9:30-5:30
Est. 1948. Medium. Spec: Avia. Cat: 1 pa: Avia. Buys: Ring first. cc: VAmD. Tube: Archway. "The only purely Aviation bookshop in England."
Owner: David Hatherell

IAN BINNIE (BOOKSELLER)
63 Halliford Street
Islington
London N1 2SL
(0171) 837 7372
Mon-Sat 10-5
Est. 1972. Medium. Spec: Eng Lit, Theatre/Drama: also Gen Stock. Cat: 12 pa: Lit, 4 pa: Gen. Buys: Ring first. cc: AV. Tube: Angel. "Ring 11-12 am."
Owner: Ian Binnie

R.A. BOON
251 Holloway Road
London N7
(0171) 700 0243
Mon-Sat 9:30-5
Medium. Spec: Theol: also Gen Stock and Hist, Lit, Tech. Cat: 24 pa: Theol, occ: Med. Buys: Ring first. cc: AV. Tube: Holloway Rd.
Owner: W. Brown

CHURCH STREET BOOKSHOP
142 Church Street
Stoke Newington
London N16 0JU
(0171) 241 5411
Mon-Sun 11:30-6
Est. 1994. Large. Gen Stock and Pbk Lit, Pbk Acad. Buys: Ring first. Bus: 73.
Owner: Tim Watson

CROUCH END BOOKSHOP
60 Crouch End Hill
London N8 8AG
(0181) 348 8966
Mon-Fri 9-6, Sat 9:30-6, Sun 11-4
Est. 1970. Small. Spec: Lit: also Gen Stock and Biog, Art. Buys: Anytime. Book search. cc: AV. Bus: 41.
Owner: Marsh Carters

FANTASY CENTRE
157 Holloway Road
London N7 8LX
(0171) 607 9433
Mon-Sat 10-6
Est. 1972. Medium. Spec: SF: also Fantasy, Horror. Cat: 10 pa. Buys: Anytime. Book search. Tube: Holloway Rd. "Mainly s'hand, out of print and 1sts, but some new titles."
Owners: Ted Ball & Erik Arthur

MICHAEL FINNEY BOOKS AND PRINTS
11 Camden Passage
Islington
London N1 8EA
(0171) 226 9280
Tue-Sat 10-5
Small. Spec: Plate books, Nat Hist: also Topog. Buys: Ring first. cc: AVAm. Tube: Angel. "Also prints and gen antiques. Special areas - David Roberts, Spain, Mediterranean."
Owner: Michael Finney

FISHER AND SPERR
High Street
Highgate
London N6 5JB
(0181) 340 7244
Mon-Sat 10-5:30
Est. 1930. Large. Gen Stock and Art, London, Sets. Buys: Anytime. Book search. cc: AVAm. Tube: Archway/ Highgate. "Between Archway and Highgate tube. Probably the largest s'hand and atqn bookshop in North London. Stock on 4 floors, covering all subjects."
Owner: J.R. Sperr

MARTIN GLADMAN
235 Nether Street
Finchley
London N3 INT
(0181) 343 3023
Tue-Fri 11-8, Sat 10-6 (or by appt)
Est. 1991. Medium. Spec: Hist, Humanities: also Gen Stock and Mil. Buys: Ring first. Book search. Tube: West Finchley. "Easy parking outside West Finchley tube, 30 min from Leicester Sq. Emphasis on humanities. Fresh stock daily. Mince pies at X'mas time."
Owner: M. Gladman

HOUSEMAN'S BOOKSHOP
5 Caledonian Road
London N1 9DX
(0171) 837 4473
Mon-Sat 10-6
Est. 1947. Small. Spec: Gay (Studs & Fict), Peace Studies: also Anarchism, Soc Sci, WS. Buys: Ring first. cc: AV. Tube: Kings Cross. "Small specialist s'hand section within shop selling new books and stationery."
Owner: Peace News Trustee

INTERCOL LONDON
Upper Gallery
11 Camden Passage
London N1 8DY
(& 43 Templars Crescent
London N3 3PR)
(0181) 349 2207
Fax (0181) 346 9539
Wed & Sat 9:30-5:30
Est. 1979. Medium. Spec: Maps, Playing Cards: also Gen Stock and Finance. Cat: 3 pa: Maps (inc. books), Currency, Playing Cards. Book search. cc: AVAm. Tube: Angel.
Owner: Yasha Baresiner

JUDITH LASSALLE
7 Pierpont Arcade
Camden Passage
London N1 8EF
(0171) 354 9344
Wed 7:30-4, Sat 9:30-4 (or by appt)
Est. 1765. Small. Spec: Chld: also Chld Games, Pre 1914 Optical, Toys, Peepshows. Buys: Ring first. cc: AVE. Tube: Angel. "And the unusual."
Owner: Judith Lassalle

THE MILITARY HISTORY BOOKSHOP
2 The Broadway
Friern Barnet Road
London N11 3DU
Tue-Fri 10-3
Est. 1970. Large. Spec: Mil Hist. Cat: 6 pa: Mil Hist. Buys: Ring first. Book search. cc: AVAmJ. BR: New Southgate. "Accept DM & US$ payments. Mention Skoob and get a free sample catalogue."
Owner/Mng: Mrs Ricketts

PENDLEBURY'S BOOKSHOP
Church House
Portland Ave, Stamford Hill
London N16 6HJ
(0181) 809 4922
Mon-Fri 10-5, Sat 10:30-4:30
Est. 1983. Large. Spec: Theol, Rel: also Gen Stock and Ornith, Bindings, Collectables. Cat: 6 pa: Theol. Buys: Anytime. Book search. cc: AVAm. BR: Stoke Newington. "The largest s'hand theol bookshop in England set in period church building."
Owner: John Pendlebury

PORCUPINE BOOKCELLAR
5 Caledonian Road
London N1 9DX
(0171) 837 4473
Mon-Sat 11-6
Medium. Spec: Pol, Fem: also Gen Stock and Atec, Lit, Film. Cat: 2 pa: Pol, Psy. Buys: Ring first. Book search. cc: AV. Tube: Kings Cross. "In the basement of Houseman's Bookshop."
Owners: B. Buitekant, A. Burgin, & A. Donaldson

RIPPING YARNS
355 Archway Road
London N6 5AB
(0181) 341 6111
Mon-Fri 10:30-5:30, Sat 10-5, Sun 11-4
Est. 1983. Medium. Spec: Chld: also Gen Stock and Theatre, Fict, Trav. Cat: occ. Buys: Ring first. Book search. cc: AV. Tube: Highgate. "Parking up to 1 hour - 20 yards up Archway Rd. north of shop and in side roads. Masses of cheap interesting books on every subject. Smaller specialist stock at Combined Harvest (off Portobello Market), 128 Talbot Road, W11, Mon, Wed, Fri, 10-5."
Owner: Celia Mitchell

ROBBIE'S BOOKSHOP
118A Alexandra Park Road
Muswell Hill
London N10 2AE
(0181) 444 6957
Mon-Sat 9-5:30, Thur close
Est. 1984. Small. Gen Stock and Penguins, Vintage books. Buys: Anytime. BR: Alexandra Palace. "Opp The Maid of Muswell Pub."
Owner: Robbie Conrich

JOHN TROTTER BOOKS
80 East End Road
London N3 2SY
(0181) 346 7430 (tel/fax)
Mon-Thur 10-5, Fri 10-3, Sun 10-1
Est. 1983. Medium. Spec: Judaica, Mid E: also Theol. Cat: 2-4 pa: Listed subj. Buys: Ring first. Book search. cc: AV. Tube: Finchley Central. "10 min walk from tube. Shop opp Manor View, N3, parking. Same premises as Manor House Books (new stock)."
Owner: John Trotter

UPPER STREET BOOKSHOP
182 Upper Street
London N1 1RQ
(0171) 359 3785
Mon-Sat 10:30-6:30
Est. 1981. Medium. Spec: Art, Photo: also Gen Stock and Atec, Lit, Mod 1sts. Buys: Anytime. cc: AV. Tube: Highbury & Islington. "Also atqn, Hist, Cinema, Design. Good quality s'hand atqn stock."
Owner: Derek Potter

VORTEX BOOKS
139-141 Church Street
Stoke Newington
London N16 0UH
(0171) 254 6516
Mon-Fri 11-6, Sat 10-6, Sun 12-6
Est. 1984. Large. Spec: Mod 1sts: also Gen Stock and Art, Hbk Fict, Pol. Buys: Anytime. cc: AVE. BR: Stoke Newington & Bus: 73. "73 Bus from Islington, Euston, or Kings Cross, or Stoke Newington BR from Liverpool St. - 15 min. The bookshop with cafe above including jazz bar in good shopping area."
Owners: I. Kinnersley & D. Mossman

G.W. WALFORD
15 Calabria Road
Highbury Fields
London N5 1JB
(0171) 226 5682
Mon-Fri 9:30-5
Est. 1948. Medium. Spec: Illus: also Gen Stock and Nat Hist, Topog. Cat: reg: Gen. Buys: Ring first. Tube: Highbury & Islington. "Also Sci, Soc Hist, rare, atqn, and standard Lit sets."
Owner: G.W. Walford

LONDON - NORTH-WEST

THE ABBEY BOOKSHOP
4D Market Hall, Camden Lock
Chalk Farm Road
London NW1 8AT
(0181) 740 0713
Mon-Sun 11-6:30
Est. 1990. Small. Spec: Irish Interest: also Gen Stock and Contemporary Lit, Phil, Hist, Pol. Buys: Anytime. Tube: Camden Town/Chalk Farm Road. "Some Atqn."
Owners: C. Overfield, S. Magill & J. Hardin

ARCHIVE BOOKSTORE
83 Bell Street
London NW1 6TB
(0171) 402 8212
Mon-Sat 10-6
Est. 1971. Medium. Gen Stock and Acad, Arts, Atqn. Buys: Ring first. Tube: Edgware Road. "Offers of collections of books & sheet music always welcome."
Owner: Tim Meaker

CAMDEN ART BOOKSHOP
200B Camden Lock
Chalk Farm Road
London NW1 8AF
(0181) 740 0713
Mon-Sun 10-6
Est. 1995. Medium. Spec: C20th Art, Film: also Ethnic Art, Catalogues, Photo. Buys: Anytime. Book search. Tube: Camden Town. "North from tube towards Chalk Farm - left hand side under railway bridge. Fast-changing stock of Arts-based material. Out-of-print & secondhand."
Owners: Chris Overfield & Janna Hardin

CAMDEN LOCK BOOKS AND PRINTS
77 Camden Lock Place
London NW1 8AF
Sat-Sun 10-6
Est. 1982. Small. Spec: Pbk Fict & Classics: also Gen Stock and Hbk Trav. Buys: Anytime. Tube: Camden Town & Chalk Farm. "First shop next to the canal in west yard of Camden Lock Market. Gifts and crafts plus a fast turnover of inexpensive & interesting books in a friendly atmosphere."
Owner: Jason Burley

EXTRA COVER
101 Boundary Road
St. John's Wood
London NW8 0RG
(0171) 625 1191
Tue-Sat 10-7, Sun 10-2
Est. 1995. Medium. Spec: Cricket, Soccer & Sport. Cat: 4 pa: Cricket & Soccer. Buys: Ring first. Book search. cc: AV. Tube: St. John's Wood. "10 min from St. John's Wood tube station - ring for directions. Vast range of books, prints & ephemera relating to Cricket & Soccer."
Manager: John Eastwood

KEITH FAWKES
1-3 Flask Walk
London NW3 1HJ
(0171) 435 0614
Mon 10-5, Tue-Sat 10-5:30, Sun 1-6
Est. 1973. Medium. Spec: Lit: also Gen Stock and Hist, Art, Atqn. Buys: Ring first. Tube: Hampstead.
Owner: Keith Fawkes

FITZJOHNS BOOKS
27A Northways Parade
College Cres., Swiss Cottage
London NW3
(0171) 722 9864
Mon-Sat 11-6
Est. 1983. Medium. Spec: Psy: also Gen Stock. Buys: Ring first. Tube: Swiss Cottage. "100 yds. from tube at the bottom of Fitzjohns Avenue."
Owner: Mr K. H. Smith

STEPHEN FOSTER
95 Bell Street
London NW1 6TL
(0171) 724 0876 (tel/fax)
Mon-Sat 10-6
Medium. Spec: Arts: also Gen Stock and Lit. Buys: Ring first. cc: AVAmD. Tube: Marylebone & Edgware Rd. "Bell St. is the 1st on the left north of Marylebone off Lisson Grove. Both tube stations less than 5 min."
Owner: Stephen Foster

W.A. FOSTER
183 Chiswick High Road
London W4 2DR
Mon-Sat 10:30-5:30
Est. 1970. Medium. Gen Stock and Atqn, Illus, Fine Bindings. Buys: Ring first. Tube: Turnham Green. "Parking outside shop. Quality stock in most subjects."
Owner: W.A. Foster

HELLENIC BOOKSERVICE
91 Fortess Road
London NW5 1AG
(0171) 267 9499
Fax (0171) 267 9498
Mon-Fri 9:30-6, Sat 9:30-5:30
Est. 1956. Medium. Spec: Greece: also Classics, Trav, Byzantium. Buys: Anytime. Book search. cc: AV. Tube: Tufnell Park. "Bus 134/135 stop outside at Fortess Road Junction Pub. Anything on Greece or the islands, with small sections on Turkey and Armenia. Supply universities and libraries worldwide."
Owner: Mrs P. Constantinou & M. Williams

CHARLES HIGHAM (S.P.C.K.)
Holy Trinity Church
Marylebone Road
London NW1 4DU
(0171) 383 3097
Fax (0171) 388 2352
Mon-Fri 9-5
Large. Spec: Theol: also Atec, Mus, Topog. Buys: Anytime. Book search. cc: AV. Tube: Great Portland St. "Situated within Holy Trinity Church. Libraries, small quantities and single volumes bought at all times. Wants lists welcomed. We post books worldwide."
Manager: Michael Pickering

OFFSTAGE THEATRE & CINEMA BOOKSHOP
37 Chalk Farm Road
London NW1 8AJ
(0171) 485 4996
Mon-Sun 10-6
Est. 1982. Small. Spec: Theatre: also Cinema, Media. Buys: Ring first. Book search. cc: AV. Tube: Chalk Farm. "Our s'hand section and new s'hand basement are adjuncts to the main new bookshop, covering all the Performing Arts."
Owner: B. Schwartz

PRIMROSE HILL BOOKS
134 Regents Park Road
London NW1 8XL
(0171) 586 2022
Fax (0171) 722 9653
Mon-Sat 10-6:30, Sun 11-6
Medium. Gen Stock and Fict, Biog, Chld. Buys: Ring first. cc: AV. Tube: Chalk Farm. "In attractive street conducive to relaxed browsing. Chalk Farm Rd. 5 min. adjacent to Primrose Hill. Gen wide-ranging stock. 1/3 s'hand. 50p-£50. Special order & post service for new books."
Owner: Jessica Graham

VINTAGE MAGAZINE SHOP LTD
8-9 Greenland Place
London NW1
(0171) 482 5083
Mon-Sat 10-7, Sun 12-8
Est. 1993. Small. Spec: Magazines: also Comics. Buys: Ring first. Tube: Camden Town. "Also film magazines, posters."
Manager: Gordon Harding

WALDEN BOOKS
38 Harmood Street
London NW1 8DP
(0171) 267 8146
Thur-Sun 10:30-6:30
Est. 1979. Medium. Gen Stock and Lit, Art. Buys: Ring first. Book search. Tube: Camden Town. "Located off Chalk Farm Rd. Gen stock with emphasis on the arts and good quality pbks."
Owner: David Tobin

Thomas Luck Kingsbury

AL-SAQI BOOKS
26 Westbourne Grove
London W2 5RH
(0171) 229 8543
Mon-Sat 10-6
Est. 1978. Small. Spec: Mid E: also Islamic World, Oriental, Trav. Buys: Ring first. cc: AVAmD. Tube: Queensway/Bayswater. "Also new books."

BAYSWATER BOOKS
27A Craven Terrace
London W2 3EL
(0171) 402 7398
Mon-Sat 11-7 (ring first)
Small. Spec: Biog: also Gen Stock and Comics, Graphic novels, Fict. Buys: Ring first. Book search. cc: AVAmD. Tube: Paddington/Lancaster Gate. "Small shop with interesting and varied stock. Something for everyone, including antiquarians."
Owner: Roger Noble

S.K. BILTCLIFFE BOOKS
289 Westbourne Crewe
London W11
(0181) 740 5326 (tel/fax)
Sat 9-3:30
Est. 1987. Small. Spec: C19th App Arts & Sci: also Gen stock and C19th Exhibitions, Trade Cat, Soc Hist. Cat: 1 pa: as above. Buys: Anytime. Booksearch. cc: AV. Tube: Notting Hill Gate. "Left off Portobello Road."
Owner: Susan Biltcliffe

BOOKS & THINGS
Arbras Gallery
292 Westbourne Grove
London W11 2PS
(0171) 370 5593 (tel/fax)
Sat 7-4
Est. 1972. Small. Spec: Decorative Art, Chld, Illus: also Posters, Mod 1sts edns. Cat: 1 pa: as above. Buys: Ring first. Book search. cc: VJ. Tube: Notting Hill Gate. "Market stall."
Owner: M. Steenson

BOOKS FOR AMNESTY INTERNATIONAL
139B King Street
Hammersmith
London W6 0UY
(0181) 749 0988
Mon-Fri 10-6, Sat 10-4
Est. 1994. Medium. Spec: Fict, Arts: also Gen Stock and Hist, Chld, Lifestyles (Txts, Trav, Int Af). Buys: Anytime. Tube: Hammersmith/Ravenscourt Park. "Less than 5 min along shopping street from station. Almost opp Baushwackers Wholefood Store. Over 50 sections. Quality books at bargain prices. The Information Section inc an amnesty dedicated ref and writing area."
Managers: T. Bissett, P. McHamish, D. Langton & E. Warren

BOOKS FOR COOKS
4 Blenheim Crescent
London W11 1NN
(0171) 221 1992
Mon-Sat 9:30-6
Small. Spec: Cookery and Wine. Buys: Anytime. cc: AvAmD. Tube: Notting Hill Gate. "Close to Portobello Road."
Owner: Heidi Lascelles

DEMETZY BOOKS
113 Portobello Road
London W11
(01993) 702209 (tel/fax)
Sat 7-2:30 (otherwise ring first)
Est. 1971. Medium. Spec: Fine Leather Bindings, Plate books: also Gen Stock and Chld, Dickens 1sts, Miniatures. Buys: Anytime. Booksearch. cc: VM. Tube: Notting Hill Gate. "Portobello Rd signposted from Nottinghill Gate. Shop opposite "Earl of Lonsdale" Pub. Wide stock covering many topics. Phone beforehand if you want to be sure of finding your topics at our outlet. Will also put together large consignments of 'Bindings for Interior Decorations' if contacted previously by phone or fax."
Owners: Paul & Marie Hutchinson

FAIRCROSS BOOKS
Strand Antiques, 166 Thames Street
Strand on the Green
London W4 3QS
(0181) 994 1912
Mon-Sun 12-5
Medium. Gen Stock. Cat: 2 pa: RC. Buys: Ring first. Book search. BR: Kew Bridge/Chiswick. "Also antiques."
Owners: B.A. & M. Sheppee

MUSIC AND VIDEO EXCHANGE BOOKSHOP

56 Notting Hill Gate
& 14 Pembridge Road
London W11 3HT
(0171) 229 8420
Mon-Sun 10-8
Est. 1985. Medium. Gen Stock and Art, Lit, US Comics. Buys: Anytime. cc: V. Tube: Notting Hill Gate. "Also records including classical selections. We buy, sell, exchange ALL s'hand books without exception. Nothing legal refused."

NOTTING HILL BOOKS

132 Palace Gardens Terrace
London W8 4RT
(0171) 727 5988
Mon-Sat 10:15-6, Thur 10:15-1
Est. 1969. Medium. Spec: Art, Lit Crit: also Gen Stock and Hist. Buys: Ring first. Tube: Notting Hill Gate. "Sell mainly remainders, some s'hand & review copies. Emphasis on scholarly rather than frivolous books, with a good pbk stand for students. Also 'coffee-table' books."
Owner: Sheila Ramage

FEM POEL ANTIQUARIAN BOOKS

The Arcade
113 Portobello Road
London W11
Sat 8:30-2
Est. 1983. Small. Spec: Gen and Continental Atqn. Buys: Anytime. Book search. Tube: Notting Hill Gate.
Owner: Fem Poel

BERNARD J. SHAPERO RARE BOOKS

80 Holland Park Avenue
London W11 3RB
(0171) 493 0876
Fax (0171) 379 4928
Mon-Fri 10-7, Sat 10-5
Est. 1979. Medium. Spec: Lit, Trav: also Gen Stock and Topog, Nat Hist, Illus. Cat: 6 pa. Buys: Anytime. Book search. cc: AVAmD. Tube: Holland Park. "Very near tube. Medium-sized print gallery downstairs."
Owner: Mr B. Shapero

THE TRAVEL BOOKSHOP LTD

13 Blenheim Crescent
London W11 2EE
(0171) 229 5260
Mon-Sat 10-6
Est. 1980. Medium. Spec: Trav: Cat: 4 pa: Trav. Buys: Ring first. Book search. cc: AVAm. Tube: Ladbroke Grove/Notting Hill Gate. "Stock both old & new travel books on all countries of the world. Travel taken in broadest sense, so include Hist, Fict set abroad, Anthrop, etc."
Owners: Sarah Anderson & Simon Gaul

WHOLEFOOD BOOKS

24 Paddington Street
London W1N 8DR
(0171) 935 3924
Mon-Thur 8:45-6, Fri 8:45-6:30, Sat 8:45-1
Small. Spec: Nutrition: also Health, Organic Culture, Alt Therapies. Buys: Ring first. cc: AV. Tube: Baker Street. "A book dept within a wholefood shop. Small selection of out-of-print books on these subjects. A larger number of new books."
Owner: Mrs Barham

THE ABBEY BOOKSHOP
4 The Apprentice Shop
Merton
London SW19 2DR
(0181) 740 0713/889 1674
Sat-Sun 10-5:30
Est. 1990. Small. Spec: Irish Interest, Contemporary Fict: also Gen Stock and Womens Stud, Psy, Phil. Buys: Anytime. Book search. Tube: Colliers Wood/South Wimbledon. "Situated in Craft Village (former Liberty's site) to rear of Sainsbury Savacentre. Merton Abbey Mills has four bookshops and a thriving weekend market which often includes bookstalls in addtion to bookshops."
Owners: C. Overfield & J. Hardin

J.A. ALLEN & CO. LTD (THE HORSEMAN'S BOOKSHOP)
1 Lower Grosvenor Place
Buckingham Palace Road
London SW1W 0EL
(0171) 834 5606
Fax (0171) 233 8001
Mon-Fri 9-5:30, Sat 9-1
Est. 1926. Medium. Spec: Horses: Cat: 6 pa: New books/occ Antq. Buys: Ring first. Book search. cc: AVAmD. Tube: Victoria. "Very specialized stock."
Owner: Joseph A. Allen

BENEDICTS BOOKSHOP
92 Lillie Road
London SW6 7SR
(0171) 385 4426
Mon-Sat 9:30-6
Medium. Spec: Lang Teaching: also Gen Stock. Buys: Anytime. Tube: West Brompton/Earl's Ct. "West Brompton tube closed Sat. Also s'hand goods."
Owner: Mr K.A. Benedict

BOOKS BOUGHT BOOKSHOP
357 Kings Road
London SW3
(0171) 352 9376
Mon-Sun 9:30-7 (occ later)
Est. 1982. Small. Gen Stock and Art, Fict, Perf Arts. Buys: Anytime. Tube: Sloane Sq./Bus: 11, 19, 22, 31. "Weekend sales:10%-20% off."
Owner: David Vale

BOOKTREE
Merton Abbey Mills
Merantun Way, South Wimbledon
London SW19 2RD
(0181) 540 2694
Fax (0181) 504 1141
Mon-Sun 10-5
Est. 1989. Spec: Crafts, Dover Books: also Craft Materials. Buys: Ring first. cc: AVAmDEJS. Tube: Colliers Wood. "Off the A3 (signs to Merton Park), A24. Northern Line. We are a craft shop with a strong selection of craft books, art source and children's activity."

JOANNA BOOTH
247 Kings Road
London SW3 5EL
(0171) 352 8998
Fax (0171) 376 7350
Mon-Sat 10-6
Est. 1965. Small. Spec: Fr: also Fine Bindings, Lit. Buys: Ring first. Book search. cc: AVAmD. Tube: Sloane Sq. "Prices range from £5-£500. Emphasis on finely bound books."
Owner: Joanna Booth

CHELSEA RARE BOOKS
313 Kings Road
London SW3 5EP
(0171) 351 0950
Fax (0171) 351 2928
Mon-Sat 10-6
Est. 1973. Medium. Gen Stock and Lit, Art. Cat: 2-3 pa. Buys: Ring first. Book search. cc: AVAmD. Tube: Sloane Sq.
Owner: Mr L.S. Bernard

CRUSAID
17-19 Upper Tachbrook Street
London SW1P 1JU
(0171) 233 8736
Mon-Fri 10:30-5:30, Sat 10-5
Est. 1994. Large. Gen Stock. Buys: Anytime. cc: AVE. BR/Tube: Victoria. "Charity shop dealing generally in all subject areas."
Managers: Ian Hankins & Pat Kemp

PAUL FOSTER'S BOOKSHOP
46-52 Church Road
Barnes
London SW13 0DQ
(0181) 748 1858
Tue-Sat 10:30-6
Spec: Illus: also Gen Stock and Atqn, Bindings, 1st edn. Cat: 2 pa: Gen. Buys: Anytime. cc: AVEJS. BR: Barnes/Tube: Hammersmith.
Owner: Paul Foster

GLOUCESTER ROAD BOOKSHOP
123 Gloucester Road
London SW7 4TE
(0171) 370 3503
Fax (0171) 373 0610
Mon-Fri 8:30-10:30, Sat-Sun 10:30-6:30
Est. 1983. Medium. Gen Stock and Lit, Hist, Art. Cat: 1 pa: Mod Lit. Buys: Anytime. Book search. cc: AVAm. Tube: Gloucester Road. "150 yards from tube. Friendly atmosphere and brightly lit shop, very long opening hours."
Owner: Nick Dennys, Manageress: Sarah Rogers

GRAYS OF WESTMINSTER
40 Churton Street
Pimlico
London SW1V 2LP
(0171) 828 4925/828 3218
Fax (0171) 976 5783
Mon-Fri 9:30-5:30, Sat 9:30-2
Est. 1987. Small. Spec: Nikon Cameras. Buys: Anytime. Book search. cc: AVAm. Tube: Pimlico. "Strictly and only new, s'hand and out-of-print Nikon books."
Owners: Gray Levett & Nick Wynne

HARRINGTON BROTHERS
253 Kings Road
Chelsea
London SW3 5EL
(0171) 352 5689
Fax (0171) 823 3449
Mon-Sat 10-6
Est. 1968. Large. Spec: Trav, Eng Lit 1st edn: also Gen Stock and Bound sets, Fore-edge paintings, Nat Hist.

Cat: 2 pa: Gen. Buys: Ring first. Book search. cc: AVAmEJS. Tube: Sloan Sq. & South Kensington. "Opp Carlyle Sq. We are constantly being told by our customers that we have the largest accessible stock in the world."
Owners: Peter & Adrian Harrington

THOMAS HENEAGE BOOKS
42 Duke Street
St. James's
London SW1Y 6DJ
(0171) 930 9223
Fax (0171) 839 9223
Mon-Fri 10-6
Large. Spec: Art, Hist: also Applied Art, Ancient Art. Cat: 4-6 pa. Buys: Ring first. Book search. cc: AV. Tube: Green Park.
Owner: Thomas Heneage

IL LIBRO
Chenil Galleries
181-183 Kings Road
London SW3
(0171) 352 9041
Mon-Sat 10-6
Est. 1978. Small. Gen Stock. Buys: Anytime. Book search. cc: AVAm. Tube: Sloane Sq./S. Kensington. "Second shop at 535 Kings Road, SW10 0S2 (0171-823 3248), stocks more prints. Tue-Sat 10-7."
Owner: G. Toscani

J. G. BOOKS
17 Streatham Vale
London SW16 5SE
(0181) 764 4669 (tel/fax)
Mon-Fri 10-6, Sat 10-5, Wed close
Est. 1980. Small. Spec: Reptiles: Cat: 2 pa: Amphibians. Buys: Ring first. BR: Streatham Common. "Also books on amphibians and Gemmology."
Owner: John Greatwood

DON KELLY BOOKS
Antiquarius M13
135 Kings Road
London SW3 4PW
(0171) 352 4690
Fax (0171) 731 0482
Mon-Sat 10-6
Est. 1980. Small. Spec: Fine & Applied Art Ref. Cat: 1 pa. Buys: Ring first. Book search. cc: AVE. Tube: Sloane Sq. "Situated in Antiquarius Antique Market, Kings Road."
Owner: Don Kelly

THE MAP HOUSE
54 Beauchamp Place, Knightsbridge
London SW3 1NY
(0171) 589 4325/584 8559
Fax (0171) 589 1041
Mon-Fri 9:45-5:45, Sat 10:30-5
Est. 1907. Small. Spec: Atlases: Cat: occ. Buys: Ring first. cc: AVAmD. Tube: Knightsbridge. "Specialist in antique maps covering all areas of the globe, also prints and engravings."
Owner: C.A. Savile

MY BACK PAGES
8-10 Balham Station Road
London SW12 9SG
(0181) 675 9346
Mon-Sat 10-8, Sat 10-7
Est. 1990. Large. Spec: Lit, Art: also Gen Stock and Mod 1sts, Acad, Atqn. Buys: Anytime. BR/Tube: Balham. "Only yards from BR & tube. Large car park next to shop. Locally famous and appreciated. Well over 20,000 books, overflowing general stock. Leisure records and collectables."
Owner: Douglas Jeffers

OLD TOWN BOOKS
30 Old Town
Clapham
London SW4 0LB
(0171) 498 0998
Tue-Fri 10-7, Sat 10-6, Sun 2-5
Est. 1991. Small. Spec: Italy, Phil: also Gen Stock. Buys: Anytime. Book search. cc: AV. Tube: Clapham Common. "Follow the pavement round from tube or refuse to get off 88 bus until it parks outside. Bargains boasted of."
Owner: John Phillimore

ORBIS BOOKS (LONDON) LTD
66 Kenway Road
London SW5 0RD
(0171) 370 2210
Fax (0171) 244 6842
Mon-Fri 9:30-5:30, Sat 9:30-4:30
Large. Spec: USSR, E. Eur, Baltic States: Cat: 2 pa. Buys: Ring first. Book search. cc: AVAm. Tube: Earl's Court. "5 min from tube, Earl's Court exit. Books in English & Polish, Russian, Czech, Slovak, Ukranian. Centre for libraries and private individuals."
Owners: J. & Dr A. Kulczycka

PAUL ORSSICH
117 Munster Road
Fulham
London SW6 6DH
(0171) 736 3869
Fax (0171) 371 9886
Mon-Fri 10-6 (or by appt)
Small. Spec: Spain & Hispanic Studies: also Illus. Cat: 2 pa: Hispanic Studies in Span. Buys: Ring first. Book search. cc: AV. Tube: Parsons Green. "200 yards from Fulham Road. Good access via No. 14 bus. Left out of tube, left at first traffic lights, right at next lights. 10 min."
Owner: Paul Orssich

PICKERING & CHATTO LTD
17 Pall Mall
London SW1Y 5NB
(0171) 930 2515
Fax (0171) 930 8627
Mon-Fri 9:30-5:30
Small. Spec: Econ: also Lit, Sci, Med. Cat: 20 pa. Buys: Ring first. Book search. cc: Am. Tube: Piccadilly Circus. "Fine 1sts & Early editions."
Mng. Dir: J. Hudson

JOHN RANDALL (BOOKS OF ASIA)
47 Moreton Street
London SW1V 2NY
(0171) 630 5331
Fax (0171) 821 6544
Tue-Fri 12-6, Sat 10-5
Est. 1979. Medium. Spec: Oriental: also Mid E. Cat: occ: Art, Gen. Buys: Ring first. Book search. cc: AVAm. Tube: Pimlico. "Specialist shop with atqn, s'hand & new books on SE Asia, India, Cent Asia, Mid E. Also some on Pacific, Siberia, Africa & Latin America."
Owner: John Randall

W.M. REEVES BOOKSELLER LTD
1A Norbury Crescent
London SW16 4JR
(0181) 764 2108
Mon-Fri 9:15-4:30
Small. Spec: Violin. Cat: 6 pa: Atqn, Mus. Buys: Ring first. BR: Norbury.
Owner: W.M. Reeves

RESPONSE BOOKSHOP
300 Old Brompton Road
London SW5 9JF
(0171) 370 4606
Fax (0171) 370 3918
Mon-Sat 9:30-5
Small. Gen Stock and Lit, Gay, Fem. Tube: Earl's Court. "Donations only."
Owner: Response Community Projects Ltd

SIMS REED LTD
58 Jermyn Street
London SW1Y 6LX
(0171) 493 5660
Fax (0171) 493 8468
Mon-Fri 10-6 (Sat by appt)
Est. 1972. Medium. Spec: Art: also Fine C19th & C20th Illus. Cat: 8-10 pa. Buys: Anytime. cc:AVAm. Tube: Green Park. "We stock rare, out-of-print & new reference books on fine & applied Art."
Directors: M. Reed, J. Sims, & N. Neve

SIMS REED LTD
43A Duke Street
London SW1Y 6DD
(0171) 493 5660
Fax (0171) 493 8468
Mon-Fri 10-6 (Sat by appt)
Medium. Spec: Art. Cat: 6-7 pa. Buys: Anytime. cc: AVAm. Tube: Green Park.
Owners: M. Reed & J. Sims

SPINK & SON LTD
5-7 King Street
St. James's
London SW1Y 6QS
(0171) 930 7888
Fax (0171) 839 4853
Mon-Fri 9:30-5:30
Est. 1666. Large. Spec: Numismatics. Cat: 10 pa: Numismatics. Buys: Ring first. cc: AVAm. Tube: Green Park/Piccadilly Circus. "Interested in buying out-of-print Numismatic books."

BARBARA STONE
Antiquarius
135 Kings Road
London SW3 4PW
(0171) 351 0963
Fax (0181) 365 2123
Mon-Sat 10:30-5:30
Est. 1975. Small. Spec: Chld: also Illus, Art, Private Press. Cat: 6 pa. Buys: Ring first. Tube: South Kensington. "Specialist in chld & Illus books."
Owner: Barbara Stone

SWANS BOOKSHOP
5 Tooting Market
Tooting High Street
London SW17 0RH
(0181) 672 4980
Mon-Sat 9-5:30, Wed close
Est. 1969. Medium. Gen Stock and Mills & Boon, War, Horror & SF. Buys: Anytime. Tube: Tooting Broadway.
Owner: R. Stacy

JOHN THORNTON
455 Fulham Road
London SW10 9UZ
(0171) 352 8810
Mon-Sat 10-5:30
Est. 1983. Medium. Spec: Theol, Classics: also Gen Stock and V Sackville-West, Gard. Buys: Ring first. Book search. Tube: Fulham Broadway. "14 bus stops outside, 11 & 22 stop on King's Road with a short walk up Gunter Grove."
Owner: John Thornton

TLON BOOKS
Unit 7-8, The Apprentice Shop
Merton Abbey Mills
London SW19 2RD
(0181) 540 4371
Mon-Fri 11-6 (Winter 10:30-5:30) Sat-Sun 10-6
Est. 1989. Medium. Spec: Hist, Soc Sci: also Gen Stock. Buys: Ring first. cc: AVE. Tube: South Wimbledon. "10 min from tube. 3 other book dealers within close proximity. Also records & ceramics. Traveller's cheques & US dollars accepted."
Owner: Marek Siemaszko

VILLAGE BOOKS
17 Shrubbery Road
London SW16 2AS
(0181) 677 2667
Mon-Sat 10:30-6 (Wed ring first)
Est. 1971. Small. Spec: Eso, Loc Hist: also Gen Stock and Latin America. Cat: occ. Buys: Anytime. Book search. BR/Tube: Streatham Hill/Streatham/Brixton. "New Esoteric Centre (Tarot, Palmistry), mail order service. Periodic fair/sales on first Sun of each month."
Owner: Mr M. Bastians

WHISTLER'S STOP BOOKSHOP
87 Replingham Road
Southfields
London SW18 5LS
(0181) 875 0449
Mon-Sat 10:30-1:30. 3-5:30
Est. 1992. Medium. Spec: Eng, Sci, Mus: also Gen Stock and cinema, Chess. Buys: Anytime. Book search. Tube: Southfields.

London - South-East

121 BOOKSHOP & ANARCHIST CENTRE
121 Railton Road
Brixton
London SE24 0LR
(0171) 274 6655
Mon 5-8, Tue & Thur 6-9, Sat 1-5
Small. Spec: Anarchism, Anarchist Hist & Theo: also WS, Animal Rights, Eco. Buys: Anytime. Tube: Brixton. BR: Herne Hill. "Also anti-racist, anti-fascist, Ireland, Gay, Secret State. Pamphlets, T-shirts, badges, magazines on above topics, advice on housing and squatting. Free information. Cafes and events-meetings, music, videos."

BOOKSHOP BLACKHEATH LTD
74 Tranquil Vale
Blackheath
London SE3 0BN
(0181) 852 4786
Mon-Sat 9:30-5 (variable)
Est. 1947. Medium. Spec: London: also Gen Stock. Buys: Ring first. BR: Blackheath. "Also prints."
Owner: Mr L. Leff

CHAPTER TWO
199 Plumstead Common Road
London SE18 2UJ
(0181) 316 4972
Fax (0181) 854 5963
Mon-Fri 9:30-5:30, Sat 10-1, Wed close
Small. Spec: Plymouth Brethren: also Dispensational Fundamental Christianity. Cat: 3-5 pa. Buys: Ring first. Book search. BR: Woolwich Arsenal. "53 bus from Trafalgar Sq. passes the door. BR from Charing Cross. Best to call us first. We are the chief suppliers in UK of 'Plymouth Brethren' literature. New & s'hand."
Owner: Edwin Cross

COFFEEHOUSE BOOKSHOP
139 Greenwich South Street
London SE10 8NX
(0181) 692 3885
Mon-Sat 10-5:30, Thur close
Est. 1978. Small. Spec: Lit: also Gen Stock and Mus, Magazines, Comics. Buys: Anytime. BR: Greenwich. "Also records, tapes, CDs, postcards etc."
Owner: Ethan Golden

COLLECTED WORKS
3 Melbourne Terrace
Melbourne Grove
London SE22 8RE
Mon-Sat 10-6
Est. 1986. Medium. Spec: Mil, Hist, Atqn, Collecting: also Gen Stock and Lit, Fict, Art, SF, Crime Fict. Buys: Anytime. BR: East Dulwich. "37 bus stops outside shop. Pace Drif, we are not in West Dulwich."
Owner: Jon Gunson

GREENWICH BOOKSHOP
37 King William Walk
London SE10 9HU
(0181) 858 5789
Mon-Sat 10:30-5:30, Sun 10-6
Est. 1970. Medium. Gen Stock. Buys: Anytime. Book search. cc: AVAmD. BR: Greenwich.
Owner: Martin Newman

HILLYERS
301 Sydenham Road
London SE26 5EW
(0181) 778 6361
Mon-Fri 9-4, Sat 9-2, Wed close
Est. 1953. Small. Gen Stock. Buys: Ring first. BR: Sydenham. "1/2 antiques and 1/2 s'hand books."
Owner: Terry Hillyer

KIRKDALE BOOKSHOP
272 Kirkdale
London SE26 4RS
(0181) 778 4701
Mon-Sat 9-5:30
Est. 1966. Medium. Gen Stock. Buys: Anytime. cc: AV. BR: Sydenham. "New & s'hand - well worth a visit."
Owner: Mrs G. Seeney

MARCET BOOKS
4A Nelson Road
Greenwich
London SE10 9JB
(0181) 853 5408/858 7524
Mon-Sun 10:30-5:30
Est. 1981. Medium. Spec: Maritime: also Gen Stock and Trav, Art, Topog. Cat: 2 pa: Trav. Buys: Anytime. cc: AV. BR: Greenwich.
Owner: Martin Kemp

ROGERS TURNER BOOKS LTD
22 Nelson Road
Greenwich
London SE10 9JB
(0181) 853 5271 (tel/fax)
Mon-Sun 10-6
Est. 1976. Medium. Spec: Atqn, Horology: also Gen Stock and Phil, Hist of Sci. Cat: 6 pa: Horology, Sci, Ling, Hist, Ger. Buys: Anytime. Book search. cc: AVAmD. BR: Greenwich.
Owners: P. Rogers & A. Turner

ANTHONY J. SIMMONDS
23 Nelson Road
Greenwich
London SE10 9JB
(0181) 853 1727
Fax (0181) 305 0649
Mon-Sat 10-6
Est. 1972. Medium. Spec: Maritime Cat: 1 pa. Buys: Ring first. Book search. BR: Greenwich. "We sell new, s'hand & atqn Naval books."
Owner: Mr A.J. Simmonds

THE SOUTH LONDON BOOK CENTRE
11-19 Stockwell Street
Greenwich
London SE10 9JN
(0181) 853 2151
Mon-Fri 10-6, Sat-Sun 9-5
Est. 1987. Medium. Spec: Art, Maritime. also Gen Stock and Mod 1sts, Archeo. Buys: Anytime. BR: Greenwich. "Ten dealers represented offering a wide range of stock - paperbacks to collectors items."
Owner: Mr Les Berry

SPREADEAGLE BOOKSHOP
8 Nevada Street
Greenwich
London SE10 9JL
(0181) 305 1666
Mon-Sun 10-1:30, 2:30-5:30
Est. 1954. Medium. Gen Stock and Topog, Hist, Cinema. Buys: Anytime. cc: AVAmD. BR: Greenwich. "Opp. the Theatre. Also stock printed ephemera."
Owner: Richard Moy

TLON BOOKS
Elephant & Castle Shopping Centre
London SE1 6TE
(0171) 701 0360
Mon-Sat 11-6
Est. 1993. Medium. Spec: Hist, Soc Sci: also Gen Stock. Buys: Ring first. cc: AVDE. Tube: Elephant & Castle. "Only books sold at this branch."
Owner: Marek Siemaszko

WARWICK LEADLAY GALLERY
5 Nelson Road
Greenwich
London SE10 9JB
(0181) 858 0317
Fax (0181) 853 1773
Mon-Sat 9:30-5:30, Sun & Public Hols 11-5:30
Large. Spec: Illus, Nelsoniana: also Atlases, Hist, Topog. Cat: occ. Buys: Ring first. cc: AVAmDS. BR: Greenwich. "Primarily print & map dealers."
Owner: Warwick Leadlay

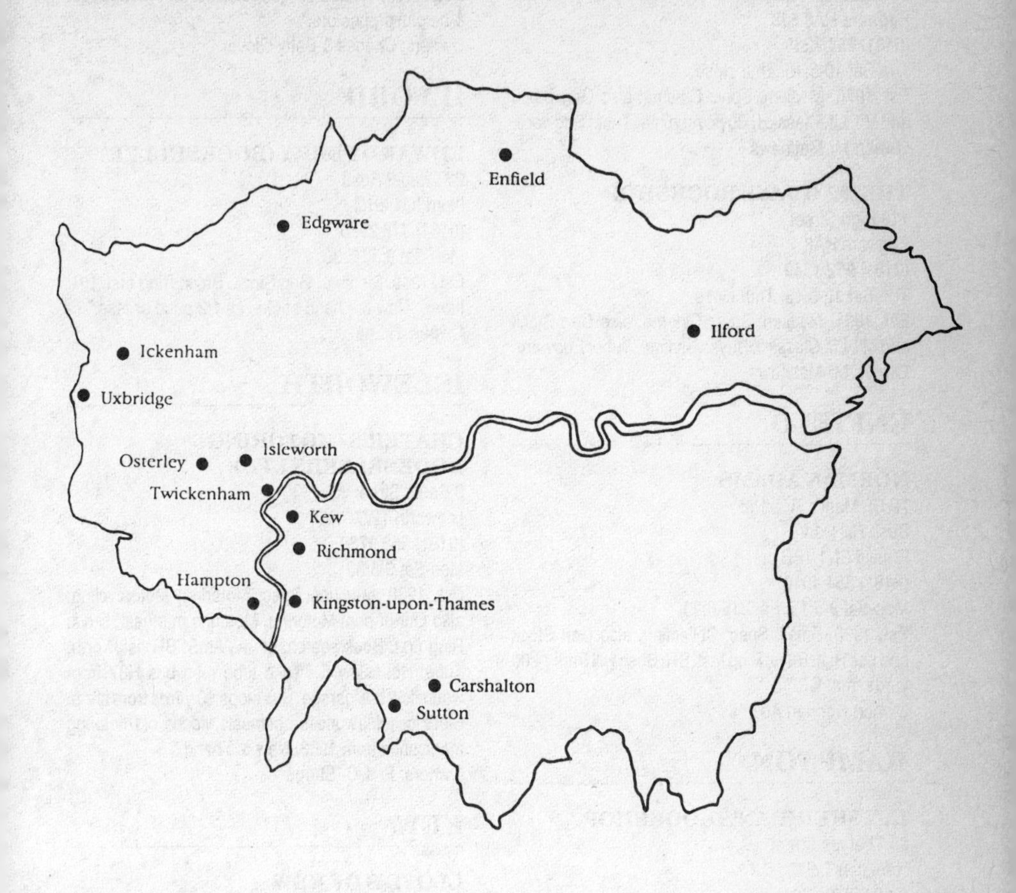

CARSHALTON

CROYDON BOOKSHOP
304 Carshalton Road
Carshalton SM5 3QB
(0181) 643 6857
Tue-Sat 10:30-5:30
Est. 1953. Large. Gen Stock. Buys: Anytime. BR: Carshalton.
Owners: P. Reding & P.J. Rogers

EDGWARE

BOOKMARK
67 High Street
Edgware HA8 7DD
(0181) 905 6993
Tue-Sat 10-5:30, Wed 10-4
Medium. Spec: SF, Football: also Gen Stock and Sport. Buys: Anytime. Tube: Edgware.
Owner: Mark Matthews

THE TWO JAYS BOOKSHOP
14 Whitchurch Lane
Edgware HA8 6JZ
(0181) 951 3266
Tue-Sat 10-5:15, Thur close
Est. 1976. Medium. Spec: Cinema: also Gen Stock and Mil, Lit, Classics. Buys: Anytime. Tube: Edgware.
Owner: Mr Matthews

THE TWO JAYS BOOKSHOP
119 High Street
Edgware HA8
(0181) 952 1349
Tue-Sat 10-5:15, Thur close
Est. 1994. Medium. Spec: Cinema: also Gen Stock and Mil, Lit, Classics. Buys: Anytime. Tube: Edgware.
Owner: Mr Matthews

ENFIELD

NORMAN ADAMS
72 St. Mark's Road
Bush Hill Park
Enfield EN1 1BB
(0181) 364 4010
Mon-Sat 9-5:15, Fri 9:15-6:30
Est. 1990. Small. Spec: Collecting: also Gen Stock and Loc Hist. Buys: Ring first. BR: Bush Hill Park. "200 yards from BR."
Owner: Norman Adams

HAMPTON

IAN SHERIDAN'S BOOKSHOP
34 Thames Street
Hampton TW12 2DX
(0181) 979 1704
Mon-Sun 10:30-7 (Winter 10:30-6)
Est. 1960. Large. Gen Stock and Atqn. Buys: Ring first. BR: Hampton. "In the village of Hampton, 1 mile from Hampton Court Palace."
Owner: Ian Sheridan

ICKENHAM

THE HAYES BOOKSHOP
6 Glebe Avenue
Ickenham UB10 8PB
(018956) 37725
Tue-Sat 9:30-5:30 (Mon by appt)
Est. 1970. Medium. Gen Stock and Remainders. Buys: Anytime. Book search. Tube: Ickenham. "Good, clean, warm. Well-arranged stock with knowledgeable & helpful proprietors."
Owners: Charles & Betty Glover

ILFORD

EDWARD TERRY (BOOKSELLER)
26 Chapel Road
Ilford IG1 2HG
(0181) 478 2850
Mon-Sat 9:30-5:30
Est. 1940. Medium. Gen Stock. Buys: Ring first. BR: Ilford. "New & s'hand books, all 1/2 price or less."
Owner: T. Lea

ISLEWORTH

CHATER'S (MOTORING BOOKSELLERS LTD)
8 South Street
Isleworth TW7 7BG
(0181) 568 9750
Mon-Sat 9-5:30
Est. 1966. Medium. Spec: Motoring, Motorcycling: also Out-of-print Motoring, Motoring manuals. Buys: Ring first. Book search. cc: AVAmS. BR: Isleworth, Tube: Hounslow E. "Take tube then bus H37 from Hounslow bus garage. Bus stops 10 yards from shop. Stock includes workshop manuals, videos, old motoring magazines from 1903. New & s'hand."
Owners: F. & C. Stroud

KEW

LLOYD'S OF KEW
9 Mortlake Terrace
Kew TW9 3DT
(0181) 940 2512
Mon-Fri 10-4, Sat 10-5:30, Wed close
Small. Spec: Gard: also Gen Stock and Botany. Cat: 1 pa: as above. Buys: Anytime. Book search. cc: AVAm. Tube: Kew Gardens. "Shop is just off Kew Green at junction of Kew Road and Mortlake Road, close to Botanic Gardens. Parking available nearby."
Owner: Daniel Lloyd

OSTERLEY

OSTERLEY BOOKSHOP
168A Thornbury Road
Osterley TW7 4QE
(0181) 560 6206
Mon-Sun 10-5:30
Est. 1976. Medium. Gen Stock. Buys: Anytime. Tube: Osterley. "Situated in the old Osterley station. Follow sign from tube to Osterley Park. Stock changes frequently."
Owners: Ms P.Smith & Mr A. Vesely

RICHMOND

W. & A. HOUBEN
2 Church Court
Richmond TW9 1JL
(0181) 940 1055
Mon-Sat 10-6
Est. 1960. Medium. Gen Stock and Lit, Hist, Trav. Buys: Anytime. cc: AV. Tube: Richmond.
Manager: Chris Dunlop

THE RICHMOND BOOKSHOP
20 Red Lion Street
Richmond TW9 1RW
(0181) 940 5512
Fri & Sat 9:30-6
Medium. Spec: The Arts, Humanities: also Gen Stock and Biog, Mil, Eng & For Topog. Buys: Ring first. BR/ Tube: Richmond. "Stock contains a high percentage of review copies and books published during the C20th."
Owners: R. Rey & J. Prescott

SUTTON

LENS OF SUTTON
4 Westmead Road
Sutton SM1 4JT
(0181) 642 0981
Mon-Sat 11-6, Wed 11-2
Small. Spec: Railways, Buses: also Trams. Buys: Ring first. BR: Carshalton.
Owner: John L. Smith

TWICKENHAM

ANTHONY C. HALL
30 Staines Road
Twickenham TW2 5AH
(0181) 898 2638 (tel/fax)
Mon-Fri 9-5:30, ec Wed
Est. 1966. Large. Spec: Russia, E. Eur: also Gen Stock and Mid E, Asia, Africa. Cat: 3 pa: as above. Buys: Ring first. Book search. cc: AV. BR: Strawberry Hill. "Booksearch only in specialist subjects."
Owner: Anthony C. Hall

MARION PITMAN BOOKS
29 Hampton Road
Twickenham TW2 5QE
(0181) 898 7165
Tue, Thur & Sat pm (ring first)
Est. 1978. Medium. Gen Stock. Buys: Ring first. BR: Strawberry Hill. "Bus from Twickenham. BR: 281/267 - changing to bric-a-brac and collectables, book stock decreasing. One person business - opening variable - ring first."
Owner: M. Pitman

UXBRIDGE

T.H. BARNARD
11 Windsor Street
Uxbridge UB8 1AB
(01895) 258054
Mon-Sat 9:30-5, Wed close
Medium. Gen Stock. Buys: Anytime. Tube: Uxbridge. "5 min from tube."
Owner: T.H. Barnard

Bedfordshire

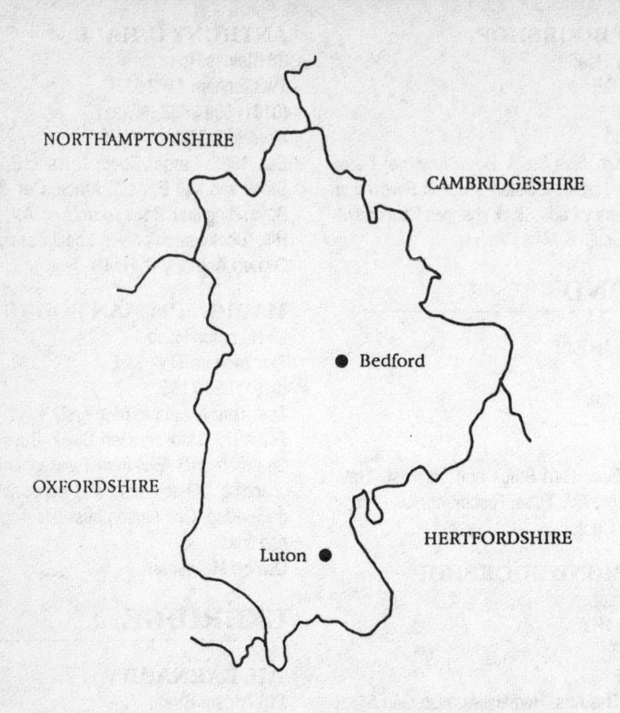

BEDFORD

THE EAGLE BOOKSHOP

103 Castle Road
Bedford MK40 3QP
(01234) 269295
Mon-Sat 10-6, Wed close
Est. 1991. Medium. Spec: Sci: also Gen Stock. Buys: Ring first. Book search. BR: Bedford. "Small family-run bookshop selling a wide range of s'hand, out-of-print & collectable books."
Owner: Peter Budek

RICHARD WILDMAN

20 Mill Street
Bedford MK40 3HD
(01234) 343905
Mon-Sat 12-6
Small. Gen Stock. Buys: Ring first. BR: Bedford. "Small general stock classified systematically."
Owner: Richard Wildman

LUTON

FOYE GALLERY

15 Stanley Street
Luton LU1 5AL
(01582) 38487
Mon-Sat 9:30-5
Est. 1960. Small. Gen Stock. Buys: Ring first. cc: AmD. BR: Luton. "Maps and prints, reprints, framing, and restoration services available. Watercolours for sale."
Owner: Michael Fleming

BERKSHIRE

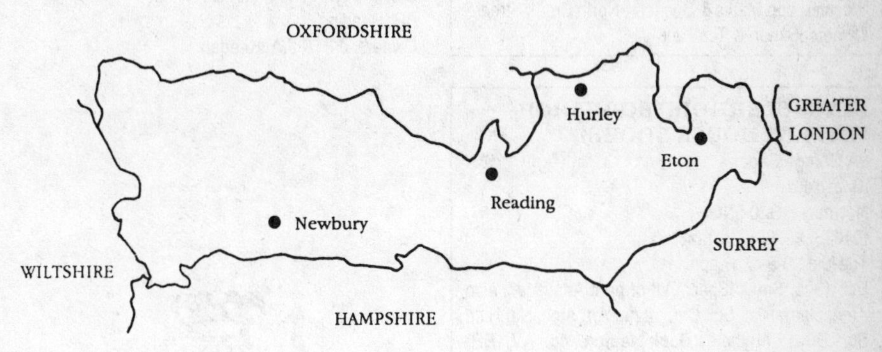

ETON

ETON ANTIQUE SHOP

88 High Street
Eton SL4 6AF
(01753) 855534
Mon-Sat 10-5:30, Sun 12-6
Est. 1976. Medium. Gen Stock and Atqn. Buys: Anytime. Book search. "Very good selection of illus and leather bound books always in stock. Also maps and prints."
Owner: Miss D. Kernec

HURLEY

RUSSELL JONES BOOKS

The Coach House
High Street
Hurley SL6 5NB
(01628) 824237
Mon-Sat 8-7 (ring first)
Est. 1958. Medium. Spec: Farm Machinery, Tractors: also Early Civ Eng/Rd Trans, Steam Cars. Cat: 12 pa: as above. Buys: Ring first. BR: Hurley. "Located in village High Street and easy to find. UK and Int'l leading specialist in these subjects."
Owner: Russell Jones

NEWBURY

INVICTA BOOKSHOP
8 Cromwell Place
Newbury RG13 1AF
(01635) 31176
Mon-Sat 10:30-5, Wed close
Est. 1969. Medium. Spec: Cookery: also Gen Stock and Sci. Buys: Ring first. Book search. BR: Newbury. "Located opp Marks & Spencer, North Brook Street."
Owners: Simon & Tim Hall

KINGSCLERE OLD BOOKSHOP (WYSEBY HOUSE BOOKS)
2A George Street
Kingsclere
Newbury RG20 5NQ
(01635) 297995 (tel/fax)
Tue-Sat 10-5 or by appt
Est. 1995. Small. Spec: Out of print Arts, Atec: also Atqn, Gard, Hist, Sci. Cat: 12 pa: Art, Atec, Nat Hist, Sci. Buys: Anytime. Book search. cc: AV. BR: Basingstoke/Newbury. "Kingsclere is near M3 & M4."
Owner: Dr Tim Oldham

READING

KEEGAN'S BOOKSHOP
Merchant's Place
Friar Street
Reading RG1 1DT
(01734) 587253
Mon-Sat 9-5:30
Est. 1979. Medium. Spec: Rail, Trans, Mil: also Gen Stock. Buys: Ring first. cc: AV.
BR: Reading.
Owners: J.P. & J.A. Keegan

Bristol

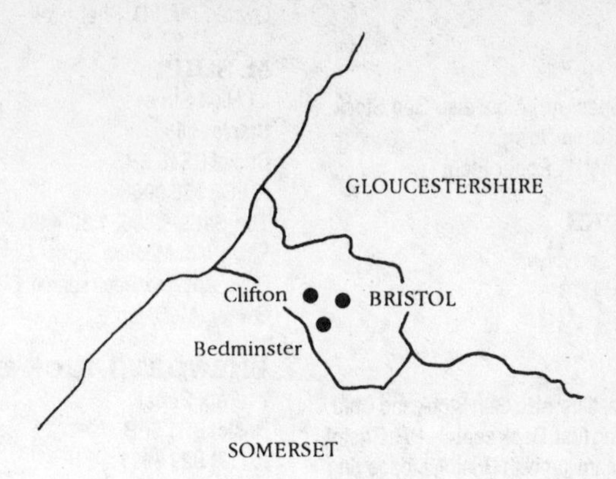

BRISTOL

BEWARE OF THE LEOPARD

77 The Covered Market
St. Nicholas Street
Bristol BS1 1LJ
(0117) 925 7277
Mon-Sat 10-4
Small. Spec: Lit, Humanities: also Gen Stock. Buys: Anytime. BR: Bristol Temple Meads. "Situated in Central Bristol in market behind historic Corn Exchange, 2 multi-storey car parks nearby. A fast-changing and very resonably-priced range of books covering most subjects."
Owner: David Jackson

JOHN BRACEWELL BOOKSHOP (ex JOHN ROBERTS BOOKSHOP)

43 Triangle West
Clifton
Bristol BS8 1ES
(0117) 926 8568
Mon-Sat 9:30-5:30
Est. 1955. Medium. Gen Stock. Cat: occ: Gen. Buys: Ring first. Book search. cc: AV. BR: Bristol Temple Meads. "Good selection of prints, mostly topographical of UK, some maps."
Owner: John Bracewell

BRISTOL BOOKS (ACADEMIC)

180C Cheltenham Road
Montpelier
Bristol BS6 5RB
(0117) 924 5458
Fax (0117) 924 6248
Mon-Sat 10-6
Est. 1993. Medium. Spec: Phil, Psy: also Gen Stock and Pol, Classics, Lit Crit. Cat: 6 lists pa: Misc. Buys: Ring first. Book search. BR: Temple Meads/Montpelier. "Near to Montpelier branch-line BR. Wide range of general academic subjects."
Owner: Garth O'Donnell

BRISTOL BOOKS

180 Cheltenham Road
Montpelier
Bristol BS6 5RB
(0117) 924 5458
Fax (0117) 924 6248
Mon-Sat 10-6
Est. 1985. Medium. Spec: Lit Crit, Phil: also Gen Stock and Ling, Black Studies. Buys: Anytime. Book search. BR: Bristol Temple Meads. "Largest s'hand bookshop in Bristol at the moment."
Owner: Garth O'Donnell

BRISTOL BOOKS (BEDMINSTER)

5 North Street
Bedminster
Bristol BS3 1EN
(0117) 963 4716
Mon-Sat 10-5:30
Medium. Spec: Beat & Pulp: also Gen Stock. Buys: Anytime. Book search. BR: Bristol Temple Meads.
Owner: Garth O'Donnell

COTHAM HILL BOOKSHOP
39A Cotham Hill
Bristol BS6 6JY
(0117) 973 2344
Mon-Sat 9:30-5:30
Est. 1981. Medium. Spec: Art, Atqn: also Gen Stock. Buys: Anytime. BR: Clifton Down.
Owners: Michael Garbett & Roger Plant

GOLDNEY BOOKS
18 Clifton Road
Clifton
Bristol BS8 1AQ
(0117) 923 7408
Wed-Sat 10:30-5:30
Small. Spec: Mod 1sts, Illus: also Gen Stock and Chld, Wine, Local. Buys: Ring first. Book search. BR: Bristol Temple Meads. "If unfamiliar with Bristol, please ring for directions. Selected stock with emphasis on condition & our spec. subjects. Mail order service."
Owners: Annette Appleton & Steve Newland

HARLEQUIN BOOKS
70 High Street
Staple Hill
Bristol BS16 5HN
(0117) 970 1801
Mon-Sat 10-5:30
Est. 1995. Small. Spec: Topog, Trans: also Gen Stock and Fict, Ref. Buys: Anytime. Book search. BR: Bristol Parkway. "Aim for M32 junction 1 roundabout, follow signs to Staple Hill."
Owner: B.W. Ball

PATTERSON & LIDDLE
2C Chandos Road
Redland
Bristol BS6 6PE
(0272) 731205
Mon-Sat 10-6
Est. 1983. Medium. Spec: Railways (BR): also Gen Stock and Canals, Bristol, Fine Bindings, Avia. Buys: Anytime. Book search. cc: AV. BR: Redland. "Local maps and prints, railway posters, easy parking."
Owners: John Patterson & Steve Little

S.P.C.K
79 Park Street
Bristol BS1 5PF
(0117) 926 8568
Mon-Sat 9-5:30, Fri 9:30-5:30
Medium. Spec: Religious books. Buys: Ring first. cc: AV. BR: Bristol Temple Meads. "Large stock of remainder & s'hand books."
Owner: Mr B.D. Shellswell

M. SHIPP
21 High Street
Staple Hill
Bristol BS16 5HB
(0117) 956 9966
Tue-Sat 9-12:30, 1:30-4:30, Wed close
Est. 1946. Medium. Spec: Collecting: also Gen Stock. Buys: Anytime. Book search. BR: Bristol Temple Meads.
Owner: M. Shipp

UNSWORTH, RICE & COE
71 Park Street
Bristol BS1 5PB
(0117) 929 9991
Fax (0171) 930 4443
Mon-Sat 10-6, Sun 12-4:30
Est. 1994. Large. Spec: Arts, Soc Sci: also Gen Stock and Acad. Buys: Anytime. Book search. cc: AVAmDS. BR: Bristol Temple Meads. "Good quality s'hand & cut-price books."
Owners: C. Unsworth, T. Rice & S. Coe

WELLINGTON BOOKS
4 Waterloo Street
Clifton Village
Bristol BS8 4BT
(0117) 973 9848
Mon-Sat 10-6
Est. 1991. Medium. Spec: Sci, Tech: also Gen Stock and Atec. Buys: Anytime. Book search. cc: AV. BR: Bristol Temple Meads. "We're 5 min walk from the Clifton Suspension Bridge. Our one claim to fame: we do not stock children's books."
Owner: Mr L. Gasparro

THE WISE OWL BOOKSHOP
26 Upper Maudlin Street
Bristol BS2 8DJ
(0117) 926 2738
Mon-Sat 10:30-5:30
Est. 1969. Medium. Spec: Mus: also Gen Stock and Theatre. Cat: occ. Buys: Anytime. BR: Bristol Temple Meads. "Also records, tapes & CDs."
Owner: Mrs P.K. Gilbert

BUCKINGHAMSHIRE

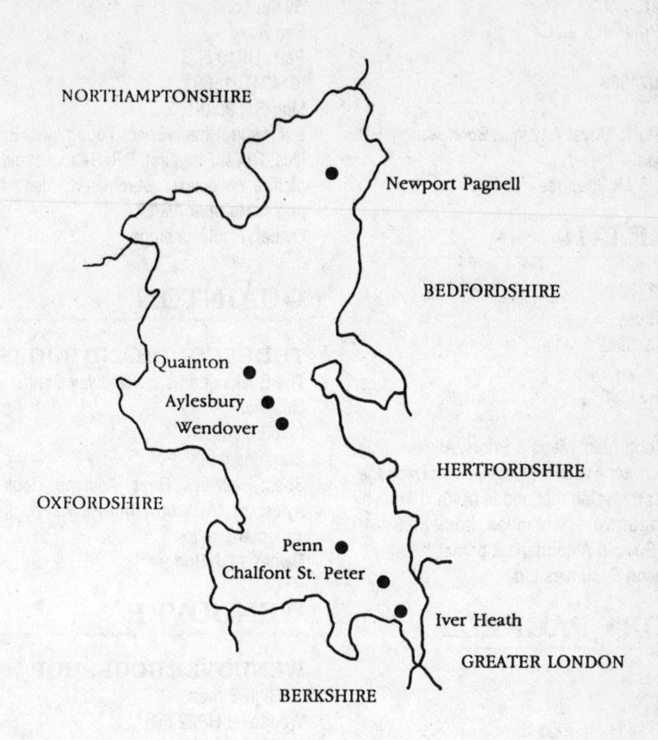

AYLESBURY

THE BOOKSHOP

Square Edge
38 Kingsbury
Aylesbury HP20 2JE
(01296) 89480
Mon-Sat 10:30-5
Est. 1990. Medium. Spec: Bucks, New Zealand: also Gen Stock and Arts, Hist, Lit. Cat: New Zealand. Buys: Anytime. cc: AV. BR: Aylesbury. "Located in Kingsbury, in the historic core of Aylesbury. 5 min walk from BR."
Owner: Marilyn Norwood

PETER EATON (BOOKSELLERS) LTD

Lilies
Weedon
Aylesbury HP22 4NS
(01296) 641393
Fax (01296) 641048
Mon-Sat 10-5
Est. 1945. Large. Gen Stock. Buys: Ring first. BR: Aylesbury.
Owner: Margaret Eaton

CHALFONT ST. PETER

FAIRCROSS BOOKS
27 High Street
Chalfont St. Peter SL9 9QE
(01753) 883222
Fax (01494) 874838
Tue-Sat 9:30-5
Small. Gen Stock. Buys: Anytime. Book search. BR: Gerrards Cross.
Owners: B.A. & M. Sheppee

IVER HEATH

POSTAPRINT
Taidswood House
Iver Heath SL0 0PQ
(01895) 833720
Fax (01895) 834890
Mon-Fri 9-5
Small. Cat: Cont: Antq, Maps & Prints, Atlases, Illus. Buys: Ring first. cc: AV. BR: Slough, Tube: Uxbridge. "40 min by car from Central London (A40). 10 min by car from Heathrow. Two miles from M25/M40 interchange. Spec in Atqn maps & prints."
Owner: Hemicon Securities Ltd

NEWPORT PAGNELL

KEN'S
29 High Street
Newport Pagnell MK16 8AR
(01908) 610003
Mon-Sat 9:30-5, Thur close
Est. 1983. Small. Gen Stock. Buys: Ring first. BR: Milton Keynes. "Specialist in written and printed ephemera. V. large stock of magazines- posters, autographs, etc. Book-readers only."
Owner: Ken Graham

PENN

PENN BARN
By the pond
Elm Road
Penn HP10 8LB
(01494) 815691
Mon-Sat 9:30-1, 2-5
Est. 1968. Small. Spec: Topog: also Bindings, Atqn, Illus. Buys: Ring first. BR: Beaconsfield. "Libraries & picture collections purchased. Also stock maps & prints. Member ABA."
Owner: Paul Hunnings

QUAINTON

THE SECONDHAND BOOKSHOP
The Buckinghamshire Railway Centre
Quainton
(01635) 200507
Sun (ring first)
Spec: Railways. Buys: Anytime. Book search. BR: Aylesbury. "Aylesbury 6 mi. Railway books, magazines, ephemera, relics."
Owner: M.J. Bridger

WENDOVER

WENDOVER BOOKSHOP
35 High Street
Wendover HP22 6DU
(01296) 696204
Mon-Sat 9-5:30
Small. Spec: Hist: also Gen Stock. Cat: 2 pa: Hist. Buys: Ring first. BR: Wendover.
Owners: D. & D.B. Harrison

CAMBRIDGESHIRE

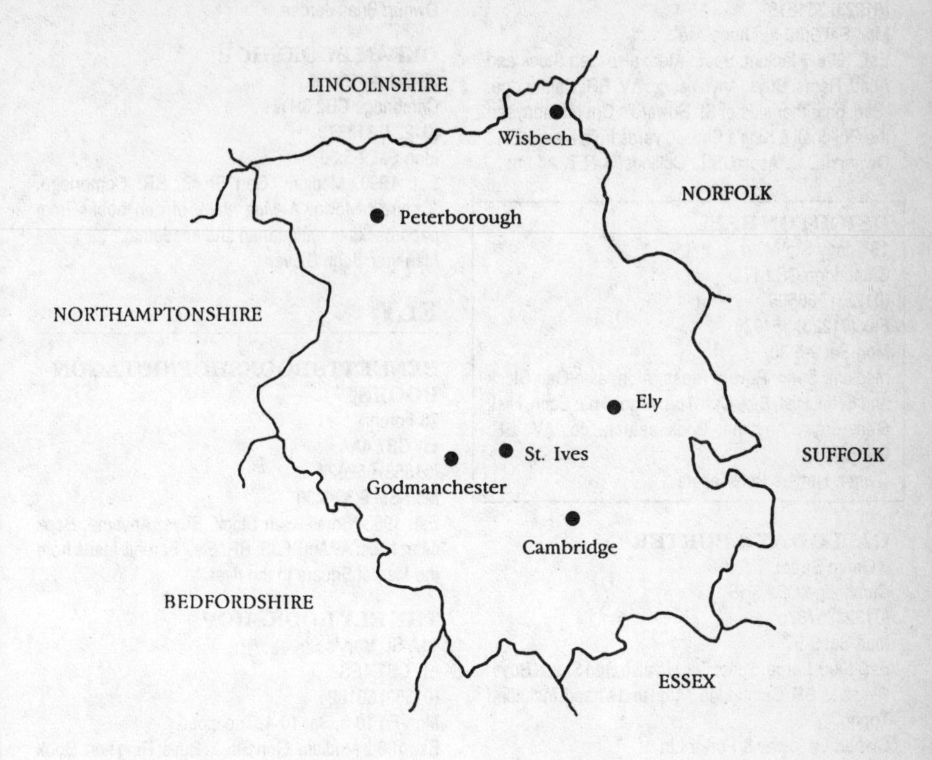

CAMBRIDGE

ALISTER & GARON BOOKS

70 King Street
Cambridge CB1 1LN
(01223) 62086
Mon-Sat 9:30-6
Est. 1981. Medium. Gen Stock. Buys: Ring first. cc: AVAmDS. BR: Cambridge. "Also large stock of records, tapes, & CDs."
Owner: Ian Alister

THE BOOKSHOP

24 Magdalene Street
Cambridge CB3 0AF
(01223) 62457
Mon-Sat 10-6, Sun 11-6
Est. 1970. Large. Spec: Fict, Pol: also Gen Stock and Lit. Buys: Anytime. BR: Cambridge. "Also includes stock from Ian Patterson (Leftwingery and Modernism), Peter Riley (Poetry)."
Owners: Hazel Hare & Andrew Seear

G. DAVID
16 St. Edward's Passage
Cambridge CB2 3PJ
(01223) 354619
Mon-Sat 9:30-5, Thur close
Est. 1896. Medium. Spec: Atqn: also Gen Stock and Acad, Rems. Buys: Anytime. cc: AV. BR: Cambridge. "Sitd. on either side of St. Edward's Church between the Guildhall & King's Coll. 50 yards from Market Sq."
Owners: D.C. Asplin, B.L. Collings, & N.T. Adams

DEIGHTON BELL
13 Trinity Street
Cambridge CB2 1TD
(01223) 568585
Fax (01223) 354936
Mon-Sat 9-5:30
Medium. Spec: Private Press, Atqn: also Gen Stock and Econ, Hist, Bibl. Cat: 3 pa: Atqn, 6 pa: Econ, Hist, Gen. Buys: Anytime. Book search. cc: AV. BR: Cambridge.
Owner: Heffers Booksellers

GALLOWAY & PORTER
3 Green Street
Cambridge CB2 3HS
(01223) 67876
Mon-Sat 9-5
Est. 1900. Large. Spec: Sci, Lit: also Gen Stock. Buys: Ring first. BR: Cambridge. "Atqn and s'hand, including Topog."
Owner: Galloway & Porter Ltd

THE HAUNTED BOOKSHOP
9 St. Edwards Passage
Cambridge CB2 3PJ
(01223) 312913
Fax (01223) 568189
Mon-Sat 10-5
Est. 1987. Small. Spec: Illus, Chld: also Gen Stock. Buys: Anytime. BR: Cambridge.
Owner: Sarah Key

BRIAN JORDAN MUSIC BOOKS FACSIMILES
10 Green Street
Cambridge CB2 3JU
(01223) 322368
Mon-Sat 9:30-6
Small. Spec: Mus: also Printed Mus, Mus Lit. Buys: Ring first. cc: AV. BR: Cambridge. "Centrally located in Cambridge off Trinity St. Serious music only."
Owner: Brian Jordan

OXFAM BOOKSHOP
28 Sidney Street
Cambridge CB2 3HW
(01223) 313373
Mon-Sat 9-5:30
Est. 1990. Medium. Gen Stock. BR: Cambridge. "Centre of town. A wide stock of gen books from paperbacks to antiquarian and academic."
Manager: John Glover

ELY

BENNETTS BOOKSHOP/OCTAGON BOOKS
23 Forehill
Ely CB7 4AA
(01353) 662027
Mon-Sat 9:30-5:30
Est. 1983. Small. Gen Stock. Buys: Anytime. Book search. cc: AVAmDEJS. BR: Ely. "Forehill leads from the Market Square to the river."

THE ELY BOOKSHOP
11A St. Mary's Street
Ely CB7 4ES
(01353) 661824
Mon-Fri 10-3, Sat 10-4, Tue close
Est. 1986. Medium. Gen Stock. Buys: Ring first. Book search. BR: Ely. "5 min walk from BR in town centre."
Owner: Michael G. Kousah

JOHN LEWCOCK
6 Chewells Lane
Haddenham
Ely CB6 2SS
(01353) 741152 (tel/fax)
Mon-Sat 9-5 or by appt
Small. Spec: Maritime: Cat: 6 pa: Maritime. Buys: Ring first. Book search. cc: AV. BR: Ely. "Can collect from Ely BR by prior appointment. Outside normal hours, visiting can be arranged by appointment."
Owner: John Lewcock

GODMANCHESTER

THE BOOKSHOP
11 Post Street
Godmanchester PE18 8BA
(01480) 455020
Tue-Sat 9:30-1, 2-5:30
Est. 1972. Small. Spec: Countryside, Local: also Gen Stock and Aircraft, Cars. Buys: Ring first. Book search. cc: AV. BR: Huntingdon. "Off A1 at Brampton Hut to Huntingdon, around ring road to Godmanchester. Shop is in C17th timber framed building. New books, esp chld's."
Owners: J. Lewis & D. Lewis

PETERBOROUGH

T.V. COLES
981 Lincoln Road
Peterborough PE4 6AH
(01733) 577268
Mon-Sat 9-4:30
Small. Spec: Mil: also Gen Stock. Buys: Anytime. BR: Peterborough. "Also substantial stock of medals and postcards."
Owner: T.V. Coles

FITZWILLIAM ANTIQUES CENTRE
Fitzwilliam Street
Peterborough PE1 2RX
(01733) 65415
Mon-Sat 10-5, Sun 12-5
Est. 1991. Small. Spec: Nat Hist, Old Towns: also Gen Stock and Atqn. Buys: Ring first. cc: AV. BR: Peterborough. "1/2 mi from BR & 4 mi from A1. 40 dealers - all specialising in different lines (porcelain, silver, furniture, coins)."
Dealers: John Gerrison & Gail Pears

DAVID HOLMES
12 Eastfield Road
Peterborough PE1 4AN
(01733) 51152
Tue-Sat 10-5, Thur 10-8
Small. Spec: Private Press, Art: also Gen Stock and Drawings, Etchings. Cat: 2-3 pa: Indiv Artists. Buys: Anytime. BR: Peterborough. "Small, odd and unusual C20th Br. Art. Also original lithos, etchings, drawings, woodcuts and Rigby Graham archive."
Owner: David Holmes

OLD SOKE BOOKS
68 Burghley Road
Peterborough PE1 2QE
(01733) 64147
Tue-Sat 10:30-5:30
Est. 1983. Medium. Spec: Local: also Gen Stock and Nat Hist, Fict, Trav. Buys: Anytime. BR: Peterborough. "We also stock paintings, prints, maps, & antiques."
Owners: Peter & Linda Clay

ST. IVES

BRUNNER BOOKS
1 White Hart Court
St. Ives PE17 4EA
(01480) 300032
Mon-Sat 9-5
Est. 1985. Small. Spec: Mil, Avia: also Gen Stock. Buys: Anytime. Book search. cc: AV. BR: Huntingdon. "Also new books."
Owners: Peter & Rosemary de Brunner

WISBECH

GRACETITLES BOOKS
1 Union Street
Wisbech PE13 3DJ
(01945) 466141 (tel/fax)
Mon-Sat 10-5:30
Est. 1995. Small. Spec: Mus, Local, Topog: also Gen Stock and Sheet Music, Prints, Maps. Buys: Anytime. Book search. BR: King's Lynn/March. "12 mi from K.L. BR, 10 mi from March. Central shopping area."
Owners: Keith & Grace Plumridge

CHESHIRE

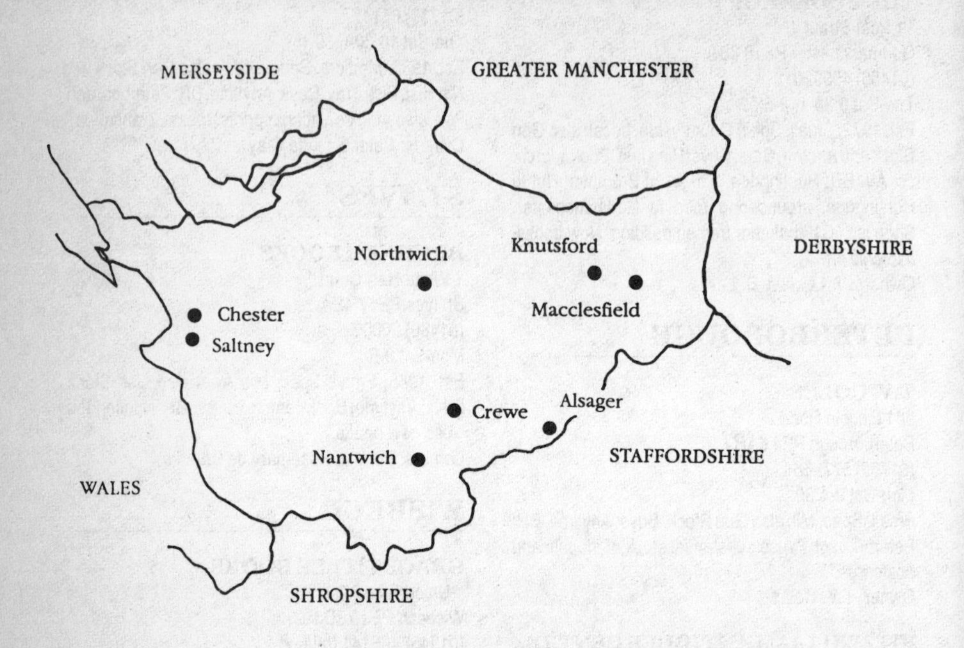

ALSAGER

FOREST BOOKS
The Bookshop Upstairs
14B Lawton Road
Alsager ST7 2AF
(01270) 882618
Mon & Wed 10:30-5, Tue-Sat 10:30-5:30, Thur & Fri 10:30-7 (or by appt)
Est. 1993. Small. Gen Stock and Drama, Loc Hist, Arts. Buys: Ring first. BR: Alsager. "M6 at Sandbach, then A533 for about 3 miles. Free car parking. Selection of Atqn & new books."
Owner: Mrs E. Mann

CHESTER

CHAPTER & VERSE BOOKSHOP
45 Brook Street
Chester CH1 3DZ
(01244) 347839
Mon-Sat 9:30-6
Est. 1994. Small. Gen Stock and Nat Hist. Buys: Anytime. Book search. BR: Chester. "Large pbk exch. Purchase novels & spec. interest."
Owner: Gavin Floyd

MADE OF HONOUR ANTIQUES
11 City Walls
Chester CH1 1LD
(01244) 314208
Mon-Sat 9:30-5:30
Small. Spec: Po, Illus: also Gen Stock and Lit Crit, Art, Textiles. Buys: Anytime. cc: AV. BR: Chester. "Next to Eastgate Clock on the city walls."
Owner: Joyce Whitehead

S.P.C.K
7-11 St. Werburgh Street
Chester CH1 2EJ
(01244) 323753 (tel/fax)
Mon-Sat 9-5:30
Medium. Spec: Theol: also Gen Stock and Hist, Topog. Buys: Ring first. Book search. cc: AV. BR: Chester. "Also new books."
Manager: Ian Vollands

STOTHERT ANTIQUARIAN BOOKS
4 Nicholas Street
Chester CH1 2NX
(01244) 340756
Mon-Sat 9:30-1, 2-5:30
Est. 1976. Small. Spec: Local: also Gen Stock and Atqn, Topog. Buys: Anytime. BR: Chester.
Owners: Mr T.M. & Mrs E.N. Stothert

WORDS & MUSIC
2 City Walls
Northgate Street
Chester CH1 2JG
(01244) 311910
Mon-Sun 10-5
Est. 1991. Small. Spec: Pol, Drama: also Mod 1sts, Mus, Lit. Buys: Anytime. Book search. BR: Chester. "We also carry a small stock of Classical & Jazz recordings in all formats."
Owner: Stephen Whitaker

CREWE

THE BOOK CELLAR
225 Nantwich Road
Crewe CW2 6BY
(01270) 252748
Mon-Sat 9-6
Est. 1995. Medium. Spec: Biog, Genealogy: also Gen Stock and Topog, Hist, Heraldry. Cat: 1 pa: Gen. Buys: Ring first. BR: Crewe. "Cheshire's newest old book shop. Free catalogue. Mailing list. Keen to acquire small or large collections of any books."

COPNAL BOOKS
18 Meredith Street
Crewe CW1 2PW
(01270) 580470
Mon-Sat 9:30-5, Wed close
Large. Spec: Theol: also Gen Stock. Buys: Ring first. BR: Crewe.
Owner: Mr P. Ollerhead

KNUTSFORD

LION GALLERY & BOOKSHOP
15A Minshull Street
Knutsford WA16 6HG
(01565) 652915
Fax (01565) 750142
Fri 10:30-5, Sat 10-5 (or by appt)
Est. 1965. Small. Spec: Atqn. Buys: Anytime. Book search. cc: AVAmD. BR: Knutsford. "Probably the largest variety of Atqn maps & prints in the world. Also watercolours & oils."
Owner: Raymond Hepner

MACCLESFIELD

BRIDGEWATER BOOKS
28 Sunderland Street
Macclesfield SK11 6JL
(01625) 424763
Mon-Sat 9-5, Wed close
Est. 1982. Small. Gen Stock. Buys: Anytime. BR: Macclesfield. "50% s'hand, 50% remainders."
Owner: Mr Bisknell

MACCLESFIELD OLD & RARE BOOKS
124 Chestergate
Macclesfield SK11 6DH
(01625) 425352
Sat & Sun 10-5:30
Est. 1988. Small. Spec: Br Topog, Lit: also Gen Stock and Illus, Classics, Psychoanalysis. Buys: Anytime. Book search. BR: Macclesfield. "Small but good quality shop 1/2 mile from BR. Good car parking nearby."
Owner: Colin Tucker

NANTWICH

GUILDMASTER BOOKS
81 Welsh Row
Nantwich CW5 5ET
(01270) 629108
Mon-Sat 10-Dusk
Est. 1990. Medium. Spec: Hist: also Gen Stock. Buys: Anytime. BR: Nantwich.
Owner: Brownsword Hulland

THOMAS & GREENS ANTIQUARIAN & SECONDHAND BOOKROOM
84 London Road
Nantwich CW5 6LT
(01270) 627779
Wed, Fri-Sun 7:30pm-9pm
Est. 1990. Small. Spec: Eng Civil Wars, Hist: also Gen Stock and Lit, Topog. Cat: Reg. Buys: Ring first. Book search. BR: Nantwich. "Not necessary from Nantwich. London Rd. is a major thoroughfare. A small business with an emphasis on condition across the board."
Owners: Thomas & Greens

NORTHWICH

CASTLE BOOK CENTRE
85 Chester Road
Castle
Northwich CW8 1HH
(01606) 781269
Mon-Sat 10-5:30
Est. 1985. Large. Gen Stock. Buys: Ring first. BR: Green Bank. "Both new & s'hand. Prepared to order books."
Owners: Mr G. Grocier & Ms E. Dunn

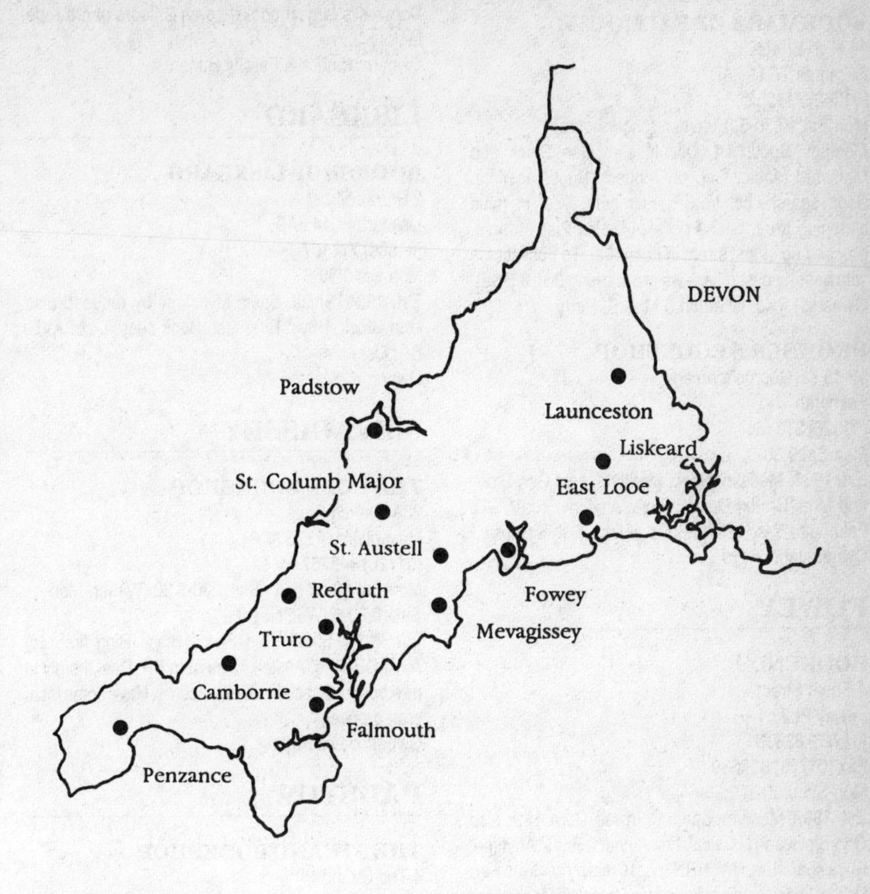

CAMBORNE

VICTORIA GALLERY

28 Cross Street
Camborne TR14 8EX
(01209) 719268
Mon 1-5:15, Tue-Fri 11-5:15, Sat 10-1, Thur close
Est. 1984. Medium. Spec: Loc, Min: also Gen Stock and Topog, Sport, Nat Hist. Buys: Anytime. BR: Camborne. "We have an excellent selection of books. Very good value. Antiques, silver, & jewellery as well."
Owners: Bernard & Jennifer Maker

EAST LOOE

THE OLD HALL BOOKSHOP & GALLERY

Shutta Road
East Looe PL13 1BJ
(01503) 263700
Mon-Sat 10-5 (Winter, ring first)
Est. 1985. Medium. Spec: Loc: also Gen Stock. Buys: Ring first. cc: AV. BR: East Looe. "We can be found 50 yards up slope from Barclays Bank in town centre. Also maps, prints, and paintings."
Owners: A. & M.W. Proud

FALMOUTH

BOOKMARK OF FALMOUTH
34 High Street
Falmouth TR11 2AD
(01362) 211252
Mon-Sat 10:30-5 (Summer, longer hours)
Medium. Spec: Art, Occult: also Gen Stock and Maritime, Magic. Cat: on request. Buys: Anytime. Book search. cc: V. BR: Falmouth. "Not in main shopping area, pass Prince of Wales Pier on right, proceed up oldest street in Falmouth. To book lovers with hearing difficulties - we are learning BSL & SSE."
Owners: Mrs J. Charlton & Miss S. Parry

BROWSER'S BOOKSHOP
13-15 St. George's Arcade
Falmouth
(01326) 313464
Mon-Sat 9:30-5
Est. 1983. Medium. Spec: Maritime: also Gen Stock and Mus, Crafts, Occult. Buys: Anytime. cc: V. BR: Falmouth. "Also sells prints, paintings & sheet music."
Owner: John Floyd

FOWEY

BOOKENDS
4 South Street
Fowey PL23 1AR
(01726) 833361
Fax (01726) 833630
Mon-Sat 9:30-1, 2:30-6
Est. 1982. Medium. Spec: Cornwall, Corn. Hist: also Gen Stock and Nautical, Loc Authors. Buys: Anytime. Book search. cc: AV. BR: Par. "10 min by car from Par. One of few s'hand bookshops in Cornwall. Good stock of Cornish Lit."
Owner: Mrs Christine Alexander

LAUNCESTON

HUTTON BOOKS
8 Race Hill
Launceston PL15 9BA
(01566) 776503
Mon-Sat 10-5, Thur close
Est. 1990. Medium. Spec: Loc Hist, Farming: also Gen Stock and Country Sports, Illus. Cat: irreg: Gen. Buys: Anytime. Book search. cc: AVE. BR: Plymouth. "Off A30, through town centre under Southgate Arch, straight on up Race Hill. Shop opp carpark entrance. Cornwall's largest bookshop on 2 floors of old rope factory."
Owners: Patrick & Felicity Hutton

LISKEARD

BOOKSHOP LISKEARD
2 Barras Street
Liskeard PL14 6AD
(01566) 774107
Mon-Sat 9:30-5
Est. 1984. Small. Spec: Mycology by request: also Gen Stock. Buys: Ring first. Book search. cc: AVE. BR: Liskeard.
Owner: K. Stanton

MEVAGISSEY

THE LOFT BOOKSHOP
23A Church Street
Mevagissey PL26 6SP
(01726) 843757
Mon-Sat 10:30-5:30, Sun 1:30-5:30 (Winter, Mon-Sat 10:30-5, Wed close)
Est. 1988. Small. Gen Stock. Buys: Ring first. cc: AVAm. BR: St. Austell. "5 mi from BR. Deal mainly in new books. Special orders welcome. Have some local craft produce."
Owner: David Payn

PADSTOW

THE STRAND BOOKSHOP
4 The Strand
Padstow PL28 8AZ
(01841) 532236
Mon-Sat 9-9, Wed 9-1 (Winter 9-5)
Est. 1963. Small. Gen Stock. Buys: Ring first. cc: AV. BR: Bodmin Parkway. "Mostly new but with a small s'hand department."
Owners: M.A. Rowe, S.A. Tregaskes, & P.M. Bates

PENZANCE

NEW STREET BOOKS
4 New Street
Penzance TR18 2LZ
(01736) 62758
Mon-Sat 10-5
Small. Spec: Cornwall: also Gen Stock. Cat: 1 pa: Cornwall. Buys: Anytime. BR: Penzance. "Centrally located off Market Street."
Owner: B.J. Maker

PENZANCE RARE BOOKS
43 Causewayhead
Penzance TR18 2SS
(01736) 62140/50237
Mon-Sat 9:30-5
Est. 1991. Medium. Gen Stock and Arts, Eso, Poetry, C19th Lit. Buys: Anytime. Book search. BR: Penzance. "Large carpark. Vegetarian and other restaurants nearby. Shop has interesting tiled Victorian shopfront."
Owner: Patricia Johnstone

ST. AUSTELL

KEMYEL BOOKS
21 High Cross Street
St. Austell PL25 4AN
(01726) 70296
Mon-Sat 9:30-5
Small. Spec: Cornish: also Gen Stock. Buys: Anytime. BR: St. Austell. "Gen. stock of good s'hand books."

ST. COLUMB MAJOR

COLLECTOR'S CORNER
7 Bank Street
St. Columb Major TR9 6AT
(01637) 880715 (home)
Mon-Sat 9-5
Est. 1988. Small. Gen Stock. Buys: Anytime. Book search. BR: St. Columb Road. "Small unspoilt town location. Interesting and varied stock, antique maps, prints, ephemera, collectables. Olde worlde atmosphere."
Owners: Robert & Marilyn Bosisto

TRURO

JUST BOOKS
9 Pydar Mews
Truro TR1 2UX
(01872) 42532
Mon-Sat 10-5, Thur close
Est. 1986. Small. Gen Stock. Buys: Anytime. Book search. BR: Truro.
Owner: Wendy Barritt

S.P.C.K
8 St. Mary's Street
Truro TR1 2AF
(01872) 72771
Mon-Fri 9-5:30, Sat 9-5
Est. 1950. Small. Spec: Theol: also Gen Stock. Buys: Ring first. cc: AV. BR: Truro.
Owner: Robin Davidson

CUMBRIA

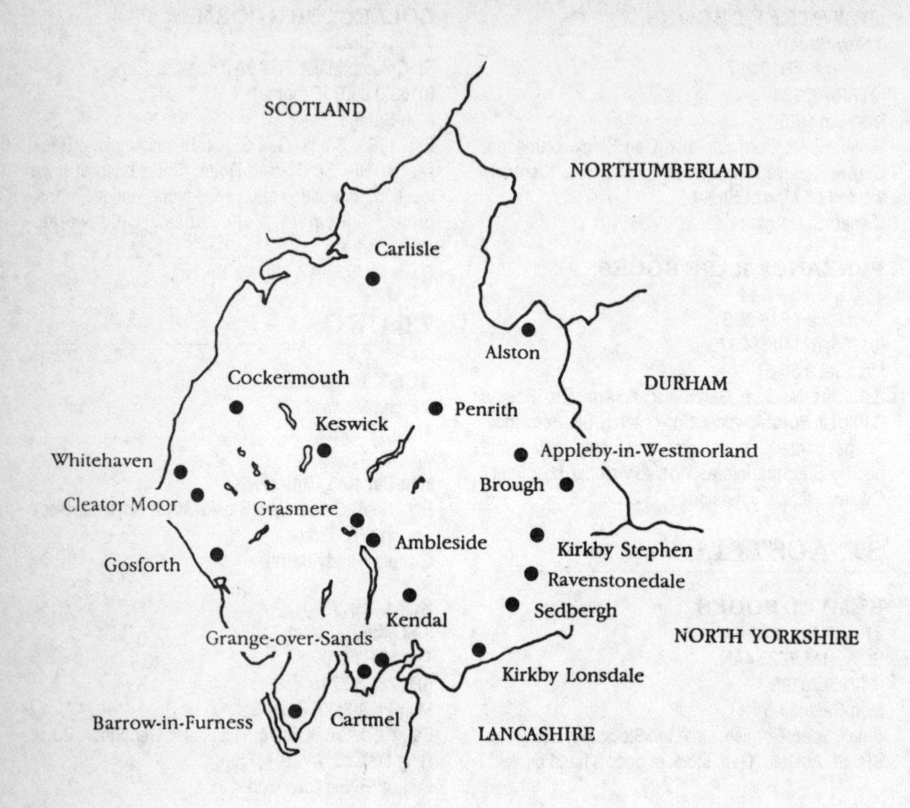

ALSTON

INCREDIBLE (DURHAM BOOK CENTRE)

Front Street
Alston CA9 3HU
(01434) 381006
Easter-Oct 10:30-4:30, Tue close
Medium. Gen Stock. Buys: Ring first. "Ring to confirm if open when travelling. 3 rooms of stock. Worth a detour."
Owner: A. Dumble

AMBLESIDE

THE LITTLE BOOKSHOP

1 Cheapside
Ambleside CA22 0AB
(015394) 32094
Fax (015394) 31905
Mon-Sun 10-5 (usually)
Est. 1994. Medium. Spec: Mount, Trav: also Gen Stock and Topog, Eng Lit. Cat: 2 pa: 1 Mount, 1 Gen. Buys: Anytime. Book search. cc: AV. BR: Oxenholme/ Penrith. "Behind Barclays Bank- main street in Ambleside. No facilities for the disabled. 3 floors of books."
Owner: Frank Grant

ROB SHEPPARD BOOKS
1 Church Street
Ambleside LA22 0BU
(015394) 31788
Mon-Sun 10-5:30
Medium. Gen Stock. Buys: Anytime. cc: AVE. BR: Windermere. "In centre of Ambleside near Tourist Info. Open seven days a week."
Owner: Rob Sheppard

APPLEBY-IN-WESTMORLAND

BARRY McKAY RARE BOOKS
Kingstone House
Battlebarrow
Appleby-in-Westmorland CA16 6XT
(017683) 52282
Fax (017683) 52946
Ring first
Small. Spec: Bibl, Printing: also Private Press, Ephemera, Topog. Cat: 4-6 pa: as above. Buys: Ring first. cc: AV. BR: Kirkby Stephen. "Small spec. stock. US$ cheques accepted. PBFA. Appointment advisable."
Owner: Barry McKay

BARROW-IN-FURNESS

THE MOSTLY BOOKS SHOP
247 Rawlinson Street
Barrow-in-Furness LA14 1DW
(01229) 836808/825097 (eve)
Tue-Fri 11-5, Sat 11-4:30, Thur close
Est. 1981. Small. Spec: Tech, Building Craft: also Gen Stock and Trans, Atec, Loc Hist. Cat: 2+ pa: as above. Buys: Anytime. Book search. BR: Barrow. "On- and off-street parking nearby. Other areas of interest include Furness."
Owner: Harvey Leeson

BROUGH

SUMMERFIELD BOOKS
High Street
Brough CA17 4BX
(017683) 41577 (tel/fax)
Mon-Sun 9-6 (ring first)
Small. Spec: Botany, Forestry, Hortic: also Nat Hist. Buys: Ring first. Book search. cc: AV. BR: Kirkby Stephen. "5 miles from BR, 2 min from A66 Transpennine Road, 20 min from M6."
Owner: J.M. Atkins

CARLISLE

BOOKCASE
17 Castle Street
Carlisle CA3 8TP
(01228) 44560 (tel/fax)
Mon-Sat 10-5
Est. 1978. Large. Spec: Cumbria, Lit: also Gen Stock and Nat Hist, Hist, Theol. Buys: Anytime. Book search. cc: AV. BR: Carlisle. "Situated mid-way bet Castle and Cathedral. Over 70,000 books on 3 floors of Georgian town house. 10,000 classical LPs and large stock of new classical CDs. Also remainder shop at 56 Castle Street."
Owners: S. & G. Matthews

MAURICE DODD BOOKS
112 Warwick Road
Carlisle CA1 1LF
(01228) 22087/26396 (tel/fax)
Mon-Fri 9-5, Sat 9-12 (or by appt)
Est. 1945. Medium. Spec: Cumberland, Westmorland: also Gen Stock and Lit, Hist, Sci. Cat: 2 pa: Gen. Buys: Ring first. cc: AV. BR: Carlisle. "Please phone before making any special journey. Junction 43 of M6 is start of Warwick Rd. Shop is approx 1 mile along here."
Owners: R.J. & G.E. McRoberts

CARTMEL

PETER BAIN SMITH (BOOKSELLER)
Market Square
Cartmel LA11 6QB
(015395) 36369
Mon-Sat 11-6, Sun 1-6 (Win, Wed-Sun, 1:30-4:30)
Large. Spec: Lake District, Eng Topog: also Gen Stock and Eng Lit, Chld. Buys: Anytime. Book search. BR: Grange-Over-Sands. "Located in centre of pretty village square with parking and pubs nearby. Children's bookroom. Pbks to antiquarian. Been here 20 years and our many reg customers return again and again."
Owner: Peter Bain Smith

NORMAN KERR (BOOKSELLERS)

The Square
Grange-over-Sands
Cartmel LA11 6PX
(015395) 36247
Ring first
Est. 1933. Medium. Gen Stock. Cat: 1 pa: Cumbria, Gen. Buys: Ring first. BR: Grange-over-Sands. "ABA and PBFA members."
Partners: H. & J.M. Kerr

OVER SANDS BOOKS

The Old Waiting Room
The Station
Grange-over-Sands
Cartmel LA11 7HR
(01524) 65061 (Ansaphone- Day)
Summer 10-6, Winter 10:45-6:45
Est. 1995. Small. Spec: Morecambe Bay Area, Loc & Mil Hist: also Gen Stock and Biog, Topog, Trav. Cat: occ lists. Buys: Anytime. Book search. BR: Grange-over-Sands. "From M6 (Junc 36) follow Barrow in Furness/Grange signs (A590 - B5278). Former waiting room on picturesque South Lakeland Station. Probably the nearest bookshop to the sea in Britain."
Owners: Eric R. Wilkinson & Stephen R. Tyson

CLEATOR MOOR

SQUARE BOOKS

Unit 1, The Business Centre, Cragg Road
Cleator Moor CA25 5PT
(01946) 63398
Irregular - phone first
Small. Gen Stock. Cat: on req: Cumbriana/Gen. Buys: Ring first. Book search. BR: Whitehaven. "Quality miscellany. Everchanging stock. Lake District Bookfair organisers."
Owner: Richard Byers

COCKERMOUTH

THE PRINTING HOUSE

102 Main Street
Cockermouth CA13 9LX
(01900) 824984
Mon-Sat 9-5:30
Est. 1978. Medium. Spec: Local: also Gen Stock and Mount, Poetry. Buys: Ring first. cc: AV. BR: Workington. "Printing and a good selection of remainders. Also maps and prints. New books at our other premises - The New Bookshop, 42-44 Main St., Cockermouth, (01900) 822062."
Owner: David R. Winkworth

GOSFORTH

ARCHIE MILES BOOKSHOP

Beck Place
Seascale
Gosforth CA20 1AT
(019467) 25792
Tue-Sat 10-6 (in season, Sun 2-6) Winter: variable
Est. 1870. Medium. Gen Stock. Cat: occ. Buys: Anytime. Book search. BR: Seascale. "Situated on edge of Lake District National Park. 9 miles from Wasdale Head, 3 miles from sea."
Owner: Mrs C.M. Linsley

GRASMERE

BRIDGE BOOKS
Church Bridge
Grasmere LA22 9SN
(015394) 35029 (tel/fax)
Easter-Nov: Mon-Sun 9:45-6, Winter 10-5 (erratic)
Est. 1993. Small. Spec: Lakes/Cumbria Topog, Hist, Authors, esp Wordsworth: also Atqn maps & prints (Cumbria, N Counties). Cat: 6+ pa: Lakes Hist & Topog, Wordsworth. Buys: Ring first. Book search. cc: AVAmJS. "Centre of village by bridge opp church. Also new books, maps, cards."
Owner: John Taylor

KENDAL

EWEN KERR BOOKS
1 Yard 51
Stramongate
Kendal LA9 4BH
(01539) 720659
Fax (01539) 730739
Mon-Sat 10-5, Thur close
Est. 1983. Medium. Spec: C18th Lit: also Gen Stock and Lake District, Art, Mount. Cat: 4-5 pa: as above. Buys: Ring first. BR: Oxenholme/Kendal. "Direction-ask for Hayton Winkley Solicitors."
Owner: Bryan Peet

KIRKLAND BOOKS
68 Kirkland
Kendal LA9 5AP
(01539) 740841
Mon-Sat 10-5, Thur close
Est. 1987. Medium. Spec: Loc Hist, Topog: also Gen Stock and Mount, Lit, Art. Buys: Ring first. BR: Kendal via Oxenholme. "Ample parking in Kendal Parish Church. Public car park directly opp. shop. 3 floors of books in listed building."
Owner: David Stockley.

THE RIVERSIDE BOOKSHOP
Yard 39
Highgate
Kendal LA9 4ED
(01539) 735173
Mon-Sat 10-4:30 Thur close
Est. 1993. Small. Spec: Chld novels/annuals: also Gen Stock and Mod Fict. Cat: occ: Chld. Buys: Ring first. Book search. BR: Oxenholme. "Central position in yard near Town Hall. Small shop with books on most subjects."
Owner: Paul Lee

ROB SHEPPARD BOOKS
Units D1-D3 Kendal Indoor Market
Westmoreland Centre
Kendal LA9 4TN
(01539) 727504/731116
Mon-Sat 8:30-5
Est. 1978. Medium. Gen Stock. Buys: Anytime. cc: AVE. BR: Kendal/Oxenholme. "Easy parking in adjacent Westmoreland Centre car park. Open 6 days a week."
Owner: Rob Sheppard.

KESWICK

BOOKENDS
66 Main Street
Keswick
(017687) 75277
Mon-Sun 9:30-6:30
Est. 1991. Small. Gen Stock. Buys: Ring first. cc: AV. BR: Penrith. "New & remainder shop with popular s'hand stock."
Owners: S. & G. Matthews

KESWICK BOOKSHOP
4 Station Street
Keswick CA12
(017687) 75535
Most days 10-5 (ring first)
Small. Spec: Mount, Loc Topog: also Gen Stock and Art. Buys: Ring first. BR: Penrith. "Atqn & s'hand books, maps & prints."
Owners: Jane & John Kinnaird

KIRKBY LONSDALE

BECK HEAD BOOKS
10 Beck Head
Kirkby Lonsdale LA6 2AY
(015242) 71314
Tue, Thur-Sat 10-5 (Summer), Thur-Sat (Winter)
Est. 1984. Medium. Spec: Arts, Lit: also Gen Stock and Juvenile, Topog. Buys: Anytime. BR: Oxenholme/Lancaster. "Good, clean, organised, reasonably priced, (hopefully) interesting stock. Also Atqn maps, prints, old postcards & printed ephemera."
Owner: Mrs Barbara French

KIRKBY STEPHEN

VIVIAN WRIGHT
Fletcher Hill, Market Street
Kirkby Stephen CA17 4QQ
(017683) 71735
Mon, Wed, Fri, Sat 10-5
Medium. Spec: Atec: also Gen Stock. Cat: occ: Atec. Buys: Ring first. BR: Kirkby Stephen. "Easy parking. Carefully selected, wide range of Atqn, out-of-print books, prints, and maps."
Owners: V. & B. Wright

RAVENSTONEDALE

THE BOOK HOUSE
Gray Garth
Ravenstonedale CA17 4NQ
(015396) 23634
Mon-Sat 9-5, Tue & Sun close
Medium. Spec: Industrial Hist, Railways: also Gen Stock and Chld, Gard, Lit. Cat: 2 pa: Ind. Hist, 2 pa: Rail. Buys: Ring first. Book search. cc: AV. BR: Kirkby Stephen. "Ravenstonedale is off A685, 5 miles from Kirkby Stephen & 7 miles from Junc. 38 on M6. Book house is former Victorian Vicarage opp. the village school. Books on 3 floors. Bed & Breakfast at £13.50-reduction for dealers."
Owners: C.R. & M. Irwin

SEDBERGH

THE BOOK CELLAR
86 Main Street
Sedbergh LA10 5AD
(015396) 21097
Fax (015396) 21424
Mon, Tue, Fri, Sat 10:30-5
Est. 1994. Small. Spec: Loc Topog, Trav: also Gen Stock. Buys: Ring first. BR: Oxenholme. "Varied gen stock."
Owner: C.J. Chambers

R.F.G. HOLLETT & SON
6 Finkle Street
Sedbergh LA10 5BZ
(015396) 20298
Fax (015396) 21396
Mon-Sat 10-12, 1:15-5
Est. 1969. Large. Spec: Nat Hist, Sporting: also Trav, Topog, Fine Art. Cat: 1 pa: Gen. Buys: Anytime. Book search. BR: Oxenholme. "8 miles from BR. Cheap parking nearby. Rare Atqn books of all kinds. Large stock of fine & interesting books. ABA."
Owners: R.F.G. & C.G. Hollett

WHITEHAVEN

MICHAEL MOON'S BOOKSHOP
41-43 Roper Street
Whitehaven CA28 7BS
(01946) 62936
Mon-Sat 9:30-5 (Wed close, out of season)
Est. 1970. Large. Spec: Hist: also Gen Stock and Topog, Nat Hist. Cat: 3-4 pa: Hist, Gen. Buys: Ring first. BR: Whitehaven/Corkickle/Bransty "Largest of its kind in Cumbria. 1.25 miles of shelves in 6,000 sq. ft. New gallery open. ABA/PBFA."
Owners: Michael & Sylvia Moon

DERBYSHIRE

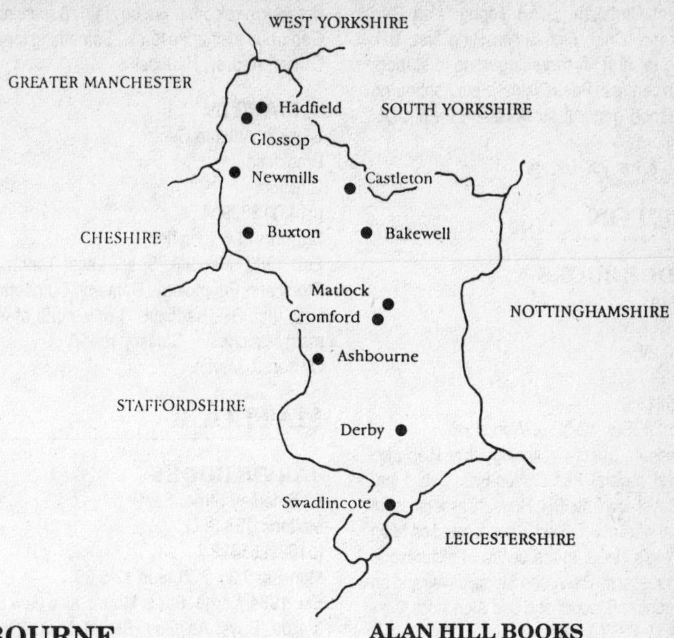

ASHBOURNE

PAMELA ELSOM ANTIQUES

5 Church Street
Ashbourne
(01335) 343468
Tue-Sat 10-5, Mon 2-5, Wed close
Est. 1963. Small. Gen Stock. Buys: Ring first. BR: Derby. "Bookshop at back of antique shop."
Owner: Pamela Elsom

BAKEWELL

ABBEY PRINTS & BOOKS

Stall 1, Bakewell Antiques Centre
King Street
Bakewell
(01529) 812496/(0114) 274 9538 (home)
Mon-Sat 10-5, Sun 11-5
Small. Spec: Atqn: also Gen Stock. Buys: Ring first. cc: AVAmD. BR: Matlock. "Aim to keep a reasonably good stock including interesting Atqn & illus books. Also original etchings by well-known artists, paintings & fine prints."
Owner: Robert Manger

ALAN HILL BOOKS

2 Buxton Road
Bakewell DE4 1DA
(01629) 815010
Fri, Sat, Mon 10-5
Est. 1987. Medium. Gen Stock. Buys: Ring first. cc: AV. "On the A6 road. Other branch in Sheffield."
Owner: A.D. Hill

BUXTON

HALL BANK BOOKSHOP

9 Hall Bank
Buxton SK17 6EW
(01298) 70889
Mon-Sat 10-5:30 (Winter, Tue-Sat 10:30-5)
Est. 1987. Medium. Spec: Topog: also Gen Stock and Biog, Drama, Theatre. Buys: Anytime. Book search.
Owner: David Huxley

HARTINGTON CHAPEL BOOKSHOP

Hall Bank
Hartington
Buxton SK17 0AT
(01298) 84569/84319

Wed-Sun 2-5 (Easter-end Oct) Sat-Sun 2-5 (Nov-Easter)
Medium. Spec: Christian, Local Topog: also Gen Stock and Trans, Chld, Fict. Buys: Ring first. BR: Buxton. "Phone first if travelling long distance. Hartington is in centre of Peak District, near Ashbourne & Bakewell. Good general stock, also LPs & CDs. Browsers welcome."
Owners: Anne & Patrick Rogers

CASTLETON

HAWKRIDGE BOOKS
The Cruck Barn
Cross Street
Castleton S30 2WH
(01433) 621999
Fax (01433) 621862
Mon-Sat 10-5:30, Sun 12-5:30, Wed close
Est. 1995. Medium. Spec: Ornithology, Nat Hist: also Gen Stock and several Fict & Non-Fict. Cat: 1 pa: Ornithology. Buys: Anytime. BR: Hope. "Castleton is on the A625, 17 mi west of Sheffield. Shop located on Main St. opp The Nag's Head. In the centre of picturesque Castleton, famous for its Blue John Stone, caves and an ideal walking centre. Secondhand and Atqn stock."
Owners: Dr & Mrs J. Tierney

CROMFORD

SCARTHIN BOOKS
The Promenade
Scarthin
Cromford DE4 3QF
(01629) 823272
Fax (01629) 825094
Mon-Sat 10-6, Sun 12-6
Est. 1974. Large. Gen Stock and Sci, Mus, Nat Hist. Buys: Ring first. BR: Cromford. "Under one roof, a varifying very well-organised traditional s'hand & atqn bookshop, plus an exceptional range of new books."
Owner: Dr David Mitchell

GLOSSOP

THE GEORGE STREET LOFT
31 George Street
Glossop SK13 8AY
(01457) 863413
Wed-Sat 10-5
Est. 1986. Medium. Gen Stock. Buys: Ring first. cc: AV. BR: Glossop. "Interesting selection of books in good condition & reasonable order. Friendly staff. Browsers welcome. We buy fairly & price moderately. Generous exchange terms. Something for everyone."
Owner: Andrew Hancock

J. MARTIN
Glossop Antique Centre
Brookfield
Glossop
(01457) 363904
Sat-Sun 11-5 (ring first)
Est. 1980. Medium. Spec: Local Topog: also Gen Stock and Egyptology, Romany, Cumberland. Buys: Ring first. BR: Hadfield. "1 mile north of Glossop on main Manchester-Glossop road."
Owner: J. Martin

MATLOCK

JARVIS BOOKS
57 Smedley Street East
Matlock DE4 3FQ
(01629) 55322
Mon-Sat 9:30-5:30, Sun 12-5:30
Est. 1984. Large. Spec: Mount: also Gen Stock. Cat: 3-4 pa. Buys: Anytime. BR: Matlock. "Good quality general stock; some atqn."
Owners: Grant & Valerie Jarvis

SWADLINCOTE

G.K. HADFIELD
Rock farm
Chilcote
Swadlincote DE12 8DQ
(01827) 373466
Fax (01827) 373699
Tue-Sat 9-5
Small. Spec: Horology, Sundials: also Musical Boxes & Automata, Early Woodwork & Lathes. Cat: 1 pa: In print; 3 pa: Out of print. Buys: Ring first. Book search. cc: AVAm. BR: Burton-upon-Trent. "A42/M42 junction 11 exit service roundabout then to No Man's Heath. Take 1st right to Chilcote for 1 3/4 miles. Shop is 1/2 way through village on right; old-fashioned pub-style sign."
Owners: G. & J. Hadfield, D. & N. Hadfield-Tilly

DEVON

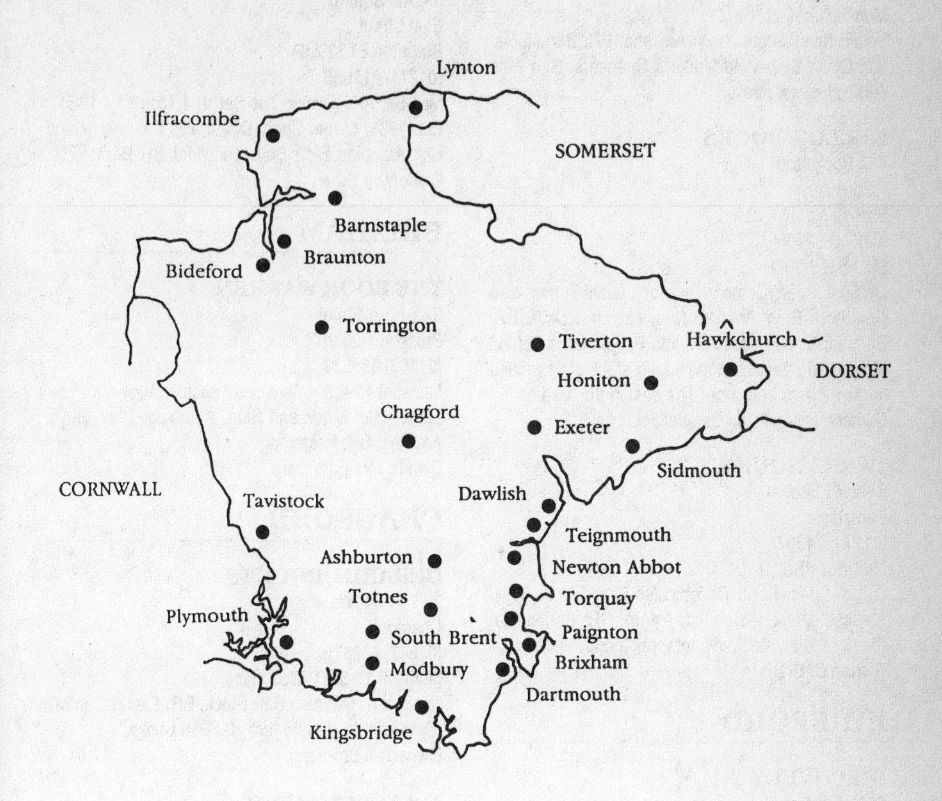

ASHBURTON

DARTMOOR BOOKSHOP
2 Kingsbridge Lane
Ashburton TQ13 7DX
(01364) 53356
Mon-Sat 9:30-5:30
Est. 1972. Large. Spec: Nat Hist, Travel: also Gen Stock and Countryside. Buys: Anytime. cc: AV. BR: Newton Abbott. "Interesting stock of books on 3 floors."
Owners: Paul & Barbara Heatley

BARNSTAPLE

BARNSTAPLE PANNIER MARKET
Butchers Row
Barnstaple EX32
(01271) 79084
Mon-Sat 9-4
Medium. Spec: Atqn. Buys: Ring first. BR: Barnstaple. "Collector's market Weds; Atqn and s'hand books."
Various dealers

THE BOOK & TEAPOT SHOP
Paiges Lane
Barnstaple EX32
(01271) 22900
Mon-Sat 9:30-4:30
Small. Spec: Atqn. Buys: Anytime. BR: Barnstaple. "Off Cross St. behind Marks & Spencers. Gen Atqn and collectors' books."

KELLOW BOOKS
The Bookshop
Paiges Lane
Barnstaple E31 1BA
(01271) 22900
Mon-Sat 9:30-4
Medium. Spec: Company History, Local Topog: also Gen Stock. Buys: Anytime. Book search. cc: AVE. BR: Barnstaple. "Off Cross St. into Paiges Lane behind Marks and Spencer. Good quality stock of all second hand subjects plus atqn. The best in the area."
Owners: Peter & Jan Combellack

TARKA BOOKS
5 Bear Street
Barnstaple
(01271) 74997
Mon-Sat 10-5:30
Large. Spec: North Devon: also Gen Stock. Buys: Anytime. Book search. cc: AVAm. BR: Barnstaple. "Book repairs, stock of prints, photocopy service."
Owner: C. Branson

BIDEFORD

DISCOVERY
66A High Street
Bideford
(01237) 473577
Mon-Fri 10:30-3:30, Sat 9:30-4, ec Wed
Est. 1978. Small. Gen Stock. Buys: Anytime. BR: Barnstaple. "Small, scruffy, and cheerful. Also CDs, records, tapes, and videos."

PETER HAMES
The Old Bridge Antiques Centre
Bideford EX39 2DR
(01237) 478592/421065 (eve)
Mon-Sat 9:30-5:30 (ec Wed)
Est. 1979. Small. Spec: Devon: also Gen Stock and Motoring, Atqn, Jazz. Buys: Ring first. BR: Barnstaple.
Owner: Peter Hames

BRAUNTON

THE BOOK CELLAR
5A The Square
East Street
Braunton EX33 2JD
(01271) 815655
Mon-Sat 10-5 (Winter: Tue-Sat 10-4, Mon & Fri 10-5)
Est. 1985. Large. Spec: Dogs: also Gen Stock and Hist, Autobiog, Biog. Buys: Ring first. BR: Barnstaple.
Owner: Mr Stow

BRIXHAM

THE BOOK WARREN
9A Bolton Street
Brixham TQ5 9BZ
(01803) 858531
Mon-Sat 10-4:30 (Wed close ec July-Aug)
Large. Gen Stock and Biog, Autobiog, Chld. Buys: Anytime. BR: Paignton.
Owner: Mrs E.M. Dare

CHAGFORD

GERARD BROOKES
78 The Square
Chagford
(01647) 432670
Mon-Sat 10-5:30, Wed close
Spec: Nat Hist: also Gen Stock. BR: Exeter Central. "Specialist in old and rare Nat Hist books."
Owner: G. Brookes

DARTMOUTH

CHANTRY BOOKSHOP AND GALLERY
11 Higher Street
Dartmouth TQ6 9EB
(01803) 832796/834208
Mon-Sat 10:30-5 (close Jan-Feb)
Est. 1968. Small. Gen Stock. Buys: Ring first. cc: AVAm. BR: Dartmouth. "We're in a backstreet beside Cherub Pub. Specialise in antique prints, Br counties and world ant. maps, sea and battle charts, town plans (European)."
Owner: M.P. Merkel

EXETER

ANTIQUE AND COLLECTORS CENTRE
The Quay
Exeter EX4
Mon-Sun 10-6 (Summer), 10-5 (Winter)
Medium. Gen Stock and Early Penguins. Buys: Ring first. BR: Exeter Central. "Large s'hand stock."
Dealers: Allen, Desforges, Jenkins, Morris

BARBICAN BOOKS
39 New Bridge Street
Exeter EX4 3AH
(01392) 216716
Mon-Sat 9:30-6 (Sometimes Sun).
Buys: Ring first. BR: Exeter Central. "Easy to find. Make your way to the River Exe– shop is on right. Extensive range of s'hand and atqn books in stock covering a wide range of subjects."
Owners: D. Carreyett & A. Hart

DICKENS BOOKSHOP
13 City Arcade, Fore Street
Exeter EX4 3JE
(01392) 431587
Mon-Sat 10-5:30
Est. 1971. Medium. Spec: Devon: also Gen Stock and General Academic. Buys: Ring first. cc: AVAmEJ. BR: Exeter Central. "Member PBFA."
Owner: Mr R.C. Parry

EXETER RARE BOOKS
12A Guildhall Shopping Centre
Exeter EX4 3HG
(01392) 436021
Mon-Sat 10-1, 2-5
Est. 1971. Medium. Spec: Devon Topog: also Gen Stock. Buys: Anytime. cc: AV. BR: Exeter Central. "In heart of City, adjacent to large carpark."
Owner: R. Parry (ABA)

EXETER RARE BOOKS
Guildhall Shopping Centre
Queen Street
Exeter EX4 3HG
(01392) 436021
Mon-Sat 10-1, 2-5
Est. 1981. Small. Spec: Devon and West Country Topog: also Gen Stock. Buys: Ring first. cc: AVAmEJ. BR: Exeter Central. "1st floor gallery in Victorian arcade in precinct, next to M&S. Member ABA. Selection of antiquarian and quality secondhand books on most subjects."
Owner: R.C. Parry M.A.

PENNIES
Unit 2, Wessex Estate, Station Road
Exeter EX4 4N2
(01392) 71928
Mon-Sat 9-6
Est. 1983. Small. Gen Stock. Buys: Ring first. BR: Exeter St. Davids. "S'hand furniture, bric-a-brac, antiques."
Owner: Mrs Penelope Clark

QUAY BOOKS
3 Crane Cellars
47 The Quay
Exeter EX2 4AN
(01392) 426793
Thur-Sun 11-4; longer in Summer
Small. Gen Stock and Penguin Pbk. Buys: Ring first. Book search.
Owner: Nick Allen

S.P.C.K
1-2 Catherine Street
Cathedral Yard
Exeter EX1 1EX
(01392) 73640
Mon-Sat 9-5:30
Est. 1946. Medium. Spec: Theol: also Gen Stock. Buys: Anytime. Book search. cc: AV. BR: Exeter Central.
Manager: Mr Richard Hammond

JOEL SEGAL BOOKS
37B Fore Street
Topsham
Exeter EX3 0HR
(01392) 877895
Mon- Sat 9:30-4:30 (Apr-Oct), 10:30-5 (Nov-Mar)
Gen Stock. Buys: Anytime. "Close to Topsham's attractive and historic estuary waterfront. Large quay side carpark. Gen stock of s'hand and out of print books covering wide range of subjects."
Owner: Joel Segal

HAWKCHURCH nr. Axminster

MYLES W. THIMBLEBY
Woodcote Farm, Crewkerne Road
Hawkchurch nr. Axminster EX13 5UN
Every Morning
Est. 1964. Medium. Spec: Country Matters: also Gen Stock and Juvenile. Buys: Anytime. BR: Axminster. "Not in village on Main Axminster/ Crewkerne Road."
Owner: Myles W. Thimbleby

HONITON

FOUNTAIN ANTIQUES
132 High Street
Honiton EX14 8JP
(01404) 42074
Mon-Sat 9:30-5:30
Small. Gen Stock and Atqn Ref, Loc Topog. Cat: 3 pa: Gypsies. Buys: Anytime. cc: AV. BR: Honiton.
Owner: Mr Graham York

HIGH STREET BOOKS
150 High Street
Honiton EX14 8JX
(01404) 45332
Mon-Sat 10-5
Small. Gen Stock. Buys: Anytime. cc: AV. BR: Honiton. "Easy-on-street parking outiside. Varied general stock of Atqn., s'hand and out of print bks., prints and maps bought and sold."
Owners: D. Spark, J. Ryan, & G. Tyson

HONITON OLD BOOKSHOP
51 High Street
Felix House
Honiton EX4 8PW
(01404) 47180 (tel/fax)
Mon-Fri 10-5:30, Sat 9:30-5:30
Medium. Spec: Trav, Topog: also Gen Stock and Chld, Atqn. Cat: 4 pa: Br Topog, Trav. Buys: Anytime. BR: Honiton. "Easy to find at the east end of High St., easy parking outside shop. Good general and 'better' quality stock, although some pbks also sold."
Owner: Roger Collicott

JOHN WIGNALL FINE BOOKS
174 High Street
Virginibus
Honiton EX14 8LA
(01404) 43460
Fax (01404) 47377
Mon-Sat 10-5:30 (ec Race days)
Medium. Spec: Field Sports, Rural Life: also Working Dogs. Buys: Anytime. BR: Honiton. "Superlative selec. of books on most subjects from Atqn to Occult."
Owner: John Wignall

ILFRACOMBE

FITZJOHN'S BOOKS
44 Fore Street
Ilfracombe
(01271) 866888
Mon-Sat 10-5
Est. 1987. Large. Spec: Sci, Tech: also Gen Stock and Theol. Buys: Ring first. BR: Barnstaple. "Large, clean, attractively priced general stock."
Owner: Kenneth H. Smith

LYNTON

BERRYS OF LYNTON
42 Lee Road
Lynton EX35 6BS
(01598) 752633
Mon, Wed, Sat 10:30-1, 2:30-4:30
Est. 1983. Small. Spec: West Country: also Gen Stock. Buys: Anytime. cc: AV. "Also painting, watercolours. Beautiful countryside in Exmoor."
Owner: Frank Windsor

MODBURY

LAMB'S TALES
63 Brownston St
Modbury PL21 0RQ
(01548) 830317
Mon-Sat 9:30-12:30, 1:30-5 (ec Wed)
Small. Gen Stock. Buys: Anytime. BR: Plymouth. "On Plymouth-Kingsbridge bus route. Select stock of interesting s'hand books. Bibliophiles welcome. Incorporates Welsh dresser antiques."
Owners: James & Elizabeth Lamb

NEWTON ABBOT

LINDY'S BOOKSHOP
58A Queen Street
Newton Abbot TQ12 2BZ
(01626) 63221 (tel/fax)
9:30-5:30 (Thur 9:30-1)
Est. 1984. Medium. Spec: Theol and Mus: also Gen Stock and Prints, Old Adverts, Postcards, Records. Cat: 6 pa: Theo & Mus. Buys: Ring first. Book search. BR: Newton Abbot.
Owner: Mark Lacey

PAIGNTON

BIDDY'S BOOKSHOP
99C Dartmouth Rd
Goodrington
Paignton TQ4 6NT
(01803) 556151
Mon-Sun 11-4 (Apr-Jun, Sep-Oct 9-5:30, Jul-Aug 9-9)
Est. 1990. Large. Gen Stock. Buys: Anytime. Book search. BR: Paignton. "On bus route. On-road parking and large car park around the corner. Good pub opposite with large carpark."
Owner: Biddy Nicholls

THE OLD CELTIC BOOKSHOP
43 Hyde Road
Paignton TQ4 5BP
(01803) 558709
Mon-Sun 9:30-6; June-Sept 9:30-9:30
Large. Spec: Atqn, Chld: also Gen Stock. BR: Paignton. "1000's of paperbacks with half-price exchange. New books at up to 80% off - something for everybody."

THE POCKET BOOKSHOP
159 Winner Street
Paignton TQ3 3BP
(01803) 529804
Mon-Sat 10:30-6 (Nov-Mar Mon close)
Est. 1985. Medium. Gen Stock. Buys: Ring first.
BR: Paignton.
Owner: L.Corrall

PLYMOUTH

BARBICAN BOOKSHOP
24 Southside Street
Plymouth PL1 2LD
(01752) 664957
Mon-Sat 10:30-5
Est. 1965. Medium. Gen Stock. Buys: Anytime. BR: Plymouth.
Owners: A. & D. Clement

CORNERSTONE BOOKS
New Street Antiques Centre
The Barbican
Plymouth PL1 2NB
(01752) 661165
Mon-Sat 10-5
Est. 1986. Medium. Spec: Local: also Gen Stock and Mil, Art, Occ. Buys: Anytime. BR: Plymouth. "15 min walk from City Centre, situated in historic barbican area. The Centre has 4 floors of antiques, crafts, and books. Restaurant on top floor."
Owner: Mark Treece

THE SEA CHEST NAUTICAL BOOKS
Queen Anne's Battery Marina
Coxside
Plymouth PL4 0LP
(01752) 222012
Fax (01752) 252679
Mon-Sat 9-5:30
Est. 1987. Small. Spec: Nautical. Cat: 1 pa: New Books. Buys: Anytime. Book search. BR: Plymouth. "The only specialist nautical b'shop in Plymouth. New nautical books, admiralty charts agent, stock always wanted."
Owner: Robert Dearn

SIDMOUTH

DEVONSHIRE HOUSE ANTIQUES CENTRE
All Saints Road
Sidmouth EX10 8ES
(01395) 512588
Mon-Sat 10-5 (Sun, May-Oct, 2-5)
Medium. Spec: Atqn. Buys: Ring first. BR: Exeter Central. "3 atqn booksellers within the shop with wide range of subjects."
Owners: B. Dunstan-Smith, W. Gillian & J. Godfrey

SOUTH BRENT

JAMES A MITCHELL
The Manor
North Huish
South Brent TQ10 9NQ
(01364) 72288
Mon-Sat 9-7
Est. 1970. Medium. Gen Stock. Buys: Anytime. BR: Totnes. "For North Huish, come to Avonwick on former B3210 from Totnes, or from South Brent A38 Junction."
Owner: James A. Mitchell

TAVISTOCK

BLACK BIRD BOOKS
3A The Old Dairy, Paddons Row
Tavistock PL19 0HF
(01822) 618822
Mon-Sat 9-5 (Summer), 10-5 (Winter)
Est. 1993. Medium. Spec: Ornithology, Railway: also Gen Stock and Pol, Mil, Africa. Buys: Anytime. cc: AVE. BR: Plymouth. "Bus to Tavistock. Go past Woolworths to Goodes, cross road through tunnel. A good clean general stock covering most subjects."
Owner: J. Black

TEIGNMOUTH

QUAYSIDE BOOKSHOP
43 Northumberland Place
Teignmouth TQ14 8DE
(01626) 775436 (tel/fax)
Mon-Sat 9-5:30
Small. Spec: Hbk Fict: also Gen Stock and Hist, Maritime. Buys: Anytime. cc: AV. BR: Teignmouth. "Close to the sea, harbour, and carparks. S'hand dept. at rear of new b'shop. Stock is very general."
Owners: V.K. & T. Marston

TIVERTON

ANGEL HILL BOOKSHOP
17 Angel Hill
The Barn
Tiverton EX16 6PE
(01884) 257783/4
Mon-Sat 9-5
Medium. Spec: Eso, Phil: also Gen Stock and Lit, Theol. Buys: Ring first. Book search. BR: Tiverton Parkway. "Limited booksearch. Much enlarged stock and area devoted to book at No.17 apart from my own stock. Well worth a visit."
Owner: R.A. Spiers

THE FOUNTAIN PICTURE SHOP
17 Angel Hill
Tiverton EX16 6PE
(01884) 257784
Mon-Sat 9-5 (or by appt)
Medium. Spec: Art: also Gen Stock. Buys: Anytime. BR: Tiverton Parkway. "Buses from BR (7 miles) infrequent. More frequent service from Exeter BR. More than 1 bookseller on the premises. Pass through courtyard to find more."
Owner: R.A. Chandler

TORQUAY

BOOKBARN
53 Market Street
Torquay TQ1 3AW
(01803) 298160
Mon-Sat 10-5:30
Est. 1976. Large. Gen Stock and Thrillers, Romance, SF and Paperbacks Buys: Anytime. BR: Torquay. "Books sold at approx. 1/2 retail price with 1/2 price back exchange avail."
Owners: Mr & Mrs D. Carpenter

TORBAY RARE BOOKS
10 Lucias Street
Torquay TQ2 5UN
(01803) 215672
Thur-Sat 10-5
Medium. Gen Stock. Cat: 3-4 pa: Single subj lists. Buys: Anytime. BR: Torquay. "In historic heart of Torquay opp. old Tor Church. Customer parking at rear. A wide-ranging but selected stock of books and ephemera."
Owners: Steven & Elizabeth Wycherley

TORRINGTON

TOR BOOKS
1 South Street
Torrington EX38 8HE
(01805) 623791
Thur-Sat 9-5
Est. 1986. Medium. Spec: Travel, Topog: also Gen Stock and Mil, Arts, Biog. Buys: Anytime. Book search. BR: Barnstaple. "Centre of Torrington - 12 miles from Barnstaple or 7 miles from Bideford. Stocks the odd and the curious."
Owners: Peter & Doreen Mitchell

TOTNES

THE BOOKSHOP
72 Fore Street
Totnes TQ9 5RU
(01803) 864088
Mon-Sat 9:30-5, Thur 9:30-1
Est. 1971. Medium. Gen Stock. Buys: Anytime. BR: Totnes.
Owner: Ken Parnell

COLLARDS BOOKSHOP
4 Castle Street
Totnes TQ9 5NU
(01548) 550246
10-5 restricted in Winter
Est. 1970. Medium. Spec: Crime Fict: also Gen Stock and "Alternative" living. Buys: Anytime. BR: Totnes. "Follow signs to the castle. Customer has just said: You've got some really nice books!"
Owner: Mrs Belle Collard

HARLEQUIN
41 High Street
Totnes TQ9 5NP
(01803) 866406
Mon-Sat 9-5:30
Est. 1982. Medium. Gen Stock. Buys: Anytime. BR: Totnes.
Owner: Paul Wesley

THE MAGPIE
Rutherfold Square
Totnes TQ9 5ST
(01548) 830082 (home)
Mon-Sun 10-5, Wed-Thur close
Est. 1990. Medium. Spec: West Country, Collecting: also Gen Stock. Buys: Anytime. BR: Totnes. "At the top of the town, near car parks. An interesting shop for collectors. Also sells general ephemera, general memorabilia, and antique buttons."
Owners: H. & D.E. Helmer

PEDLARS PACK BOOKS
4 The Plains
Totnes
(01803) 866423
Mon-Sat 9-5
Medium. Gen Stock. Cat: 2 pa: Mod 1sts, Soc Sci, Atqn. Buys: Ring first. Book search. BR: Totnes. "At the bottom of town, nearby parking. Also CDs, records, tapes, maps, and postcards."
Owners: Peter & Angela Elliott

DORSET

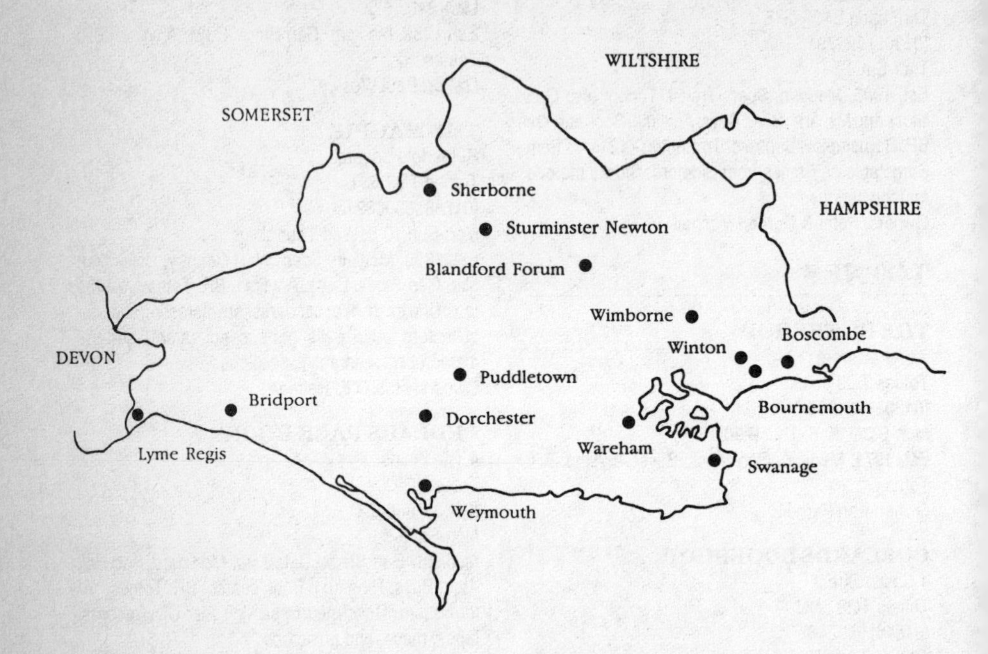

BLANDFORD FORUM

ANCIENT AND MODERN BOOKSHOP

84 Salisbury Street
Blandford Forum DT11 7QE
(01258) 455276
Mon-Sat 9:30-12:30, 1:30-5:30, Wed close
Est. 1989. Small. Spec: Mil: also Gen Stock and Trav. Buys: Anytime. BR: Poole. "Also sells small antiques."
Owner: Margaret A. Davey

BOSCOMBE

THE ASHLEY BOOKSHOP

30B Ashley Road
Boscombe BH1 4LH
(01202) 302499
Mon-Sat 10-5:30
Est. 1968. Large. Gen Stock and Lit, Topog, Chld. Buys: Anytime. BR: Pokesdown/Bournemouth Cent. "Academic focus– we cater a lot for students. Also 8 cabinets full of leather-bound & Atqn."
Owners: Mr & Mrs D.J. Horne

BIZZY LIZZY
708 Christchurch Road
Boscombe BH1
(01202) 303942
Mon-Sat 9:30-5:30, 9:45-5 (Winter)
Est. 1982. Large. Gen Stock. Buys: Anytime. BR: Bournemouth Central. "Books in good condition. Also sell new ceramics. Fairly friendly on a good day."

H. & S.J. ROWAN
459 Christchurch Road
Boscombe BH1 4AD
(01202) 398820
Mon-Sat 9-6
Est. 1968. Large. Spec: Atqn: also Gen Stock and Avia, Art, Mil. Buys: Anytime. Book search. BR: Bournemouth Central.
Owner: Harold Rowan

BOURNEMOUTH

HOLDENHURST BOOKS
275 Holdenhurst Road
Bournemouth BH8 8BZ
(01202) 397718
Mon-Sat 10-5:30, Wed close
Est. 1985. Medium. Spec: Motoring, Motor Cycling: also Gen Stock and Mil, Avia. Buys: Anytime. BR: Bournemouth. "Turn left out of station. Shop is 1/4 mile away."
Owner: R.W. Reese

YESTERDAY'S BOOKS
65-67 Bennett Road
Bournemouth BH8 8RH
(01202) 302023
Mon-Sat 9:30-5:30
Est. 1984. Medium. Spec: Africana: also Gen Stock and Lit. Cat: 4 pa: Africana. Buys: Anytime. Book search. BR: Bournemouth. "Easy Parking. Friendly welcome, dealer discount."
Owners: D. & J.L. Weir

BRIDPORT

PIC'S BOOKSHOP
11 South Street
Bridport DT6 3NR
(01308) 425689
Mon-Sat 9-5, Thur 9-1
Est. 1981. Medium. Gen Stock and Classics, Art. Buys: Anytime. BR: Dorchester. "Shop with practical touch–50 classifications."
Owner: Peter Craddock

DORCHESTER

BOOKS & BYGONES IN DE DANANN
25-27 London Road
Dorchester
(01305) 250066
Mon-Sat 9-5
Est. 1982. Medium. Spec: Nat Hist: also Gen Stock and Dorset, Topog, Arch. Buys: Anytime. Book search. BR: Dorchester.
Owners: N.T. Armitage & F.W. Barrett-Selbie

THE DORCHESTER BOOKSHOP
3 Nappers Court
Dorchester DT1 1EE
(01305) 269919
Mon-Sat 10-5
Est. 1993. Small. Gen Stock. Buys: Anytime. BR: Dorchester. "Right opp. big car park. Side arcade, next to coffee-shop. Friendly. Leather-bound volumes to cheap paperbacks."
Owner: Michael Edmonds

WORDS ETCETERA
2 Cornhill
Dorchester DT1 1BA
(01305) 251919
Mon-Sat 9:30-5:30, Sun 1-5 (Summer)
Est. 1995. Large. Spec: Mod 1sts, Arts: also Gen Stock. Cat: 2 pa: Mod 1sts. Buys: Ring first. Book search. cc: AVJS. BR: Dorchester. "We have 18 other booksellers on the first floor of our shop. Also periodic exhibitions of poetry and paintings."
Owner/Manageress: Jucian Nangle/Fiona Seare

LYME REGIS

BOOKS & PRINTS
7 Drake's Way
Lyme Regis DT7 3QP
(01297) 443464
Fax (01395) 513255
Mon-Sun 10:30-5:30 (Summer; occ later), Fri-Mon 10:30-5 (Winter)
Medium. Spec: Lit, Poetry: also Gen Stock and Loc Topog, Art, Nat Hist. Cat: 4 pa: Art, Po, Lit, Gen. Buys: Anytime. Book search. cc: AVE. BR: Axminster. "Atqn prints also sold. Special interest ring first, esp. Winter."
Owners: N. Cozens, I.Mostyn, & J.Vaupres

GUILDHALL EMPORIUM
6 Bridge Street
Lyme Regis DT7
(01297) 442088
Mon-Sun 10-6
Small. Gen Stock. Buys: Ring first. BR: Axminster. "Part of the Fossil Shop. Wide selection of subjects sold by several dealers."
Various dealers

MARINE-WORKSHOP BOOKSHOP
Old Bonded Store
The Cobb
Lyme Regis DT7 3JF
(01297) 442088
Mon-Sun 10-6
Est. 1960. Medium. Gen Stock and Lit, Hist, Topog. Buys: Anytime. Book search. cc: AV. BR: Axminster.
Owner: Mr B. Landon

SERENDIP
11 Broad Street
Lyme Regis DT7 3QD
(01297) 442594
Fax (01297) 443036
'Normal'
Small. Gen Stock. Buys: Anytime. Book search. cc: AV. BR: Axminster. "Also new books. Serendip is one of a family trio of bookshops, this being the only one with a s'hand section."
Owners: Messrs. C., S. & M. Chapman

PUDDLETOWN

ANTIQUE MAP & BOOKSHOP
32 High Street
Puddletown DT2 8RU
(01305) 848633
Mon-Sat 9-5 (occ close 1-2)
Est. 1977. Medium. Spec: Thomas Hardy, Illus: also Gen Stock and Fine Bindings, Lit, Sport. Cat: 4 pa: Misc. Buys: Anytime. Book search. cc: AV. BR: Dorchester. "We are always interested to buy good Atqn. & s'hand books on all subjects."
Owners: H.M. & C.D. Proctor

SHERBORNE

A1 CRIME FICTION
Westridge House
3 Horsecastles Lane
Sherborne DT9 6DW
(01935) 814989
Mon-Sun 8am-9pm (ring first)
Large. Spec: Crime. Cat: 3 lists weekly: Crime Fict. Buys: Anytime. Book search. cc: AV. BR: Sherborne. "Opp. Skippers Pub car park. Viewing 7 days a week (8-9) but ring first as I could be away buying. Also wants lists."
Owner: D.L. Ireland

CHAPTER HOUSE BOOKS
Trendle Street
Sherborne DT9 3NT
(01935) 816262
Mon-Sat 10-1, 2-5
Est. 1988. Large. Gen Stock and Pictures. Buys: Ring first. Book search. BR: Sherborne. "Also book repairs and binding."
Owners: Carol & Robert Hutchinson

STEVEN FERDINANDO AT THE SWAN GALLERY
51 Cheap Street
(Cnr. Cheap St. & Swan Yard)
Sherborne DT9
(01935) 814465
Mon-Sat 9:30-5, Wed 9:30-1
Est. 1979. Medium. Spec: Local: also Gen Stock and Lit, Thomas Hardy, Topog. Cat: occ. Buys: Ring first. cc: AV. BR: Sherborne. "No rubbish. Specialities are Dorset, Powys & Barnes."
Owner: Simon Lamb

STURMINSTER NEWTON

STOUR BOOKS
Bridge Street
Sturminster Newton DT10 1AP
(01258) 473561
Mon-Fri 10-4:30, Tue close
Est. 1982. Small. Spec: Illus, Early Motor Racing: also Gen Stock and Chld, Tech, Trans. Buys: Anytime. BR: Gillingham. "Print & picture restoration. Book binding service."
Owner: A.J. Butler

SWANAGE

ANTIQUARIAN & SECONDHAND BOOKS
55 High Street
Swanage BH19 1LT
(01929) 424088
Mon-Sat 10-10 (Summer)
Est. 1987. Medium. Gen Stock. Buys: Ring first. BR: Wareham. "30 min from BR."
Owners: Jill & Mike Blanchard

WAREHAM

BAY TREE BOOKS
2-3 St. John's Hill
Wareham BH20 4NA
(01929) 552577
Wed-Sat 10-1, 2:30-5:30
Medium. Gen Stock and Mus, Poetry, Drama. Buys: Anytime. BR: Wareham. "Wareham is an interesting old walled Saxon town and the shop is not far from the quay."
Owners: Eric & Audrey Lewis

WEYMOUTH

BOOKS & BYGONES
13 Great George Street
Weymouth DT4 7AR
(01305) 777231
Mon-Sat 10:30-5, Sun 12-5
Est. 1992. Medium. Gen Stock. Buys: Anytime. Book search. BR: Weymouth. "50 yards from the Esplanade. Antiques & ephemera. Business has been going since 1984."
Owner: Mrs D. Nash

BOOKS AFLOAT
66 Park Street
Weymouth DT4 7DE
(01305) 779774
Mon-Sat 9:30-5:30
Est. 1983. Medium. Spec: Maritime: also Gen Stock and Trans, Loc Topog, Lit. Cat: 2-3 pa: Maritime. Buys: Anytime. BR: Weymouth. "Near BR. 1 hour free parking outside shop. Specialising in maritime books, ephemera and ship models. Also old Dorset books & postcards."
Owner: John Ritchie

BOOK WORLD
59 East Street
Weymouth DT4 9PG
Winter 10-5, Summer 10-10
Est. 1993. Small. Spec: SF, Horror: also Gen Stock. Buys: Anytime. BR: Weymouth.
Owner: Mrs C. Squire

QUEST BOOKS
13A Cove Street
Weymouth DT4
(01305) 789142
Mon-Sat 10:30-1, 2-5:30
Est. 1982. Small. Gen Stock. Buys: Ring first. BR: Weymouth. "By harbour near Brewer's Quay and Town Bridge. A little of everything– Fict, Topog, Autobiog–no specialism."
Owner: Mrs J. Child

WIMBORNE

MINSTER BOOKS
11 Corn Market
Wimborne BH21 1JL
(01202) 883355
Mon-Sat 10-5
Est. 1991. Medium. Gen Stock. Buys: Anytime. cc: AVAm. BR: Poole. "Good quality gen stock."
Owner: John Child

WINTON

BOOKS RARE & SECONDHAND
1 Jewel Box Building
Cardigan Road
Winton
(01202) 521373
Mon-Sat 9-5:30
Est. 1983. Medium. Gen Stock. Buys: Anytime. BR: Bournemouth. "Price range £2.50-£2,000."
Owner: R.J. Browne

Durham

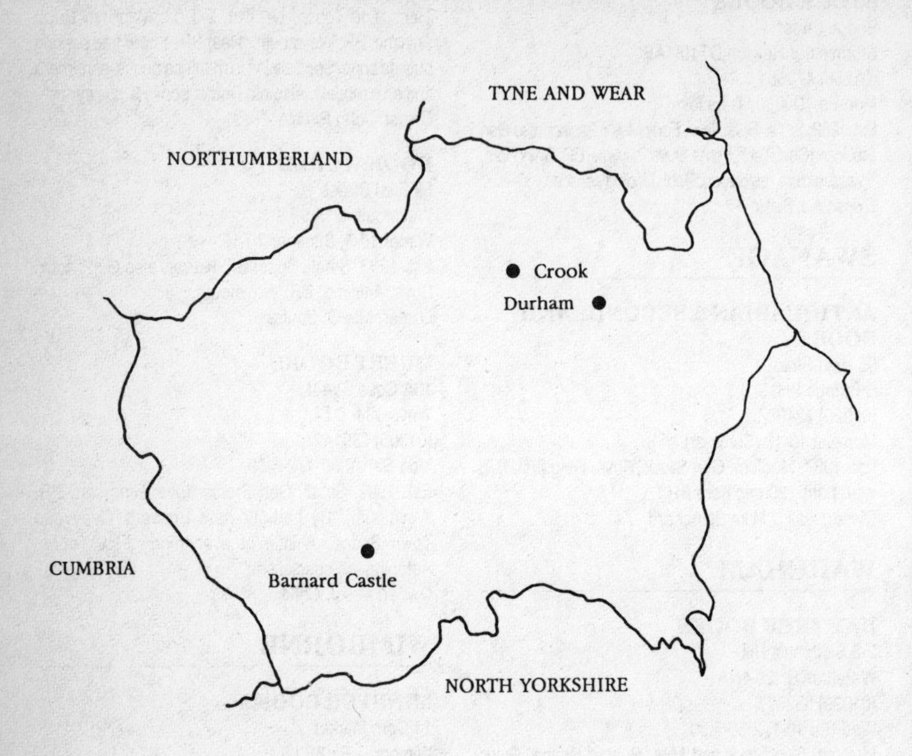

BARNARD CASTLE

CURLEWS

27 Horse Market
Barnard Castle DL12 8EJ
(01833) 631090
Mon-Sat 9-5:30, Sun 1-5
Est. 1984. Large. Gen Stock. Buys: Anytime. Book search. BR: Darlington. "Also large stock of Theo at 5 Galgate, Barnard Castle."
Owner: Maurice Abrahams

CROOK

JOHN TURTON

83 High Street
Willington
Crook DL15 0HN
(01388) 747600
Thur-Sat 10-5
Est. 1977. Large. Spec: British Topog, Atqn: also Gen Stock and Sci, Trav, Lit. Cat: 3 pa: Br. Loc Hist. Buys: Ring first. BR: Durham. "A690, 7 miles west of Durham City, next door to GPO. Without a doubt the best bookshop between Langley Moor and Crook."
Owner: John Turton

DURHAM

DILLONS UNIVERISTY BOOKSHOP
55-57 Saddler Street
Durham DH1 3EJ
(0191) 384 2095
Fax (0191) 381551
Mon-Sat 9-5:30 (Summer 11-5)
Est. 1976. Medium. Spec: Theol: also Gen Stock and Hist, Phil, Eng Lit. Buys: Anytime. Book search. cc: AV. BR: Durham.
Manageress: Miss N. Angell

J. SHOTTON
89 Elvet Bridge
Durham DH1 3AG
(0191) 386 4597
Tue-Sat 9:30-5
Est. 1968. Small. Gen Stock. Buys: Ring first. BR: Durham. "Also sells maps & prints."
Owner: J. Shotton

THOMAS RARE BOOKS
Durham Indoor Market
Market Square
Durham DH1
(0191) 373 3526 (home)
Mon-Sat 9-4
Medium. Spec: NE Hist & Topog: also Gen Stock. Cat: 1 pa: NE Topog. Buys: Anytime. Book search. cc: AV. BR: Durham. "A new post in the 20 year old indoor market."
Owner: G.L. Thomas

Charles Swainson

A.D. MDCCCXLVII.

Jacob Ley.
Student of Ch.Ch.
and Vicar of
St. Mary Magdalene,
OXFORD.

ESSEX

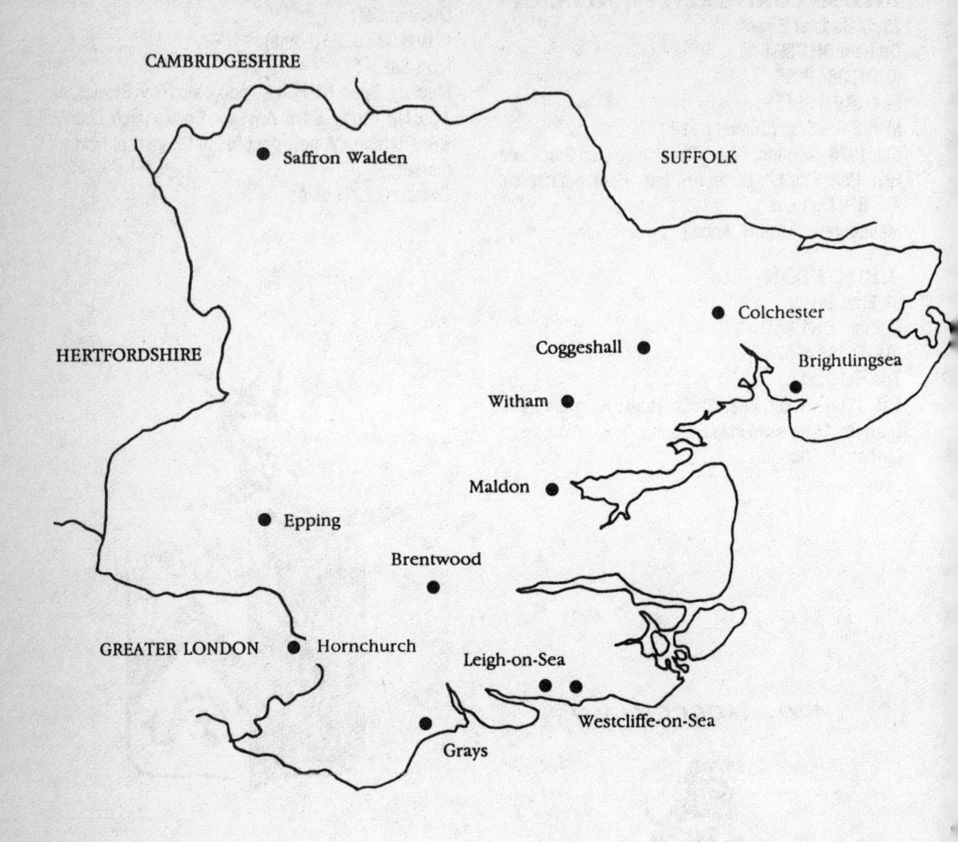

BRENTWOOD

THE BOOKEND
38 Kings Road
Brentwood CM14 4DW
Mon-Sat 10-5:30, Thur 10-1
Est. 1980. Medium. Gen Stock. Buys: Ring first. BR: Brentwood Brook Street. "1/2 mile from station towards Brentwood town."
Owners: G.E. & M.K. Smith

BRIGHTLINGSEA

VICTORIA BOOKS
22 Victoria Place
Brightlingsea CO7 0BX
(01206) 302374
Mon-Sat 10:30-4:30, Tue-Wed close, Sun 1:30-4:30
Medium. Gen Stock. Buys: Anytime. BR: Alresford. "In Brightlingsea's main shopping area, free parking outside. Owned adjoining premises since 1991. Interesting books on most subjects (no tat!) Predominantly non-fict."
Owner: G. Cawthorn

COGGESHALL

ELKIN MATTHEWS
16 Stoneham Street
Coggeshall CO6 1TT
(01376) 561730
Mon-Fri 9:30-1, 2-4:30, Sat 10-5, Wed close
Medium. Spec: Local: also Gen Stock and Chld, Illus. Cat: 3 pa: Chld, Gen. Buys: Ring first.
Owners: David & Lynn Muir

COLCHESTER

ALPHABETS (C.E. BRIGGS)
13 Trinity Street
Colchester CO1 1JN
(01206) 572751
Mon-Sat 10-5, Thur close
Est. 1975. Medium. Spec: Maritime: also Gen Stock and Gard, Atqn. Buys: Anytime. BR: Colchester. "Bunkside bargains, sailing books. Phone for details."
Owners: C.E. & S.M. Briggs

CASTLE BOOKSHOP
37 North Hill
Colchester CO5 0NZ
(01206) 577520
Mon-Sat 9-5
Est. 1947. Large. Spec: E Anglia, Mil: also Gen Stock and 1sts, Arch, Folklore. Buys: Anytime. Book search. BR: Colchester North Street. "V. large stock of good s'hand & atqn books."
Owner: R. Green

GREYFRIARS BOOKS
92B East Hill
Colchester CO1 2QN
(01206) 563138
Mon-Fri 10-5:30, Sat 9-5:30
Est. 1983. Medium. Spec: Mineralogy: also Gen Stock and Art, Lit, Nat Hist. Cat: 2 pa: Mineralogy, Mining. Buys: Anytime. BR: Colchester. "On top of hill opp. church. Emphasis on interesting books in good condition covering a broad subject range. Specialist in Mineralogy & Mining."
Owners: Roy, Pauline & Simon Taylor

EPPING

BROWSERS BOOKSHOP
9 Station Road
Epping CM16 4HA
(019925) 72260
Mon-Sat 10-5, Wed close
Est. 1990. Medium. Gen Stock. Buys: Anytime. BR: Epping.
Owners: Brian & Moira Carter

GRAYS

KENDONS
10 London Road
Grays
(01375) 371200
Thur & Sat 9:30-4
Medium. Spec: Essex Topog: also Gen Stock and Occult, Field Sports. Buys: Anytime. Book search. BR: Grays. "Situated on town centre, one-way system. 200 yds from BR, 50 yds from High Street. On 1st floor above antique shop."
Owner: R. Drake

HORNCHURCH

TALATIN BOOKS
21 Parkstone Avenue
Hornchurch RM11 3LX
(01708) 447561
Fax (01708) 442238
Est. 1987. Small. Spec: Chld, Illus: also Shorthand (all systems). Cat: 4 pa: Chld, Illus. Buys: Ring first. BR: Hornchurch. "4 miles from M25. Can provide map. VG+/Fine books only."
Owner: Maggie Stevens

LEIGH-ON-SEA

CALIVER BOOKS
816-818 London Road
Leigh-on-Sea SS9 3NH
(01702) 73986 (tel/fax)
Mon-Wed, Fri & Sat 9-6, Thur 9-8, Sun 11-5
Est. 1987. Medium. Spec: Mil, Fantasy Role-play: also C17th Hist. Cat: 15 pa: Mil. Buys: Ring first. Book search. cc: AVAmE. BR: Chalkwell. "Situated on A13, 1/2 mile west of Chalkwell schools. 1 hour by train/car from London."
Owner: D. Ryan

LEIGH GALLERY BOOKS
137 Leigh Road
Leigh-on-Sea SS9 1JQ
(01702) 715477 (tel/fax)
Tue-Sat 10-5, Wed close
Est. 1983. Medium. Gen Stock and Art, Tech, Trav. Buys: Ring first. BR: Chalkwell. "Parking outside. C19th & C20th Br & Continental prints. Also decorative & general. Jazz & classical records."
Owner: Barrie Gretton

MALDON

ALL BOOKS
2 Mill Road
Maldon
(01621) 856214
Mon-Sat 1:30-5, Sun 2-5, Wed close
Est. 1970. Large. Gen Stock and Sailing, Trans, Nat Hist. Buys: Anytime.
Owner: Barry Jenkinson

SAFFRON WALDEN

LANKESTER ANTIQUES & BOOKS
The Old Sun Inn
Church Street & Market Hill
Saffron Walden CB10 1HQ
(01799) 522685
Mon-Sat 9:30-5:30
Est. 1967. Large. Gen Stock. Buys: Ring first. BR: Audley End. "Situated in the C14th former headquarters of Oliver Cromwell. Interesting selection of 30,000 books & 4 showrooms of antiques & reproductions."
Owner: P.W. Lankester

WESTCLIFF-ON-SEA

BARRIE E. ELLEN
The Bookshop
262 London Road
Westcliff-on-Sea SS0 7JG
(01702) 338763 (tel/fax)
Tue-Sat 9:30-5, Wed close
Est. 1976. Medium. Spec: Chess: also Gen Stock and Mil, Avia, Hist. Cat: 3 pa: Chess. Buys: Ring first. cc: AV. BR: Westcliff-on-Sea. "Easy parking outside shop. Many remainders & review copies stocked. S'hand records bought & sold."
Owner: Barrie Ellen

WITHAM

BALDWIN'S SCIENTIFIC BOOKS
Fossil Hall, Boar Tye Road
Silver End
Witham CM8 3QA
(01376) 583502
Fax (01376) 584480
Mon-Sat 10-4 (ring first)
Large. Spec: Geol, Palaeontology, Mineralogy: also Gen Stock and Nat Hist, Arch, Hist of Sci. Cat: 1 pa. Book search. cc: V. BR: Witham/Braintree. "3 1/2 miles off A12 or A120 between Chelmsford & Colchester. UK's largest specialist dealer in Geology & fossils."
Owner: Stuart A. Baldwin

GLOUCESTERSHIRE

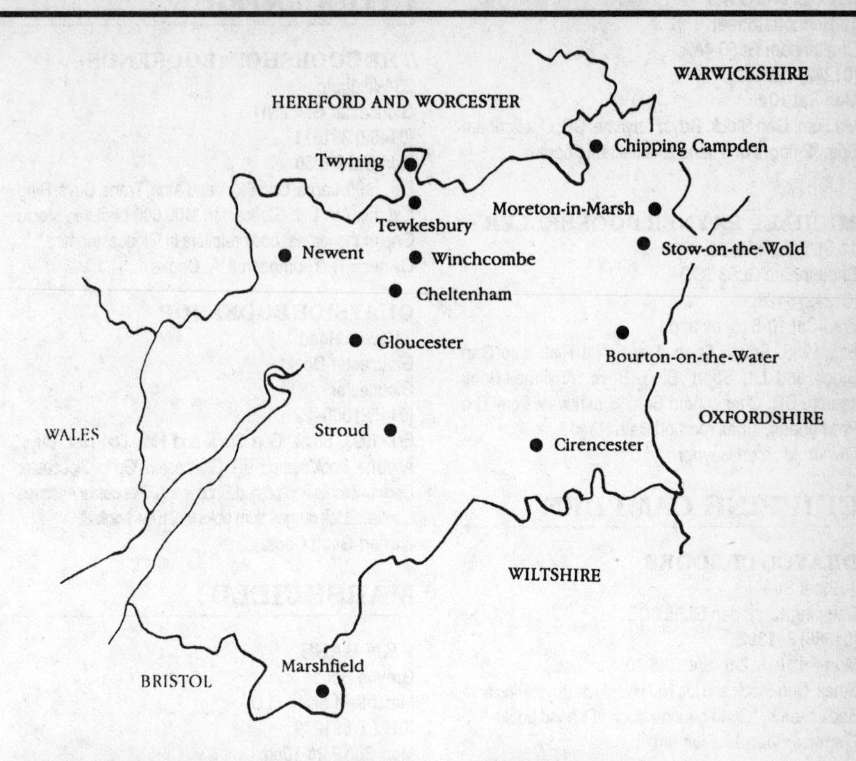

BOURTON-ON-THE-WATER

AQUARIUS BOOKS

Victoria Street
Bourton-on-the-Water GL54 2BX
(01451) 820352
Mon-Sun 9:30-6
Small. Spec: Fict: also Gen Stock. Buys: Ring first. Book search. "Near the central pedestrian bridge in village centre. Good general stock covering most categories."

CHELTENHAM

ATTIC BOOKS

14 St. James Street
(off Upper High Street)
Cheltenham GL52 2SH
(01242) 255300
Mon-Sat 9:30-5:30 (occ Sun)
Est. 1994. Small. Spec: Lit, Po: also Gen Stock. Buys: Ring first. Book search. BR: Cheltenham Spa. "Situated above Moonstone Books (Mind, Body & Spirit, new & s'hand)."
Owner: Roger Langer

ALAN HANCOX FINE BOOKS

101 Promenade
Cheltenham GL50 1NN
(01242) 513204/(0973) 166192 (mobile)
Mon-Sat 10-5
Est. 1949. Large. Spec: Mod 1sts, Atqn: also Gen Stock and Fine Art, Folio, Collecting. Cat: 1 pa. Buys: Anytime. BR: Cheltenham Spa.
Owner: Shelagh Hancox

MOSS BOOKS
13 Henrietta Street
Cheltenham GL50 4AA
(01242) 222947
Mon-Sat 10-5
Medium. Gen Stock. Buys: Anytime. BR: Cheltenham Spa. "2 floors of s'hand & collectable books."

MICHAEL RAYNER BOOKSELLER
11 St. Luke's Road
Cheltenham GL53 7SQ
(01242) 512806
Wed-Sat 10-6 (or by appt)
Est. 1988. Small. Spec: Trans, Nat Hist: also Gen Stock and Lit, Sport, Biog. Buys: Anytime. Book search. BR: Cheltenham Spa. "5 min walk from The Promenade, small road off Bath Road."
Owner: Michael Rayner

CHIPPING CAMPDEN

DRAYCOTT BOOKS
1 Sheet Street
Chipping Campden GL55 6DS
(01386) 841392
Mon-Fri 10-1, 2-5, Sat 10-5:30, Sun occ
Small. Gen Stock and Lit, Nat Hist, Arts. Buys: Ring first. Book search. "Good general stock of s'hand books."
Owner: Robert McClement

CIRENCESTER

THOMPSON'S BOOKSHOP
Dunstall House
Park Street
Cirencester GL7 2BX
(01285) 655239
Tue-Sat 10-5
Est. 1980. Medium. Spec: Atec: also Sport, Biog. Cat: 2 pa: Atec. Buys: Anytime. BR: Kemble. "Next to Museum, opp. Yew hedge."
Owners: J.M. & S.V. Thompson

GLOUCESTER

THE BOOKSHOP (BOOKENDS)
26 Westgate
Gloucester GL1 2NH
(01452) 331011
Mon-Sat 9-5:30
Est. 1990. Large. Gen Stock and Atqn, Trans. Buys: Ring first. cc: AV. BR: Gloucester. "100,000 books in stock. One of the largest book retailers in Gloucestershire."
Owners: R. Thompson & A. Cooke

QUAYSIDE BOOKSHOP
2 Severn Road
Gloucester Docks
Gloucester
(01452) 300422
Est. 1990. Small. Gen Stock and Hist, Loc Hist. Buys: Anytime. Book search. BR: Gloucester. "Go to Gloucester Docks, which is sign-posted. Shop is opp. Gloucester Antiques Centre. Stock ranges from pbks to £100+ books."
Owner: Geoff Cook

MARSHFIELD

BEN BASS
Greyne House
Marshfield SN14 8LU
(01225) 891279
Mon-Sun 9am-10pm
Medium. Spec: Arthur Machen: also Gen Stock and Lit, Biog, Spain. Cat: 4-6 pa: Misc. Buys: Ring first. Book search. BR: Bath/Chippenham. "Marshfield is 13 miles from Bristol & 10 miles from Chippenham on the A420, 10 min drive from Bath."
Owner: Ben Bass

MORETON-IN-MARSH

FOUR SHIRE BOOKSHOP
17 High Street
Moreton-in-Marsh GL56 0AF
(01608) 651451
Fax (01608) 650827
Mon-Sat 9:30-1, 2:15-5 (Summer, Sun 11-5)
Est. 1982. Medium. Spec: Needlecraft: also Gen Stock and Cotswolds, Gloucestershire. Cat: 2 pa: Craft, Needlecraft. Buys: Anytime. Book search. cc: AV. BR: Moreton-in-Marsh. "In town centre, we share a front door with Drury's Butchers."
Owners: Hazel & David Potten

NEWENT

MUSHROOMS BOOK CELLAR/ COBWEBS
10 Church Street
Newent GL18 1PP
Fax (01531) 821120
Mon-Sat 9:30-1, 2-5
Est. 1986. Large. Gen Stock and Topog, Mil, Po. Buys: Ring first. BR: Gloucester. "10 miles from BR. In the centre of Newent town. Parking outside. Generally 50p to £25 range."
Owner: J.R. Chapman

STOW-ON-THE-WOLD

BOOKBOX
Chantry House
Sheep Street
Stow-on-the-Wold GL54 1AA
(01451) 831214
Mon-Sat 10-1, 2-5, Wed close (Winter Thur-Sat 11-4:30, ring first)
Est. 1982. Medium. Spec: Lit, Art: also Gen Stock and Mus, Fine Bindings, Topog. Cat: occ. Buys: Ring first. cc: AV. BR: Kingham. "Easy drive from Cheltenham, Stratford or Oxford. Other b'shops in town. Train from Paddington is 75 min. Quality bookshop in a fine listed building."
Owners: Mrs P. Brown & C.M. Fisher

FOUR SHIRE BOOKSHOP
4 Talbot Court
Stow-on-the-Wold GL54 1BQ
(01451) 830755
Mon-Sat 9:30-1, 2:15-5 (Summer, Sun 11-5)
Est. 1982. Medium. Spec: Crafts, Design: also Gen Stock and Handicrafts. Cat: 2-3 pa: Craft, Design. Buys: Anytime. Book search. cc: AV. BR: Moreton-in-the-Marsh. "We are in the courtyard beside the Talbot Hotel, in the Square."
Owners: Hazel & David Potten

WYCHWOOD BOOKS
Sheep Street
Stow-on-the-Wold GL54 1AA
(01451) 831880
Tue-Sat 9:30-1, 2-5, Wed close
Est. 1985. Medium. Spec: Nat Hist: also Gen Stock and Lit, Topog, Biog. Buys: Ring first. "Close to corner of Church Street near Post Office. 3 floors of good s'hand Atqn books on most subjects."
Owner: Glyn Frewer

STROUD

INPRINT BOOKSHOP
31 High Street
Stroud GL5 1AJ
(01453) 759731
Fax (01453) 763414
Mon-Sat 10-5:30
Est. 1978. Medium. Spec: Cinema: also Gen Stock and Hist, Perf & Visual Art, Leisure. Cat: 1 pa: Cinema, occ. lists other subjs. Buys: Ring first. Book search. BR: Stroud. "Close to town centre car parks. Loading bay to rear of shop."
Owner: Mike Goodenough

RUTH PYECROFT BOOKS
56 Middle Street
Stroud GL5 1DZ
(01453) 755788
Mon-Sat 10:30-5:30
Est. 1994. Small. Spec: Penguins, Pans: also Gen Stock and Comparative Religions, Eso, Loc Ephemera. Cat: 4 pa: Collectable Pbks. Buys: Ring first. Book search. BR: Stroud. "5 min walk from town centre. There is a map at top of pedestrianised High Street. Wide range of s'hand books, comics & printed collectables."
Owner: Ruth Pyecroft

ALAN & JOAN TUCKER
The Bookshop
Station Road
Stroud GL5 3AP
(01453) 764738
Tue, Wed, Sat 9:30-5 (Tue & Wed close for lunch; other days by appt)
Est. 1962. Medium. Gen Stock. Cat: 1 pa: 1sts, Lit, Chld. Buys: Ring first. cc: AV. BR: Stroud. "Next to BR car park. Mostly new books (90%) with chld's & s'hand sections."
Owners: Alan & Joan Tucker

TEWKESBURY

WAYFARER BOOKS
19 & 93 Church Street
Tewkesbury GL20 5PD
(01684) 293337
Mon-Sat 10-5 (Summer, Sun)
Est. 1986. Medium. Gen Stock and Lit, Countryside, Mil. Buys: Anytime. Book search. cc: AVAmD. BR: Cheltenham. "Shop with medium but interesting & changing stock to suit all tastes & pockets."
Owner: Robert Brown

TWYNING

THE BOOK ROOM
The Post Office
Twyning GL20 6DF
(01684) 274641/295855
Tue-Sat 10-1, 2-5
Medium. Spec: Avia, Girls' School Stories: also Gen Stock and Mil, Med, American West. Cat: occ lists. Buys: Anytime. Book search. cc: AV. BR: Cheltenham. "Situated in the pretty riverside village of Twyning off A38, 3 miles north of Tewkesbury."
Owner: Kenneth Fergusson

WINCHCOMBE

ABBEY ANTIQUARIAN BOOKS
Cowl Lane
Winchcombe GL54 5RA
(01242) 602589
Mon-Sun (ring first)
Est. 1978. Medium. Spec: Atqn, Chld: also Gen Stock and Wooden & Illus, Fable books. Cat: on req. Buys: Ring first. Book search. BR: Cheltenham.
Owner: C.J. Aeschlimann

ANCHOR HOUSE BOOKSHOP
88 North Street
Winchcombe GL54 5PS
(01242) 602149
Mon-Sun 10-1, 2-5:30, Thur close
Est. 1991. Medium. Spec: Hist: also Gen Stock. Cat: 3-4 stocklists pa: Hist. Buys: Ring first. BR: Cheltenham. "Just north of Cheltenham on B4632 to Broadway & Stratford. 1 hour on-street parking usually available nearby. Long-stay car park nearby. O/S maps also sold."
Owner: Mrs M. Stephenson

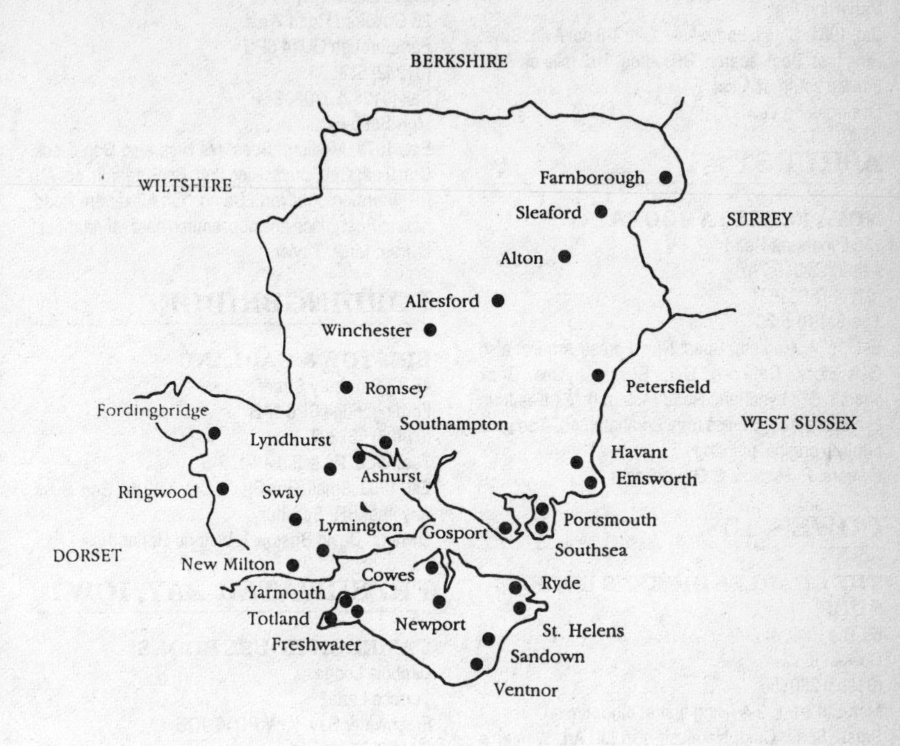

ALRESFORD

LAURENCE OXLEY

The Studio Bookshop
17 Broad Street
Alresford SO24 9AW
(01962) 732188
Mon-Sun 9-5
Est. 1950. Medium. Spec: India: also Gen Stock and Oriental. Buys: Ring first. cc: AVAmD. BR: Winchester. "Also sells maps, prints & watercolours. Framing service, oil paintings cleaned, books rebound, watercolours search."
Owner: Laurence Oxley

ALTON

ALTON SECONDHAND BOOKS

11 Normandy Street
Alton GU34 1DD
(01420) 89352
Mon-Sat 9:30-5
Est. 1989. Medium. Gen Stock. Buys: Ring first. Book search. BR: Alton. "On the main road, 100 yards from BR."
Owners: Mrs Andrews & Mrs Wilson

SOLDRIDGE BOOKS

Soldridge House
Alton GU34 5JF
(01420) 562811 (tel/fax)
Vary-Ring first
Est. 1981. Small. Spec: Avia: Cat: 4-6 pa: Avia. Buys: Ring first. Book search. BR: Alton. "1/2 mile off A31. 5 miles south of Alton."
Owner: John Lewis

ASHURST

NOVA FORESTA BOOKS

185 Lyndhurst Road
Ashurst SO40 7AR
(01703) 293389
Tue-Sat 10-5:30
Est. 1994. Medium. Spec: New Forest, Art, Po: also Gen Stock. Cat: occ: Gen. Buys: Anytime. Book search. BR: Lyndhurst Road (Ashurst). "2 miles from Lyndhurst/A35, 5 miles from Southampton. Also sells prints & original paintings."
Owners: P. Roberts & G. Peckham

COWES, IOW

THE CHARLES DICKENS BOOK-SHOP

65 The High Street
Cowes, IOW
(01983) 280586
Mon-Sat 11-1, 2-4 (Ring first at other times)
Small. Spec: Chld, Nautical: also Lit, Art, Women's Interest. Cat: occ. BR: Southampton, Red Funnel: W. Cowes. "More children's books, Theatre & Atec stored at home. ABA member."
Owner: Gaby Goldscheider

EMSWORTH

THE BOOKSHOP

The Square
Emsworth PO10 7EJ
(01243) 372617
Mon-Sat 9-5, Wed 9-1
Est. 1946. Small. Gen Stock and Atqn. Buys: Anytime. Book search. BR: Emsworth. "Main business in new books, stationery, printing."
Owner: Miss D. Way

FARNBOROUGH

FARNBOROUGH BOOKSHOP & GALLERY

26 Guildford Road West
Farnborough GU14 6PU
(01252) 518033
Fax (01252) 370309
Mon-Sat 8-6
Est. 1978. Medium. Spec: Mil Hist: also Gen Stock. Cat: 9 pa: Gen. Buys: Ring first. Book search. cc: AV. BR: Farnborough/North Camp. "Off Alexandra Road, next to Post Office and opp. church near roundabout."
Owner: Mr P. Taylor

FORDINGBRIDGE

BRISTOW & GARLAND

45-47 Salisbury Street
Fordingbridge SP6 1AB
(01425) 657337
Tue, Wed, Fri & Sat 10-1, 2-5
Est. 1992. Small. Gen Stock. Cat: 8-12 pa: Gen. Buys: Anytime. BR: Salisbury.
Owners: David Bristow & Victoria Garland

FRESHWATER BAY, IOW

CAMERON HOUSE BOOKS

Dimbola Lodge
Terrace Lane
Freshwater Bay, IOW PO40 9QE
(01983) 754960
Fax (01983) 755578
Tue-Sun 10-1, 2-5, Mon by appt
Est. 1970. Medium. Spec: Mod 1sts, C20th Illustrators: also Gen Stock and Mervyn Peake, JM Cameron, Po. Buys: Anytime. BR: Lymington. "Good quality stock in former home of pioneering photographer J.M. Cameron. Specialist in early photography books."
Owner: Mr L.J. Sklaroff

GOLDEN HOURS BOOKSHOP

113 School Green Road
Freshwater, IOW PO40 9AZ
(01983) 753434
Mon-Sat 9:30-5
Medium. Gen Stock. Buys: Anytime. Book search. "Restoration and repair of cloth & leather bound books by S.J. Briscoe."
Owner: Kate Chandler

GOSPORT

RICHARD MARTIN

21 & 23 Stoke Road
Gosport PO12 1LS
(01705) 520642/581753 (home)
Tue-Sat 10:15-1, 2:15-5 Wed close
Est. 1976. Medium. Spec: Maritime: also Gen Stock. Cat: occ: thematic. Buys: Ring first. Book search. BR: Portsmouth. "Also sells antique prints & maps, watercolours. Specialise in signed etchings by marine artist W.L. Wyllie."
Owner: Richard Martin

HAVANT

BOOKENDS

2 North Street
Havant PO9 1PR
(01705) 470094
Mon-Wed & Sat, 9:30-5, Thur 9:30-6, Fri 9:30-7
Est. 1983. Large. Gen Stock and Cookery, Crafts, Nat Hist. Buys: Ring first. Book search. BR: Havant. "Town Centre position, ample parking. Helpful, friendly & knowledgeable staff. Fast turnover, new stock added daily. Browsers welcome."
Owner: Mrs Carol Waldron

LYMINGTON

HUGHES & SMEETH LTD

1 Gosport Street
Lymington SO14 9BG
(01590) 676324
Mon-Sat 9:30-5
Est. 1976. Small. Spec: Maritime: also Gen Stock and Atqn. Buys: Ring first. cc: AV. BR: Lymington. "Also sells maps & prints."
Directors: P. Hughes & S. Smeeth

TRIANGLE BOOKS

Lymington Antiques Centre
76 High Street
Lymington SO41 9ZX
(01590) 670934
Mon-Fri 10-5, Sat 9-5
Est. 1990. Small. Spec: Art, Australia: also Gen Stock and Sheet Mus, Chld, Horse Racing. Buys: Anytime. Book search. BR: Lymington. "Free parking nearby. With over 30 dealers in antiques, jewellery, silver & collectables, the centre is well worth a visit. We also sell ephemera & prints."
Owners: M. & B. Clapham, J. Day & C. Williams

LYNDHURST

NEW FOREST BOOKS

6 High Street
Lyndhurst SO43 7BD
(01703) 282754
Mon-Wed & Sat 10-4:30 (phone other times)
Small. Spec: Golf, Hants: also Gen Stock and New Forest. Buys: Anytime. BR: Lyndhurst Road/ Brockenhurst. "Next to church, opp. Crown Hotel. Occupies part of New Forest Curiosity Shop. Small stock with high proportion of hard-to-find & obscure but cheaper non-fiction."
Owner: Roger Atkinson

NEW MILTON

BOOKS AND THINGS

99 Old Milton Road
New Milton BH25 6DN
(01425) 617521
Mon-Sat 9:30-5:30, Wed 9:30-1 (ring first)
Est. 1976. Large. Gen Stock. Buys: Ring first. BR: New Milton. "Parking outside shop. Friendly welcome and all possible help given to genuine buyers. One-man business. Health problems."
Owner: Anthony Keith

PETERSFIELD

THE PETERSFIELD BOOKSHOP

16A Chapel Street
Petersfield GU23 3DS
(01730) 263438
Fax (01730) 269426
Mon-Sat 9-5:30
Est. 1918. Large. Spec: Angling, Antique Collecting: also Gen Stock and Art, Topog. Cat: 3 pa. Buys: Anytime. Book search. cc: AVAmD. BR: Petersfield. "New books, Art materials & picture framing."
Owner: Frank Westwood

PORTSMOUTH

MILLERS BOOKS & PRINTS
55 Fawcett Road
Southsea
Portsmouth PO4 0DA
(01705) 755796
Tue-Sat 11-6, Wed close
Est. 1988. Medium. Gen Stock. Buys: Anytime. BR: Fratton/Portsmouth.
Owners: Bryan & Gill Miller

STAR BOOKSHOP
69 Fawcett Road
Southsea
Portsmouth PO4 0DB
(01705) 737077
Tue-Sat 12-6, Wed close
Medium. Spec: Lit: also Gen Stock and Mil, Trav, Topog. Cat: 1 pa: Lit, Gen. Buys: Ring first. Book search. "In street noted for its number and range of antique shops. Stock changes rapidly and is well set out, with various categories easy to locate."
Owners: Nick & Stella Purkis

WRIGHT & LOGAN
20 Queen Street
Portsea
Portsmouth PO1 3HL
(01705) 829555
Mon-Sat 9-5
Est. 1924. Small. Spec: Maritime. Buys: Ring first. cc: AVAmD. BR: Portsmouth. "Excellent parking. Near HMS Victory, Mary Rose, HMS Warrior & Naval Base. Both new & s'hand, only Naval subjects."
Owner: Ron Forrest

ROMSEY

ROMSEY BOOKSHOP
4 Abbey Walk
Church Street
Romsey SO51 8BU
(01794) 522202
Mon-Sat 9:30-5:30
Est. 1994. Medium. Spec: Mil, Mod 1sts: also Gen Stock and Lit. Cat: occ: Mil. Buys: Anytime. Book search. cc: AV. BR: Romsey. "4 miles from M27-opp. the Abbey, two doors from Post Office. Medium sized shop with pbk room & some atqn."
Owner: Ken Ford

RUSKINS 2
27 Bell Street
Romsey SO51 8GY
(01794) 523881
Mon-Sat 9:30-5:30
Est. 1975. Medium. Spec: Loc Hist, Mountbatten, F. Nightingale: also Gen Stock and Loc prints. Cat: 2 pa: Spec subjs. Buys: Ring first. Book search. cc: AV. BR: Romsey.
Owner: John Davies

RYDE, IOW

HERITAGE BOOKS
7 Cross Street
Ryde, IOW PO33 2AD
(01983) 562933
Mon-Sat 10-5, Thur close
Est. 1976. Medium. Gen Stock and Africana, Theol. Cat: 3 pa: Mod Theol. Buys: Anytime. Book search. cc: AV. BR: Ryde Esplanade. "Shop is 500 yards from Hovercraft terminal. Particularly interested in Mod Theol."
Owner: Rev D.H. Nearn

THE RYDE BOOKSHOP
135 High Street
Ryde, IOW PO33 2RJ
(01983) 565227
Mon-Sat 8:30-5:45, Thur 8:30-5
Est. 1988. Medium. Gen Stock. Buys: Anytime. cc: AV. BR: Ryde. "Also new books."
Owner: Mark D. Sames

SANDOWN, IOW

ARMSTRONG'S LITTLE BOOKSHOP
14 York Road
Sandown, IOW PO36 8ET
(01983) 406226
Mon-Sat 9:30-5:45 (Oct-Mar by appt only, not Sun)
Est. 1980. Small. Spec: IOW, Nat Hist: also Gen Stock. Buys: Ring first. BR: Sandown. "Not far from bus stop, 15 min walk from BR. Also sells stamps, coins, postcards, prints. Bookshop long but narrow. Phone first, esp if coming over from mainland."
Owners: Messrs L.E. & M.A. Armstrong

THE LITTLE BOOKSHOP
14A York Road
Sandown, IOW PO36 8ET
(01983) 406226
Mon-Sat 9-7 (Winter by appt)
Est. 1980. Small. Spec: Nat Hist, Trav: also Gen Stock. Buys: Ring first. Book search. BR: Sandown.
Owner: M.A. Armstrong

SOUTHAMPTON

H. M. GILBERT & SON
2 Portland Street
Southampton SO1 0EB
(01703) 226420
Mon-Sat 8:30-5
Est. 1859. Medium. Spec: Eng & For Lit, Hants: also Gen Stock and Topog, Maritime, Sci. Buys: Ring first. cc: AV. BR: Southampton Central. "Just off above Bar shopping precinct. We buy all types of quality books from small lots to libraries. Valuations, binding & book repair service available. Friendly service."
Owners: B.L. & R.C. Gilbert

THE SHIRLEY BOOKSHOP
2 Emsworth Road
Shirley
Southampton SO1 3LX
(01703) 510779
Mon-Fri 10:30-6, Sat 10-5
Medium. Spec: Hants: also Gen Stock. Buys: Anytime. BR: Southampton. "We are just off Shirley High St. almost opp. Woolworth's. Short ride from BR. Free parking. Shop houses good gen stock of 4 independent book dealers."
Owners: V. Ford, J. Day, W. Jackson, & C. Sweed

WARSASH NAUTICAL BOOKSHOP
6 Dibles Road
Southampton SO3 9HZ
(01489) 572384
Fax (01489) 885756
Mon-Fri 9-5:45, Sat 9-5:30
Est. 1970. Small. Spec: Maritime, Nautical: also Yachting. Cat: 3-4 pa. Buys: Ring first. Book search. cc: AVAmD. BR: Swanwick. "Also new books. Computer database of new & s'hand. Publishers of bibliography of nautical books annually. Listing available plus recently out-of-print."
Owner: Alan Obin

SOUTHSEA

ACADEMY BOOKS
13 Marmion Road
Southsea PO5 2AT
(01705) 816632
Mon-Sat 9-5
Est. 1970. Large. Gen Stock and Theol, Maritime, Conan Doyle. Cat: 2-3 pa. Buys: Ring first. BR: Southsea. "2 other s'hand b'shops within walking distance. Good selection on most subjects."
Owner: Bill Robinson

OLDFIELD GALLERY
76 Elm Grove
Southsea PO5 1LN
(01705) 838042 (tel/fax)
Mon-Sat 10-5
Small. Spec: Topog. Buys: Anytime. Book search. cc: AVAm. BR: Portsmouth Town. "Spec in atqn Br topog. Also large selection of maps C16th-C19th & early OS material. Vast selection of prints."
Owner: A. Downes

ST. HELENS, IOW

MOTHER GOOSE BOOKSHOP
Lower Green Road
St. Helens, IOW PO33 1XB
(01983) 873897
Tue-Sat 10-4, Thur close (or by appt)
Est. 1980. Medium. Gen Stock. Buys: Ring first. Book search. Ferry: Ryde.
Owner: Valerie Edmondson

SWAY nr. Lymington

BEAGLE BOOKS
1 Middle Road
Sway nr. Lymington SO41 6AT
(01590) 683421
Mon-Fri 10-1, 2-4:30, Wed & Sat 10-1
Medium. Spec: Nat Hist, Country Sports: also Gen Stock and Mil, Topog, Trav. Buys: Anytime. Book search. BR: Sway. "Friendly shop a few yards from BR and easy parking. We welcome browsers, collectors & dealers."
Owners: Jill & Tony Blakeley

VENTNOR, IOW

EMPORIUM BOOKS
58 High Street
Ventnor, IOW PO38 1LT
(01983) 852514
'Open All Hours'
Est. 1957. Large. Spec: Chld, Blyton (etc): also Gen Stock and Dandy, Beano, Biog. Buys: Ring first. Book search. BR: Shanklin. "Opp. main car park & bandstand. Big shop over 4 sites, 1000s of vintage books. 400 'Britain in Pictures'. Vast stock of antiques, postcards, stamps."
Owner: Capt Keith Hockney

VENTNOR RARE BOOKS
19 Pier Street
Ventnor, IOW PO38 1ST
(01983) 853706
Fax (01983) 853357
Mon-Sat 9-5:30, Wed close (some seasonal variation)
Est. 1972. Medium. Spec: Lit: also Gen Stock and Br Topog. Buys: Ring first. BR: Shanklin. "A wide range of stock and an enjoyable place to visit. Customers will be met at Ryde or Shanklin."
Owners: Nigel & Teresa Traylen

WINCHESTER

PETER DALY
Rear of Thompson Antiques
20A Jewry Street
Winchester SO23 8RZ
(01962) 867732 (eve)
Wed, Fri 10-4:30, Sat 10-1, 2-5
Small. Spec: Sport: also Gen Stock and Ornithology, Nat Hist, Mount. Buys: Ring first. BR: Winchester. "Also Asia & Africana."
Owner: Peter Daly

KINGSGATE BOOKS & PRINTS
Kingsgate Arch
College Street
Winchester SO23 9PD
(01962) 864710
Tue-Fri 12:30-5, Sat 10-5
Small. Spec: Loc, Topog: also Gen Stock. Buys: Ring first. cc: AV. BR: Winchester. "Under historic arch between Cathedral & Winchester College. Also sells atqn prints. Picture framing service."
Owner: Michael Folokes

S.P.C.K. BOOKSHOP
24 The Square
Winchester SO23 9EX
(01962) 866617 (tel/fax)
Mon-Sat 9-5:30
Est. 1968. Medium. Spec: Theol: also Gen Stock. Buys: Ring first. Book search. cc: AV. BR: Winchester. "Near the Cathedral. Large stock of new books."

YARMOUTH, IOW

THE BOOKSHOP
High Street
Yarmouth, IOW PO41 0PN
(01983) 760851
Mon-Sun 10-5 (Jan-Easter, Fri & Sun 10-4)
Est. 1990. Small. Gen Stock and Yachting, Nat Hist. Buys: Ring first. Book search. BR: Lymington. "2 min from Yarmouth to Lymington. Within easy reach of New Forest via ferry. Especially books on single-handed yacht voyages."
Owner: Alan Argent

Hereford and Worcester

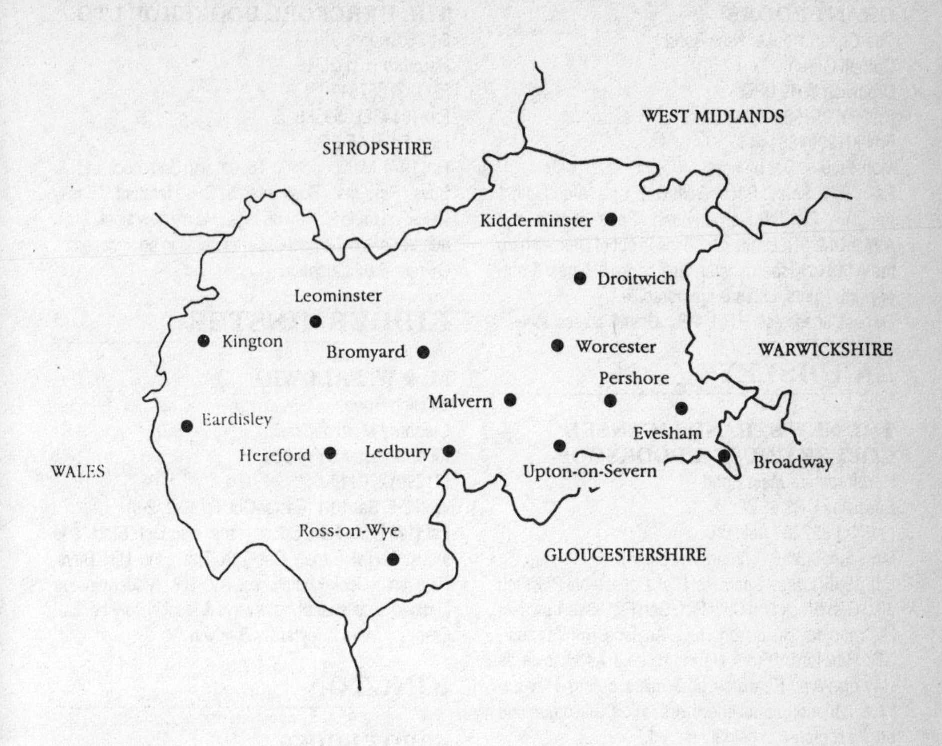

BROADWAY

BROADWAY OLD BOOKS

45 High Street
Broadway WR12 7DP
(01386) 853668
Mon-Sat 9:30-5:30, Sun 11-5
Est. 1974. Medium. Gen Stock. Buys: Ring first. Book search. cc: AV. BR: Evesham. "Parking easy. Also Antique Collectors Club new titles."
Owner: Mary-Jane Grant-Zeid

BROMYARD

LANDSMAN'S BOOKSHOP LTD

Buckenhill
Bromyard HR7 4PH
(01885) 483420 (tel/fax)
Mon-Fri 9-4:30 (Sat by appt)
Est. 1946. Medium. Spec: Agric, Hortic. cc: AV. BR: Hereford/Worcester. "Predominantly new books. Also a worldwide postal service catering for Agric."
Owner: Mr K. Stewart

DROITWICH

GRANT BOOKS
The Coach House, New Road
Cutnall Green
Droitwich WR9 0PQ
(01299) 851588
Fax (01299) 851446
Mon-Fri 9-5, Sat by appt
Est. 1971. Small. Spec: Golf: Cat: 1 pa: Atqn Golf; 1 pa: new Golf. Buys: Anytime. Book search. cc: AVAmDM. BR: Droitwich. "3 miles out of Droitwich on the A442 to Kidderminster. Golf books old, new & out-of-print. Prints, clubs & memorabilia."
Owner/Manageress: H.R.J. & S.J. Grant/Maureen Jones

EARDISLEY

THE NEW STRAND LICENSED COFFEE HOUSE & BOOKSHOP
Herefordshire Main Road
Eardisley HR3 6PW
(01544) 327285 (tel/fax)
Mon-Sun 9:30-6 (Winter, Tue close)
Est. 1986. Large. Spec: Nat Hist, Collectable Pbk Fict: also Gen Stock and Chld Fict, Gen Fict. Cat: 1 pa: Nat Hist; subject lists on req. Buys: Anytime. Book search. BR: Hereford. "From Hereford, take A438 towards Hay-on-Wye, Eardisley is 6 miles before Hay-on-Wye. A friendly atmosphere awaits you, with organised books & plenty of help if needed."
Owners: R. & A. Cardwell

EVESHAM

BOOKWORMS OF EVESHAM
81 Port Street
Evesham
(01386) 45509
Fax (01386) 750052
Tue-Sat 9:30-5, Mon by appt
Est. 1971. Medium. Spec: Trav, Hist: also Gen Stock and Lit, Bindings. Cat: occ: Gen. Buys: Anytime. Book search. BR: Evesham. "Easy to find on Evesham to Broadway Road opp. Swan Inn. Public car park at shop rear. Also book binding service. Shop praised by Angela Lambert!"
Owners: J. Slaughter & C. Garratt

HEREFORD

THE HEREFORD BOOKSHOP LTD
24-25 Church Street
Hereford HR1 2LR
(01432) 357617
Fax (01432) 353586
Mon-Sat 9:15-5:30
Est. 1974. Medium. Spec: Topog: also Gen Stock and Lit. Buys: Ring first. Book search. BR: Hereford. "Easily visited en route for Hay-on-Wye. Mainly new stock, but a number of s'hand books. Better items in book cases."
Owner: Paul Latcham

KIDDERMINSTER

M. & W. BALDWIN
24 High Street
Cleobury Mortimer
Kidderminster DY14 8BY
(01299) 270110
Wed 2-6, Sat 10-1 (Easter-Oct, Fri 10-1, 2-6)
Est. 1981. Medium. Spec: Trans: also Gen Stock and Industrial Hist, Canals. Cat: 5 pa: Trans, Ind. Hist. Buys: Ring first. Book search. cc: AV. BR: Kidderminster/Ludlow. "Publisher of waterways & local history books."
Owners: Mark & Myfanwy Baldwin

KINGTON

ARROW BOOKS
17 Duke Street
Kington HR5 3BL
(01544) 230729
Mon-Sat 10-5, Wed close
Est. 1983. Medium. Gen Stock. Buys: Ring first. BR: Leominster.
Owner: Robert Jenkins

CASTLE HILL BOOKS
12 Church Street
Kington HR5 3AZ
(01544) 231195
Fax (01544) 231161
Mon-Sat 10-5:30
Medium. Spec: Br Topog, Arch: also Gen Stock and Countryside, Local. Cat: lists. Buys: Anytime. Book search. cc: AV. BR: Hereford/Knighton. "20 min free car parking, 30 yds. Parking outside shop."
Owner: Peter Newman

LEDBURY

KEITH SMITH BOOKS
78B The Homend
Ledbury HR8 1BX
(01531) 635336
Tue-Sat 10-5
Est. 1990. Medium. Spec: John Masefield, Dymock Poets: also Gen Stock and Local. Buys: Ring first. Book search. cc: V. BR: Ledbury. "Close to town centre. Parking outside. Also sells ephemera."
Owner: Keith Smith

LEOMINSTER

MAINLY BOOKS
7 School Lane
Leominster HR6 8AA
(01568) 615722
Mon-Sat 9:30-5
Est. 1984. Medium. Gen Stock. Buys: Ring first. BR: Leominster. "We also sell paintings, maps, prints & bric-a-brac."
Owner: Mr Banks

MALVERN

THE MALVERN BOOKSHOP (M & G BOOKS)
7 Abbey Road
Malvern WR14 3ES
(01684) 575915
Mon-Sat 9:15-5
Est. 1950. Small. Spec: Mus, Horses: also Gen Stock and Art, Atec, Topog. Buys: Anytime. Book search. BR: Great Malvern. "Near Malvern Priory. 15 min walk from BR. Parking nearby. Good remainders on ground floor & s'hand upstairs with prints & maps."
Owners: J. & A. Gibbs & M. Manwaring

PRIORY BOOKS
Church Walk
Malvern WR14 2XH
(01684) 560258
Tue-Sun 10-12:45, 2-5
Est. 1985. Medium. Gen Stock and Topog, Cricket, Lit. Buys: Anytime. Book search. cc: AV. BR: Great Malvern. "Next to Somerfield (the only supermarket in town)."
Owner: Mr L. Kelly

KEITH SMITH BOOKS
32 Belle Vue Terrace
Malvern WR14 4PZ
(01684) 566199
Mon-Sat 10-5, Sun 12-5
Est. 1992. Medium. Spec: Loc Hist, Rug Making: also Gen Stock and Topog. Buys: Ring first. Book search. cc: V. BR: Great Malvern. "In town centre. Parking outside/nearby. Also at Ledbury.
Owner: Keith Smith

PERSHORE

COACH HOUSE BOOKS
17A Bridge Street
Pershore WR10 1AJ
(01386) 552801
Fax (01386) 556100
Mon-Sat 9-1, 2-5, Wed & Sun close ec by appt
Large. Gen Stock and Atqn. "Opp. MEB showrooms on main A44. Car park at rear. Quality atqn & s'hand books. Wide range of prints incl. David Shepherd limited editions."

IAN K. PUGH BOOKS
40 Bridge Street
Pershore WR10 1AT
(01386) 552681
Mon-Fri 10:30-4:30, Sat 10-5
Est. 1974. Medium. Spec: Gard: also Gen Stock and Art, Nat Hist. Buys: Ring first. BR: Pershore. "Good parking. Reserve stock held in cellar, so shelves always full."
Owner: Ian K. Pugh

ROSS-ON-WYE

ROSS OLD BOOKS AND PRINTS
51-52 High Street
Ross-on-Wye HR9 5HH
(01989) 567458
Mon-Sat 10-5
Est. 1982. Medium. Gen Stock. Buys: Anytime. cc: AV. BR: Hereford. "On the way to Hay, on A40 & close to M50. Good books & prints always wanted."

UPTON-ON-SEVERN

BOAR'S NEST TRADING POST

37A Old Street
Upton-on-Severn WR8 0DN
(01684) 592540
Mon-Sat 10-6
Medium. Gen Stock. Buys: Ring first. BR: Malvern. "Also bric-a-brac, records & CDs."

GERSHOM WOOD BOOKSELLER

The Bookshop
31 Old Street
Upton-on-Severn WR8 0HN
(01684) 593469
Mon-Sat 10-5:30
Est. 1984. Medium. Spec: Eso, Yoga: also Gen Stock and Film, Art, Cricket. Book search. BR: Worcester. "Also sell postcards, autographs, ephemera."
Owner: Gershom Wood

WORCESTER

ANDREW BOYLE (BOOKSELLERS) LTD

21 Friar Street
Worcester WR1 2NA
(01905) 611700
Mon-Fri 9:30-4, Thur & Sat close (ring first)
Est. 1930. Large. Spec: Chld: also Gen Stock and Lit, Hist, Biog. Cat: 6 pa: Gen. Buys: Ring first. BR: Worcester. "Close to Cathedral, Porcelain Factory & BR. 1 1/2 mile from exit 7 of M5. Stock includes Early Juveniles & Early Education."
Owner: Mrs P. Leeming

WATSON'S BOOKS

54 Upper Tything
Worcester WR1 1JY
(01905) 27824
Mon-Fri 10-4, Sat 10-5
Est. 1992. Large. Gen Stock. Buys: Anytime. BR: Foregate Street. "Situated on the main A38 opposite Alice Ottley School, on corner of Upper Tything and Britannia Square. Good general s'hand stock with large bargain basement."
Owner: Mrs Maggie Watson

HERTFORDSHIRE

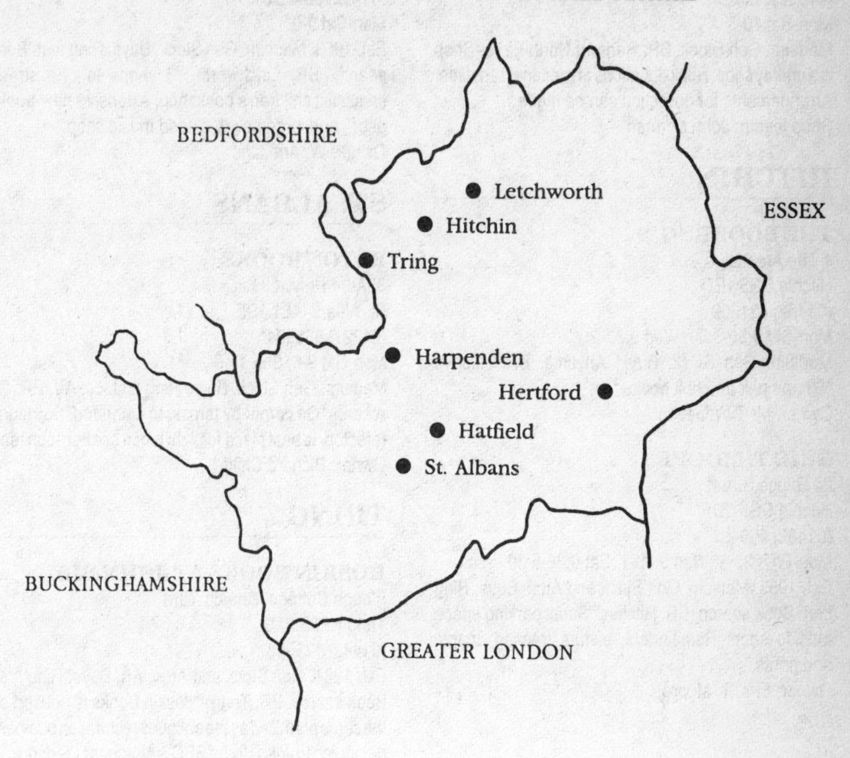

HARPENDEN

THE BOOK CABIN
379 Luton Street
Harpenden AL5 3NF
(01582) 768581
Mon-Sat 9:30-12:30, 2-5 (ring first)
Est. 1980. Small. Spec: Pre 1700: also Gen Stock and Embroidery. Cat: occ: Embroidery. Buys: Ring first. BR: Harpenden. "Easy access from M1 (2 miles from junction 9), A1 and M25. Easy parking."
Owner: G.W. Pearson

HATFIELD

BATTERDALE BOOKS
10 Batterdale
Hatfield AL9 5JF
(01707) 257217
by appointment only
Est. 1994. Small. Spec: Railways, Canals, Indus Hist: Cat: lists in above areas. Buys: Ring first. Book search. BR: Hatfield.
Owner: G.B. Steven

HERTFORD

THE OXFAM BOOKSHOP
8 Railway Street
Hertford SG14 2TH
(01992) 583221
Mon-Sat 10-5
Medium. Gen Stock. BR: Hertford North/East. "Shop is a charity shop. Book donations are received anytime. Arrangements for collection can be made."
Shop leader: John Norman

HITCHIN

THE BOOKBUG
1 The Arcade
Hitchin SG5 1ED
(01462) 431309
Mon-Sat 9:30-5:30, Wed 9:30-2
Medium. Gen Stock. Buys: Anytime. BR: Hitchin. "S'hand pbk and hbk books."
Owner: Mr T.W. Jevon

ERIC T. MOORE
24 Bridge Street
Hitchin SG5 2DF
(01462) 450497
Mon-Fri 9:30-5, Wed 9:30-1, Sat 9:30-5:30
Est. 1953. Medium. Gen Stock and Atqn. Buys: Ring first. Book search. BR: Hitchin. "Small parking space outside shop. Remainders, picture framing, maps, and prints."
Owner: Eric. T. Moore

LETCHWORTH

DAVID'S BOOKSHOP LTD
14 Eastcheap
Letchworth SG6 3DE
(01462) 684631
Mon-Sat 9-6
Est. 1963. Medium. Gen Stock. Buys: Ring first. Book search. BR: Letchworth. "3 shops in one street: specialist children's bookshop, extensive new books dept., and large new & s'hand music shop."
Owner: W. Armitage

ST. ALBANS

PATON BOOKS
32A-34 Holywell Hill
St. Albans AL1 1DE
(01727) 853984
Mon-Sat 9-6, Sun 11-6
Medium. Gen Stock. Buys: Ring first. cc: AV. BR: St. Albans. "On corner by turning to cathedral. Cathedral refectory is best place for light lunch or afternoon tea."
Owner: Richard Child

TRING

HOSKIN BOOKS AT JOHN BLY
Plough Cottage, Church Yard
Tring HP23 5AG
(01442) 823030
Est. 1981. Gen Stock and Atqn, Art. Buys: Ring first. Book search. BR: Tring. "Hoskin Books Is housed on the same premises as the antiques restoration business belonging to John Bly (of BBC's Antiques Roadshow)."
Owner: Margaret Phillips

KENT

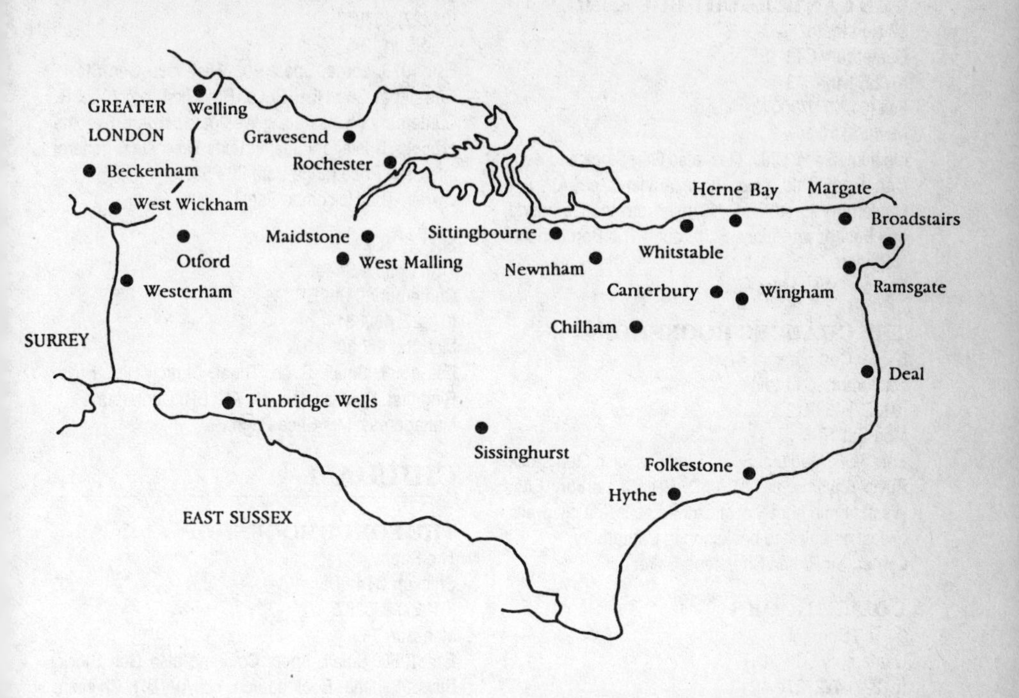

BECKENHAM

CAROUSEL

12 Beckenham High Street
Beckenham Junction
Beckenham
(0181) 650 7238
Mon-Fri 12-9, Sat & Sun 10:30-8
Est. 1993. Medium. Spec: Mil, Trav: also Gen Stock and Cookery, Perf Arts, 1st edns. BR: Beckenham Junction. "1st left from Beckenham Junction station, 30 seconds walk. Also ephemera, records, collectable pbks. Trade welcome."
Owner: Pamela Finn

BROADSTAIRS

ALBION BOOKSHOP

29 Albion Street
Broadstairs CT10 1LX
(01843) 862876
Mon-Sat 9-5
Est. 1956. Medium. Gen Stock. Buys: Ring first. cc: AV. BR: Broadstairs. "New books at No. 29, s'hand dept housed in old C17th converted chapel."
Owners: Sheila & Alan Kemp

CANTERBURY

THE CANTERBURY BOOKSHOP

37 Northgate
Canterbury CT1 1BL
(01227) 464773
Fax (01227) 780073
Mon-Sat 10-5
Medium. Spec: Chld, Illus: also Gen Stock and Kent. Cat: 1 pa: Chld, Illus. Buys: Anytime. cc: AV. BR: Canterbury East/West. "10 min from the Cathedral, due East down Palace St. through The Borough into Northgate."
Owner: David Miles

THE CHAUCER BOOKSHOP

6 Beer Cart Lane
Canterbury CT1 2NY
(01227) 453912
Mon-Sat 10-5
Est. 1956. Medium. Spec: Bindings: also Gen Stock. Buys: Anytime. cc: AVAmD. BR: Canterbury East/West. "4 min from SW of Cathedral, inside city walls. Oldest established bookshop in Canterbury."
Owner: Sir Robert Sherstone-Baker

COLLIE BOOKS

20 The Borough
Canterbury CT1 2DR
(01227) 472727
Mon-Sun 10-6
Est. 1990. Medium. Gen Stock and Arts. Cat: 15 pa. cc: AV. BR: Canterbury East.
Manager: Andrew Colla

ELHAM VALLEY BOOKSHOP

St. Mary's Road
Elham
Canterbury CT4 6TH
(01303) 840359
Tue & Thur 10-4:30, Wed close, Fri-Sat 10-5, Sun 2:30-5
Medium. Spec: Nat Hist, Trav: also Gen Stock. Buys: Anytime. Book search. BR: Folkestone Cent. "A small general s'hand bookshop in delightful village of Elham, just off village square. Coffee & tea available. 3 pubs within 50 yards offering excellent food."
Owner: Tim Parsons

PAUL HOLCOMBE

5 North Lane
Canterbury CT2 7EB
(01227) 457913
Wed-Sun 12-5
Est. 1979. Large. Spec: Bus, Hist: also Gen Stock. Cat: 1 pa: Soc Hist. Buys: Ring first. cc: AV. BR: Canterbury West. "Facing Westgate carpark. 8 rooms of books. Upstairs academic texts. Downstairs general interests. Price range from £2-£50."
Owner: The Holcombe Family

S.P.C.K

7 St. Peter's Street
Canterbury CT1 2EF
(01227) 462881
Mon-Sat 9-5:30
Est. 1933. Small. Spec: Theol, Church Hist. Buys: Ring first. Book search. cc: AV. BR: Canterbury.
Manageress: Mrs Erica Pugh

CHILHAM

THE FORGE BOOKSHOP

The Street
Chilham CT4 8DL
(01227) 730267
Mon-Sun 9-6
Est. 1980. Small. Spec: Cookery: also Gen Stock. Buys: Anytime. Book search. cc: AV. BR: Chilham. "Parking outside shop. We also sell maps, all kinds of prints and new books."
Owner: Mrs Barnes

DEAL

THE GOLDEN HIND BOOKSHOP

85 Beach Street
Deal CT14 6JB
(01304) 375086
Mon-Sun 10-5:30
Est. 1973. Medium. Spec: 1sts: also Gen Stock and Lit. Cat: 4 pa: 1sts, Gen, Arch, US Lit. Buys: Anytime. Book search. BR: Deal. "Situated on the seafront, with easy parking."
Owner: Clive Allison

FOLKESTONE

G. & D. MARRIN & SONS

149 Sandgate Road
Folkestone CT20 2DA
(01303) 253016
Fax (01303) 850956
Mon-Sat 9:30-5:30
Est. 1948. Medium. Spec: Mil: also Gen Stock and Atqn. Cat: 4 pa: Kent, WW1. Buys: Anytime. cc: AV. BR: Folkestone Central. "Also maps & prints. Specialising in World War 1."
Owners: D.I., J.G. & P.J. Marrin

GRAVESEND

RAFTERS

The Courtyard
Manor Road
Gravesend
(014747) 05672
Fri-Sat 10-4:30
Small. Gen Stock. Buys: Ring first. BR: Gravesend. "3 min walk from BR. Gen s'hand books. Also antiques, collectables & pictures."
Owner: Neil Lawrie

HERNE BAY

HERNE BAY BOOKS

2 Stanley Road
Herne Bay CT6 5SH
(01227) 365020 (tel/fax)
Wed-Sat 8:45-5
Est. 1995. Small. Gen Stock. Buys: Anytime. Book search. BR: Herne Bay. "Local neighbourhood s'hand bookshop with an ever-growing stock of cheaper titles."
Owner: R.J.C. Eburne

HYTHE

THE OLD GALLERY BOOKSHOP

125 High Street
Hythe CT21 5JJ
(01303) 269339
Mon-Sat 9-5 ec Wed
Est. 1990. Medium. Spec: Mil: also Gen Stock and Trans, Crime. Cat: 2 pa: Trans, Crime. Buys: Anytime. BR: Sandling. "Main High Street."
Owners: D. & P. Hadway

MAIDSTONE

EUNICE & CLIFF FOX

38 Union Street
Maidstone
(01622) 754774
Fax (01622) 676343
Tue-Sat 10-5
Est. 1995. Medium. Spec: Chld, Illus: also Chld Fict, Juveniles. Cat: Reg. Buys: Anytime. cc: AVAm. BR: Maidstone. "Also Picture Books & Victorian Colour Printing. Regular catalogues issued (overseas air mailed free).

MAIDSTONE BOOK & PRINT SHOP

38 Union Street
Maidstone ME14 1ED
(01622) 754774
Tue-Sat 10-5:30
Medium. Spec: Chld, Mil: also Gen Stock and Pbk, Kent, Topog. Buys: Anytime. cc: AVAmD. BR: Maidstone East. "2 miles from Junction 6, M20. 3 adjacent car parks. Friendly shop. Trade welcome. Also local & decorative prints."
Owners: Watkins & Fox

NEWNHAM nr. Sittingbourne

PERIWINKLE PRESS

47 The Street
Newnham nr. Sittingbourne ME9 0BN
(01795) 890388
Mon, Wed-Sat 10:30-6, Tue 2-6, Sun 12-6
Est. 1968. Small. Spec: Kent: also Gen Stock and Mil, Chld. Buys: Ring first. BR: Sittingbourne. "Also sells Atqn prints. Picture framing service."

RAMSGATE

MICHAEL'S BOOKSHOP

72 King's Street
Ramsgate CT11 8NY
(01843) 589500
Mon-Sat 9:30-5:30
Est. 1984. Medium. Gen Stock and Remainders. Buys: Anytime. cc: AV. BR: Ramsgate.
Owner: Michael Child

ROCHESTER

BAGGINS BOOK BAZAAR LTD
19 High Street
Rochester ME1 1QB
(01634) 811651
Fax (01634) 841851
Mon-Sun 10-6
Large. Spec: Biog: also Gen Stock and Trav, Lit, Fict. Buys: Ring first. Book search. cc: AV. BR: Rochester/ Strood. "Probably the largest s'hand bookshop in England."
Manager: Godfrey George

SISSINGHURST

THORNTON BOOKS
The Street
Sissinghurst TN17 0RS
(01580) 712965
Tue-Sat 11-6 (Winter, Fri & Sat 10-5:30)
Est. 1987. Medium. Spec: Gard, Vita Sackville-West: also Gen Stock and Nat Hist, Countryside. Buys: Ring first. BR: Staplehurst. "Opening days are designed to coincide with those of nearby Sissinghurst Castle."
Owners: John & Caroline Thornton

TUNBRIDGE WELLS

BASKERVILLE BOOKS
13 Nevill Street
Tunbridge Wells TN2 5RU
(01892) 526776/546292 (eve)
Mon-Sat 10-5, Wed close
Est. 1990. Medium. Spec: Cricket: also Gen Stock and Chld, Cinema. Buys: Anytime. BR: Tunbridge Wells. "Fast turnover, sensible prices."
Owner: Mike Banwell

HALL'S BOOKSHOP
20 Chapel Place
Tunbridge Wells TN1 1YQ
(01892) 527842 (tel/fax)
Mon-Sat 9:30-5
Est. 1898. Large. Spec: Hist, Biog: also Gen Stock and For Trav, Art, Atqn. Buys: Anytime. Book search. BR: Tunbridge Wells.
Owner: Sabrina Izzard

ANTHONY WHITTAKER
Corn Exchange Antiques
64 The Pantiles
Tunbridge Wells TN2 5TN
(01892) 539652
Fax (01892) 723494
Mon-Sat 9:30-5
Small. Spec: Fine & Applied Art, Chld: also Gen Stock and Sport, Kent & Sussex Topog. Buys: Anytime. cc: AVAmD. BR: Tunbridge Wells. "Also bindings, maps, prints & watercolours."
Owner: Anthony Whittaker

WELLING

FALCONWOOD TRANSPORT & MILITARY BOOKSHOP
5 Falconwood Parade
The Green
Welling DA16 2PL
(0181) 303 8291
Thur-Sat 9:30-5:30
Est. 1985. Medium. Spec: Mil, Avia, Motoring, Railways: also Trans, Maritime. Cat: 1 pa: Avia, WW1, Mil Vehicles. Buys: Ring first. Book search. cc: AVEJ. BR: Falconwood. "B16 bus from Falconwood station passes the door. Also back numbers of magazines on specialist subjects stored."
Owner: Andy Doran

WEST MALLING

FOXED AND BOUND BOOKSHOP
8 West Street
West Malling ME19 6QX
(01732) 847886
Mon-Sat 10-5
Est. 1989. Medium. Gen Stock. Buys: Ring first. Book search. BR: West Malling. "5 miles from Maidstone off A20. Parking in High Street & village car park. Good browsing stock, framed atqn prints of local villages. Helpful & friendly service. Trade discounts."
Owner: Lynne Rees

WEST WICKHAM

WEST WICKHAM BOOKSHOP
5 Bell Parade
Wickham Court Road
West Wickham BR4 0RH
(0181) 777 3982
Mon-Fri 9:45-5:30, Wed 9:45-1
Est. 1995. Medium. Gen Stock. Buys: Ring first. BR: West Wickham.
Owner: R. Davies

WESTERHAM

TAYLOR-SMITH BOOKS
2 High Street
Westerham TN16 1RF
(01959) 561561 (tel/fax)
Wed-Sat 10-5, Sun 2:30-5
Large. Spec: Winston Churchill: also Gen Stock and Mil, Hist, Po. Buys: Anytime. Book search. cc: V. BR: Sevenoaks/Oxted. "Under the Old Manor House, on the A25 in the centre of Westerham."
Owner: Alan Taylor-Smith

WHITSTABLE

BETHSAIDA CHRISTIAN BOOKSHOP
9 Tower Arcade
Whitstable CT5 2BJ
(01227) 265961
Mon-Sat 9:30-5, Wed close
Medium. Spec: Theol: also Gen Stock and Mus, Drama, Welsh Hymnology. Cat: 1 pa: Theol. Buys: Ring first. Book search. BR: Whitstable. "Situated near Whitstable harbour & castle. We have a large selection of new & s'hand Evangelical Protestant books. Also records"
Owner: Robin Johnson

BOOKS & PIECES
48 Oxford Street
Whitstable CT5 1DG
(01227) 771333
Tue-Sat 9:45-4:45
Medium. Gen Stock. Buys: Ring first. BR: Whitstable. "Opposite library. Small shop also selling prints, postcards & jigsaws."
Owner: Mrs J. Harvey

WINGHAM

LLOYD'S BOOKSHOP
27 High Street
Wingham CT3 1AW
(01227) 720774
Mon-Sat 9:30-1, 2:15-5
Est. 1959. Medium. Spec: Mus: also Gen Stock and Chld, Art. BR: Adisham. "Easy parking. Fairly fast turnover. Also prints & ephemera."
Owner: Jane Marrison

LANCASHIRE

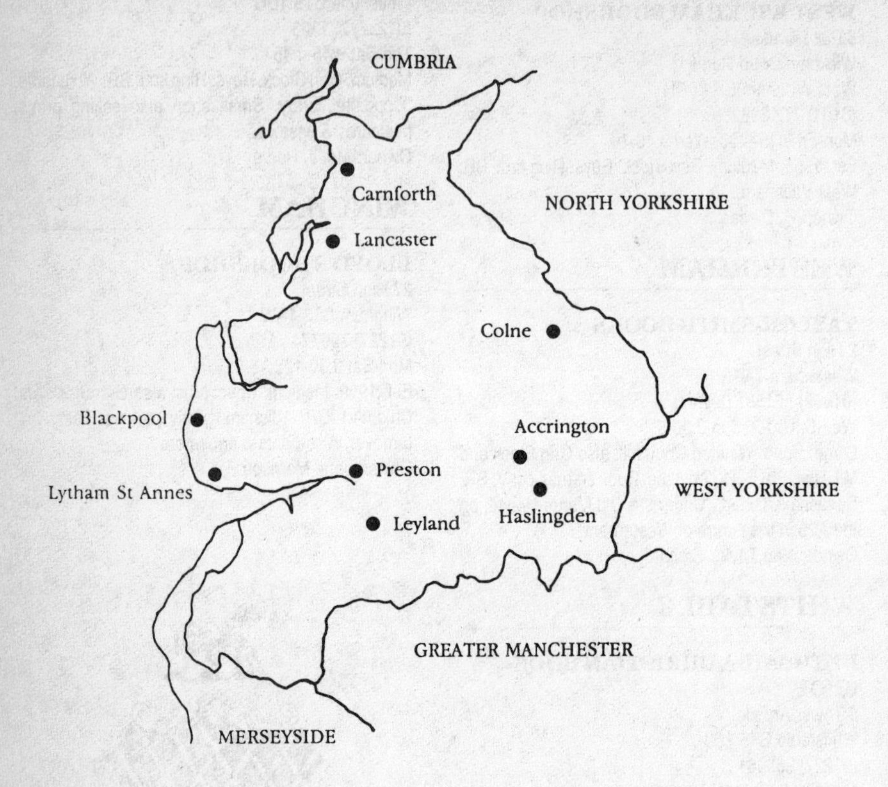

ACCRINGTON

BOWDON BOOKS

300 Union Road
Oswaldtwistle
Accrington BB5 3JD
(01254) 872978
Tue, Thur, & Fri 10-5, Sat 10-4
Est. 1987. Medium. Spec: Needlecraft, East Lancs Topog: also Gen Stock. Buys: Anytime. Book search. cc: AV. BR: Oswaldtwistle. "Although we have areas of specialisation our efforts are directed at offering a wide range gen stock, mainly non-fict, & Lit. No Mod Fict."
Owners: Gordon & Gillian Hill

BLACKPOOL

CHEVET BOOKS

157 Dickson Road
Blackpool FY1 2EU
(01253) 751858
Mon-Sat 10:15-6:15 (Summer, Mon-Sun: after Nov, ring first)
Medium. Spec: Media: also Gen Stock and Maritime. Cat: 10 pa. Buys: Ring first. BR: Blackpool North Shore. "Behind Imperial Hotel., 5 mins from town. Also stock early wireless and TV."
Owners: Mr & Mrs Myers

CARNFORTH

THE CARNFORTH BOOKSHOP
38-42 Market Street
Carnforth LA5 9JX
(01524) 734588
Fax (01524) 735893
Mon-Sat 9-5:30
Large. Spec: Biog, Hist: also Gen Stock and Art, Trav, Drama. Buys: Ring first. cc: AV. BR: Carnforth. "M6 exit 35, 4 mins from BR. Easy parking. Also new books, stationery cards, toys. Farmhouse B&B may be arranged. Near Morecombe Bay, Lake district, Yorks. Dales. Willing to travel to buy large quantities."
Owners: R.J. & C.M. Norman

COLNE

COLNE BOOKS
Shackleton Hall
Church Street
Colne BB8 0LG
(01282) 870952
Mon-Sat 9:30-4, Tue close
Est. 1989. Medium. Gen Stock. Buys: Ring first. Book search. BR: Colne. " Recycled books bought, sold, exhanged. Very good gen. stock including 1sts, signed, and rare. Small but full of surprises."
Owners: Monica Jenkins & Jim Harper

HASLINGDEN

HASLINGDEN BOOKSHOP
99 Deardengate
Haslingden BB4 5SN
(01706) 831170
Thur-Sat (but ring first)
Small. Spec: Motoring. Buys: Anytime. BR: Bury.
Owner: W. Derbyshire

LANCASTER

ATTICUS
26 King Street
Lancaster LA1 1JY
(01524) 381413
Mon-Sat 10-5:30
Est. 1988. Medium. Gen Stock and Arts, Lit, Po. Buys: Ring first. BR: Lancaster.
Owner: Tom Flemons

W.B. McCORMACK ANTIQUARIAN BOOKSELLERS
6-6A Rosemary Lane
Lancaster LA1 1NR
(01524) 36405/424991
Mon-Sat 10-5, Wed close
Est. 1962. Medium. Spec: Illus, Trav: Cat: 2 pa: Atqn, rare. Buys: Ring first. Book search. cc: AVAm. BR: Lancaster. "Close to city centre. Stock is mainly atqn and rare with some gen s'hand. Also deal in maps, prints, oils, and watercolours."
Owner: W.B. McCormack

LEYLAND

GREAT GRANDFATHER'S
82 Towngate
Leyland PR5 1LR
(01772) 422268/671424
Tue-Sat 10-5:30, Wed close
Est. 1985. Medium. Gen Stock and Nat Hist, Lancs, Topog. Buys: Anytime. BR: Leyland. "Easy access from M6 Junction 28. Large free car park nearby."
Owner: Greg Smith

LYTHAM ST. ANNE'S

THE BOOKSHELF
18 Orchard Road
Lytham St. Anne's FY8 1RY
(01253) 725704 (tel/fax)
Mon-Sat 9-5:30
Est. 1969. Medium. Gen Stock. Buys: Anytime. cc: AV. BR: St Anne's-on-Sea.
Owners: Joan & Ken Harries

PRESTON

BOOKS FOR EVERYONE
13 Lowthian Street
Preston PR1 2EP
(01772) 254857/316958 (aft.6pm)
Mon-Sat 9-5
Medium. Gen Stock. Buys: Ring first. cc: AV. BR: Preston. "We are positioned behind Orchard Street which is by Preston Market. Below the computer shop."
Owner: David Morriss

HALEWOOD & SONS
37 Friargate
Preston PR1 2AT
(01772) 252603
Mon-Sat 9:30-5:30
Est. 1867. Large. Spec: Colonial Trav, Americana: also Gen Stock and Botany, Atlases, Topog. Cat: 1 pa: Gen. Buys: Anytime. Book search. cc: AV. BR: Preston. "Atqn and expert booksellers since 1867. Indiv lists available."
Owner: H.H. Halewood

PRESTON BOOK COMPANY
68 Friargate
Preston PR1 2ED
(01772) 252603 ext 68
Mon-Sat 9:30-6
Large. Spec: Trav, Lit: also Gen Stock. Cat: 1 pa: Gen. Buys: Anytime. Book search. BR: Preston. "300 yards along from Halewoods at No.37. Something for everyone."
Owner: M. Halewood

LEICESTERSHIRE AND RUTLAND

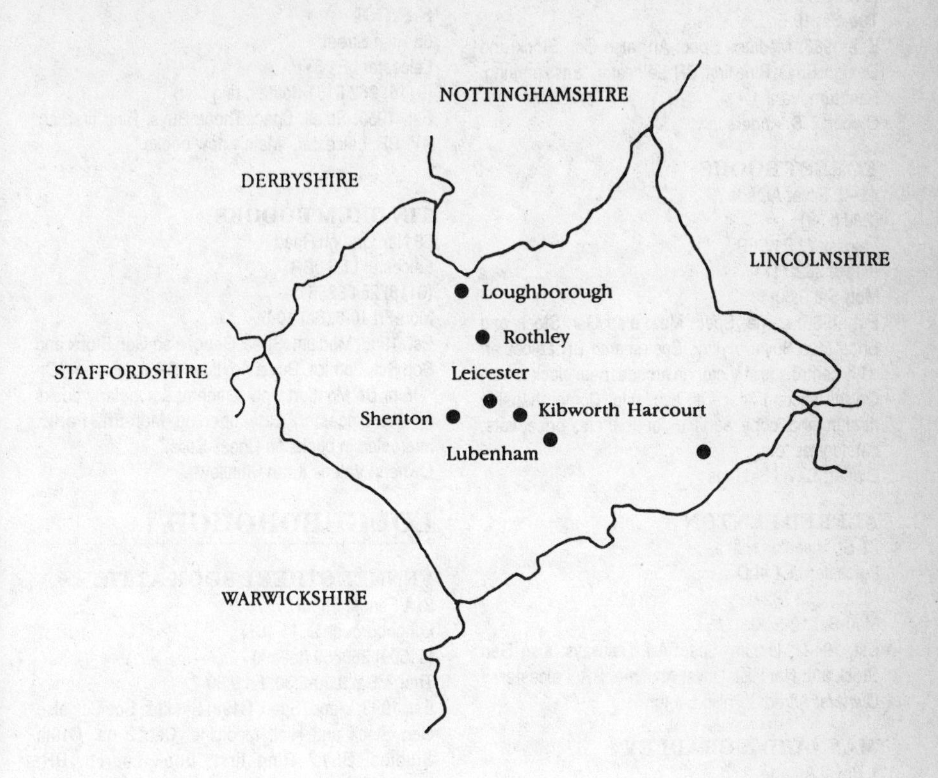

KIBWORTH HARCOURT

THE COUNTRYMAN'S GALLERY

Kibworth Harcourt LE8 0NE
(0116) 279 3211
Fax (0116) 279 2437
Tue-Sat 10-1, 2:30-5, Thur close
Est. 1985. Small. Gen Stock and Illus. Cat: occ. Buys: Ring first. Book search. BR: Market Harborough. "The gallery specialises in books and pictures for traditional field sports and the English countryside."
Owner: Pam Turnbull

LEICESTER

THE BLACK CAT BOOKSHOP

36-39 Silver Arcade
(2nd floor)
Leicester LE1 5FB
(0116) 251 2756
Mon-Sat 9:30-5
Est. 1987. Medium. Gen Stock and Peng, Classics, SF. Buys: Ring first. BR: Leicester. "Also pop & rock books and magazines, tv and film 'spin offs', Non-Fict, comics."
Owner: Mr P. Woolley

CLARENDON BOOKS
144 Clarendon Park Road
Leicester LE2 3AE
(0116) 270 1856
Tue-Sat 10-5
Est. 1986. Medium. Spec: Art: also Gen Stock and Design. Buys: Ring first. BR: Leicester. "Easy parking. Fast turnover."
Owner: T.B. Anderson

FOREST BOOKS
41-42 Silver Arcade
(2nd floor)
Leicester LE1 5FB
(0116) 262 7171
Mon-Sat 9:30-5
Est. 1986. Large. Spec: Mus: also Gen Stock and Sheet Mus. Buys: Anytime. Book search. BR: Leicester. "City centre, loc in Victorian arcade, near clock tower. On the second floor - lift available. Comprehensive design and copy service for leaflets, price lists, catalogues, etc."
Owner: David Siddons

ALFRED LENTON
27 St. Nicholas Place
Leicester LE1 4LD
(0116) 262 7827
Mon-Sat 10-5:30
Est. 1942. Medium. Spec: Art, Railways: also Gen Stock and Nat Hist. Buys: Anytime. BR: Leicester.
Owners: Alfred & Philip Lenton

MAYNARD & BRADLEY
1 Royal Arcade
Silver Street
Leicester LE1 5YW
(0116) 253 2712/626243 (appt)
Mon-Fri 9:30-5:30, Sat 9-5:30
Est. 1970. Medium. Spec: Topog: also Gen Stock and Sport, Atqn. Cat: occ: Gen. Buys: Ring first. Book search. BR: Leicester. "We stock maps and prints, some remainders and some orig works of art. Spec in Edwards, Alden, and Snaffles. Will purchase single items to complete libraries."
Owners: Messrs D. Maynard & S. Bradley

MURRAYS LIMITED
23 Loseby Lane
Leicester LE1 5DR
(0116) 262 0360
Mon-Sat 9-5
Est. 1980. Small. Gen Stock and Atqn. Buys: Ring first. BR: Leicester. "Also new books."
Owner: J. Culley

S.P.C.K
68 High Street
Leicester LE1 5YP
(0116) 262 6161 (tel/fax, ring first)
Est. 1950. Small. Spec: Theol. Buys: Ring first. cc: AV. BR: Leicester. "Mainly new books."

TIN DRUM BOOOKS
68 Narborough Road
Leicester LE3 0BR
(0116) 254 8236
Mon-Fri 10-8, Sat 10-6
Est. 1986. Medium. Spec: Geog: also Gen Stock and Soc Sci, Comics. Buys: Anytime. BR: Leicester. "On A46 nr De Montfort Univ. General & scholarly books for W. Leicester. Late opening Mon-Fri. Partic. interested in books on Coess Soils."
Owners: Valerie & Ian Smalley

LOUGHBOROUGH

FENNEL STREET BOOK ATTIC
21A Fennel Street
Loughborough LE11 1UQ
(01509) 269860 (tel/fax)
Thur & Sat 9:30-5:30, Fri 9:30-7
Est. 1993. Large. Spec: C19th Studies, Soc Sci: also Gen Stock and Hist, Medicine. Cat: 2 pa: C19th Studies. Buys: Ring first. Book search. BR: Loughborough. "Next to bus station. Also lots of ephemera."
Owner: M. Hornsby

MAGIS BOOKS
98 Ashby Road
Loughborough LE11 3AF
(01509) 210626
Fax (01509) 230349
Mon-Sat 9-5:30
Est. 1978. Medium. Spec: Occult: also Gen Stock and Eso, Phil, Magic. Cat: 12 pa. Buys: Ring first. Book search. cc: AV. BR: Loughborough. "Especially Quabala Spiritualism. Also new books. Thoth Publishers."
Owner: Tom Clarke

LUBENHAM

LEICESTERSHIRE SPORTING GALLERY
The Old Granary
Lubenham LE16 9DG
(01858) 465787
Mon-Sat 9-6, Thur close
Est. 1954. Small. Spec: Vanity fair, Shooting: also Golf, Hunting, Mil. Buys: Ring first. BR: Market Harborough. "Off M1 exit 20, follow A427 Market Harborough Road. Parking on green opp. shop."
Owner: Mr Reg Leete

ROTHLEY

POOKS MOTOR BOOKS
Fowke Street
Rothley LE7 7PJ
(0116) 237 6222
Fax (0116) 237 6491
Mon-Fri 9-5:30
Est. 1988. Large. Spec: Motoring. Buys: Anytime. cc: AV. BR: Leicester. "Also automobilia, badges & mascots."
Owners: Alison, Barrie & John Pook

SHENTON nr. Market Bosworth

MICHAEL D. RAFTERY (BOOKS)
Whitemoors Antique Centre
Shenton nr. Market Bosworth CV13 6BZ
(01455) 611017 (eve)
Mon-Sun 11-5
Est. 1976. Small. Spec: Lit, Mod 1sts: also Gen Stock and Hist, Topog, Arts. Buys: Ring first. Book search. cc: AV. "A5 - A444, rt at Fenny Drayton. Pleasant situation, close to canal, steam railway, and Bosworth Battlefield. Gardens and tea rooms on site."

UPPINGHAM

FOREST BOOKS
7 High Street
Uppingham LE15 9QB
(01572) 821173
Mon-Sat 10:15-5:30, Sun 2:15-5:15
Est. 1995. Medium. Gen Stock. Buys: Anytime. Book search. BR: Oakham. "50 yds from market place. Bus service from Leicester-Peterborough, Corby-Oakham. New shop with good general stock."
Owner: David Siddons

GOLDMARK BOOKS
Orange Street
Uppingham LE15 9SQ
(01572) 822694
Mon-Sat 9:30-5:30, Sun 2:30-5:30
Est. 1978. Large. Gen Stock. Buys: Ring first. Book search. BR: Oakham. "Next to Art and Print Gallery (part of same business). Uppingham is a beautiful market town."
Owner: Mike Goldmark

THE RUTLAND BOOKSHOP
13 High Street West
Uppingham
(01572) 823450
Tue-Sat 11-5:30
Est. 1977. Medium. Spec: Hunting, Shooting: also Gen Stock and Countryside, School Hist. Cat: occ: School Hist. Buys: Ring first. Book search. BR: Oakham. "Interesting and unusual books on all subjects."
Owners: Mr & Mrs M.E. Baines

LINCOLNSHIRE

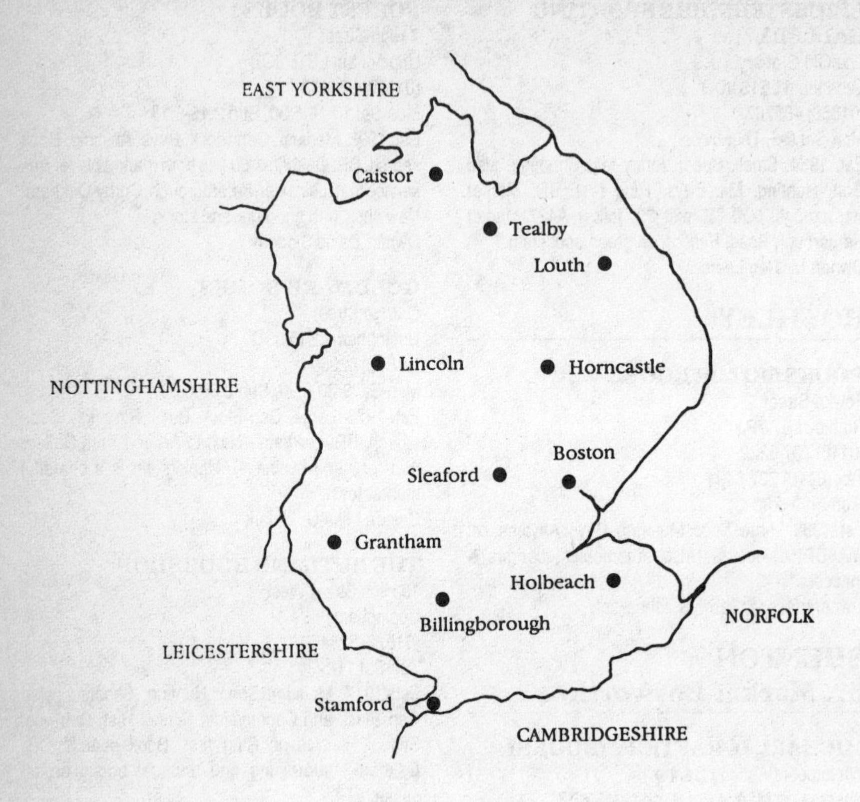

BILLINGBOROUGH

ALAN REDMOND BOOKS

25 High Street
Billingborough NG34 0QB
(01529) 240215
Sat, Sun & Bank Holidays 10-6
Est. 1981. Medium. Gen Stock. Buys: Ring first.
Owner: A.P. Redmond

CAISTOR

PLOUGH BOOKS

19 Plough Hill
Caistor LN7 6UR
(01472) 852073
Tue-Fri 10:30-5:30, Sat 9-5, Mon close
Est. 1989. Medium. Gen Stock. Buys: Ring first. BR: Market Rasen. "Opp. the Spar shop on Plough Hill. 100 yards downhill from Market Place. Shop is converted stable set back from road accessible via archway. Large selection of new local books. Art gallery and picture framing service."
Owner: Alan Dean

HOLBEACH

P.J. CASSIDY (BOOKSELLER)
1 Boston Road
Spalding
Holbeach PE12 7LR
(01406) 426322 (tel/fax)
Mon-Sat 10-6
Est. 1975. Medium. Spec: Local: also Gen Stock. Buys: Anytime. Book search. cc: AV. BR: Spalding. "Situated by traffic lights in Holbeach. Pic. framing service, maps and prints."
Owner: P. J. Cassidy

HORNCASTLE

JABBERWOCKY
14 St. Lawrence Street
Horncastle LN9 5BJ
(01507) 522112
Mon-Sat 9-5:30, Sun 1-5
Est. 1985. Medium. Gen Stock. Buys: Anytime. BR: Lincoln.
Owner: Mrs P. Flanagan

TIM SMITH BOOKS
12 North Street
Horncastle LN9
(01507) 527139 (Home)
Mon-Sat 9:30-5, Wed close
Est. 1988. Medium. Gen Stock and Sheet Music. Buys: Anytime. BR: Market Rasen. "We try and cater for all tastes."
Owner: Tim Smith

LINCOLN

GOLDEN GOOSE BOOKS
20-21 Steep Hill
Lincoln LN2 1LT
(01522) 522589
Mon-Sat 10-5:30, Wed close
Medium. Gen Stock and Art, Illus. Cat: occ. Buys: Anytime.
Owners: R. West-Skinn & Mrs A. Cochram

HARLEQUIN GALLERY
22 Steep Hill
Lincoln LN2 1LT
(01522) 522589
Mon-Sat 10-1. 2-5:30 (Wed ring first)
Est. 1964. Large. Gen Stock and Lit, Topog. Buys: Anytime. BR: Lincoln. "Also sells maps and prints. Specialist in atqn globe restoration on the premises."
Owner: R. West-Skinn

READERS REST
13-14 Steep Hill
Lincoln LN2 1LT
(01522) 543217
Mon-Sat 9:30-5, Sun 11-4
Est. 1982. Large. Gen Stock and Lit, Trav, Biog. Buys: Ring first. BR: Lincoln. "Also sells new books, cards, fancy goods, framed prints and posters. Largest s'hand bookshop in Lincoln. A quick turnover on general stock - 50,000 at last count."
Owner: Nick Warwick

READERS REST HALL OF BOOKS
St. Michael's Parish Hall
Steep Hill
Lincoln LN2 1LT
(01522) 543217
Mon-Sat 10-4, Sun 11-4
Large. Spec: Art, Hist: also Gen Stock and Remainders. Buys: Anytime. BR: Lincoln Central. "Dir. opp. main shop. The Hall carries about 20,000 books with a policy of selling cheper than most. Both shops sell T-shirts with the logo: So many books, so little time."
Owner: Kathleen Warwick

LOUTH

THE BOOK EXCHANGE
18 Queen Street
Louth LN11 9AQ
Mon-Sat 9-5, Thur 3pm close
Est. 1990. Medium. Spec: SF, Children's collectables: also Gen Stock. Buys: Anytime. Book search. BR: Grimsby. "100 yards from market place and car park. All books shelved by category and where possible alphabetically."
Owner: Julian C. Brown

BOOKSLEUTH MYSTERY BOOKSTORE

64 Legbourne Road
Louth LN11 8ER
(01507) 607651
Thur-Fri 9-5 (best to ring)
Est. 1989. Large. Spec: Crime/Mystery Fict: Cat: 1 pa: Crime Fict (92 pp. Send £2 for copy–refundable with order). Buys: Anytime. Book search. BR: Grimsby. "Possibly the largest selection of crime fiction in U.K."
Owners: Victor and Mary Brown

STAMFORD

BRIDGE BOOKSHOP

7 St. Paul's Street
Stamford PE9 2BE
(01780) 482748
Mon-Sun 10-5
Est. 1987. Medium. Spec: Motor Sport, Fens, Topog: also Gen Stock. Cat: 6 pa: Motor sport. Buys: Anytime. cc: AVD. "Moved from Cambs now just around the cor. from Staniland's. Gen stock. Large stock of local topog. Specialist motor sport and motoring stock."
Owner: James Blessett

ROBERT HUMM & CO

Station House
Stamford PE9 2JN
(01780) 66266
Fax (01780) 57929
Mon-Sat 9:30-5:30
Est. 1974. Large. Spec: Railways; also Trans. Cat: 4 pa: Trans. Buys: Ring first. cc: AV. BR: Stamford. "In the station-master's house. Deal in all aspects of trans (except private). Largest railway stock in U.K. Also periodicals, photos, timetables."
Owners: Robert & Clare Humm

ST. MARY'S BOOKS AND PRINTS

9 St. Mary's Hill
Stamford PE9 2DP
(01780) 63033
Mon-Sat 8-8
Est. 1978. Medium. Spec: Field sports, Cricket: also Gen Stock and Avia, Mil, Taxidermy. Buys: Anytime. Book search. BR: Stamford. "Beautiful stone town on A1. Well worth a visit. Very general dealer buying every area of printed matter, prints, pictures. Prices always low, aimed at dealer interest and also negotiable for quantity."
Owners: Mr & Mrs G.R. Tyers

STANILAND (BOOKSELLERS)

4-5 St. George's Street
Stamford PE9 2BJ
(01780) 55800
Mon-Sat 10-5 (or by appt)
Est. 1972. Large. Spec: Local: also Gen Stock and Topog, Atec, Hist. Cat: occ. Buys: Ring first. BR: Stamford.
Owners: M. Staniland & B. Ketchum

TEALBY

STAFFORD'S BOOKS

The Bookshop
40 Rasen Road
Tealby LN8 3XL
(01673) 838557
Thur-Sat 10:30-5:30
Est. 1983. Medium. Spec: Chld, Art: also Gen Stock and Linc, Illus, Lit. Buys: Ring first. Book search. BR: Market Rasen. "1996 is our 13th anniversary for the shop and 18th for the business."
Owner: Gillian Stafford

GREATER MANCHESTER

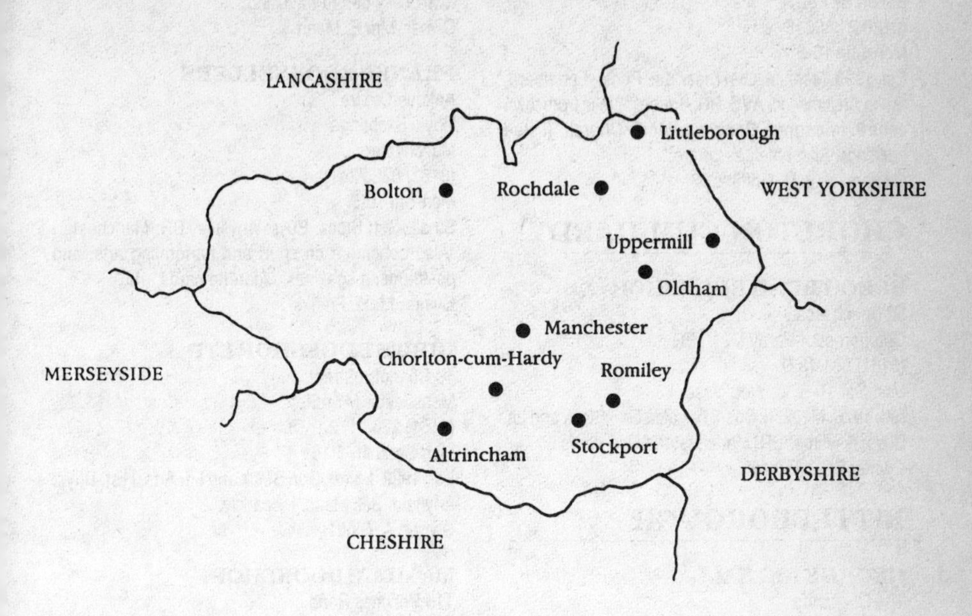

ALTRINGHAM

ABACUS BOOKS

24 Regent Road
Altringham WA14 1RP
(0161) 928 5108
Mon-Sat 10-5:30
Est. 1979. Medium. Spec: Art: also Gen Stock and Crafts, Needlework, Hist. Buys: Ring first. "Large remainder stock. General good quality."
Owner: C.D. Lawton

BOLTON

BROMLEA BOOKS

The Last Drop Village
Bromley Cross
Bolton BL7 9PZ
(01204) 596673
Mon-Fri 12-5, Sat-Sun 10-5
Medium. Spec: Illus: also Gen Stock and Chld. Buys: Anytime. Book search. cc: AV. BR: Bromley Cross. "Signposted from motorway. Village has teashop and pub. Ample parking. Regular Sunday antique fair. Also sells postcards."
Owners: Malcolm & Valerie Johnstone

IRONCHURCH BOOKS
Ironchurch Antiques Centre
Blackburn Road
Bolton BL1 8DR
(01204) 383616
Mon-Sun 10-5
Est. 1993. Medium. Gen Stock and Prints, Ephemera. Buys: Anytime. cc: AVS. BR: Bolton. "1 mile from town centre in former Congregational Church (listed building). Also antiques centre."
Owners: H. & D. Griffiths

CHORLTON-CUM-HARDY

BEECH ROAD BOOKSHOP
52 Beech Road
Chorlton-cum-Hardy M21 1EG
(0161) 881 1327
Mon-Sat 10-5:30, Wed close
Est. 1976. Medium. Spec: Art: also Gen Stock and Lit. Buys: Anytime. BR: Manchester. "Also cards."
Owner: Brian Barlow

LITTLEBOROUGH

GEORGE KELSALL
The Bookshop
22 Church Street
Littleborough OL15 9AA
(01706) 370244
Mon-Sat 10-5, Tue 1-5
Large. Spec: Topog, Soc and Indust Hist: also Gen Stock and Railway, Trans, Labour Hist. Buys: Ring first. BR: Littleborough. "Easy by rail and road (M62). Ample parking. Well-stocked general s'hand shop. Good range of subjects and prices."
Owner: George Kelsall

MANCHESTER

FOREST BOOKS
inside The Ginnel Gallery
18-22 Lloyd Street
Manchester M2 5ND
(0161) 834 0747
Mon-Sat 9:30-5:30, B/holidays close
Est. 1987. Small. Spec: Humanities: also Cost, Art Hist, Collecting. Buys: Ring first. "Lloyd Street runs one way from Deansgate to Albert Square and town hall. Also sells maps. Please phone to confirm availability before travelling."
Owner: Mrs E. Mann

FRANKS BOOKSELLERS
Antique Centre
Royal Exchange
Manchester
(0161) 832 7241
Mon-Sat 10-5
Small. Gen Stock. Buys: Anytime. BR: Manchester. "Also ephemera on sport and performing arts, and postcards, magazines, cigarette cards, etc."
Owner: Mr H. Franks

GIBB'S BOOKSHOP LTD
10 Charlotte Street
Manchester M1 4FL
(0161) 236 7179
Mon-Sat 9:15-5:15
Est. 1922. Large. Gen Stock and Lit, Arts, Hist. Buys: Anytime. BR: Manc. Piccadilly.
Owner: A. Gibb

McGILL'S BOOKSHOP
115 Princess Road
Moss Side
Manchester M14 4RB
(0161) 232 9620
Mon-Sat 12-5:30
Est. 1968. Large. Spec: Ireland: also Gen Stock and Chld, Acad, Theol, Arch, Fict. Buys: Ring first. BR: Manc. Oxford Road via Piccadilly.
Owner: James P. McGill

E.J. MORTEN (BOOKSELLERS) LTD
Warburton Street
Didsbury
Manchester M20 0RA
(0161) 445 7629
Mon-Sat 9:30-5:30, Wed 9:30-5
Est. 1959. Medium. Gen Stock and Eng Lit, Topog, Hist. Buys: Ring first. BR: Manchester. "Own parking - 12 cars. New books. Very fast turnover."
Owner: E.J. Morten

OLDHAM

OLDHAM BOOKSHOP

65 George Street
Oldham OL1 1LX
(0161) 6284693
Mon-Sat 10-6
Est. 1994. Medium. Spec: Loc Hist: also Gen Stock. Buys: Anytime. BR: Mumps - Oldham. "Easy to find, quiet part of town centre. Still finding my feet but stock improving all the time."
Owner: Bob Lees

ROCHDALE

ROCHDALE BOOK COMPANY

399 Oldham Road
Rochdale OL16 5LN
(01706) 31136/58300
Sat 10:30-5:30 (weekdays variable)
Est. 1972. Large. Gen Stock. Buys: Anytime. BR: Rochdale. "Close to M62, Junc 20. Easy parking."
Owners: John & Susan Worthy

STOCKPORT

THE HEATONS BOOKSHOP

13 School Lane
Heaton Chapel
Stockport SK4 5DE
(0161) 431 5905
Mon-Sat 10:30-4:30, Tue close
Est. 1985. Medium. Gen Stock. Buys: Ring first. BR: Stockport.
Owner: Hardy Sweeney

ROMILEY LITTLE BOOKSHOP

1 Hill Street
Romiley
Stockport SK6 3AH
(0161) 427 4853 (home)
Sat 10-4
Est. 1986. Small. Gen Stock. Buys: Ring first. Book search. BR: Romiley. "Centre of village near Methodist church – down side street. Small but we try to be helpful."
Owner: Sylvia Duckworth

TALISMAN BOOKS

42 Town Street
Marple Bridge
Stockport SK6 5AA
(0161) 449 9271
Mon-Sat 10:30-5, Sun 2-5, Wed close
Est. 1988. Medium. Spec: Horror Fict, Mod 1sts: also Gen Stock and Chld, Cookery. Cat: 2 pa: Horror Fict. Buys: Ring first. BR: Marple.
Owner: Jean Cessford

UPPERMILL

MOORLAND BOOKS

Alexandra Mill Craft Centre
Unit 20, High Street
Uppermill OL3 6HU
(01457) 871306
Wed-Fri 11-4, Sat-Sun 11-5
Est. 1982. Medium. Gen Stock. Buys: Anytime. Book search. BR: Oldham/Manchester. "Parking alongside shop."
Owner: Mrs C. Bennett

MERSEYSIDE

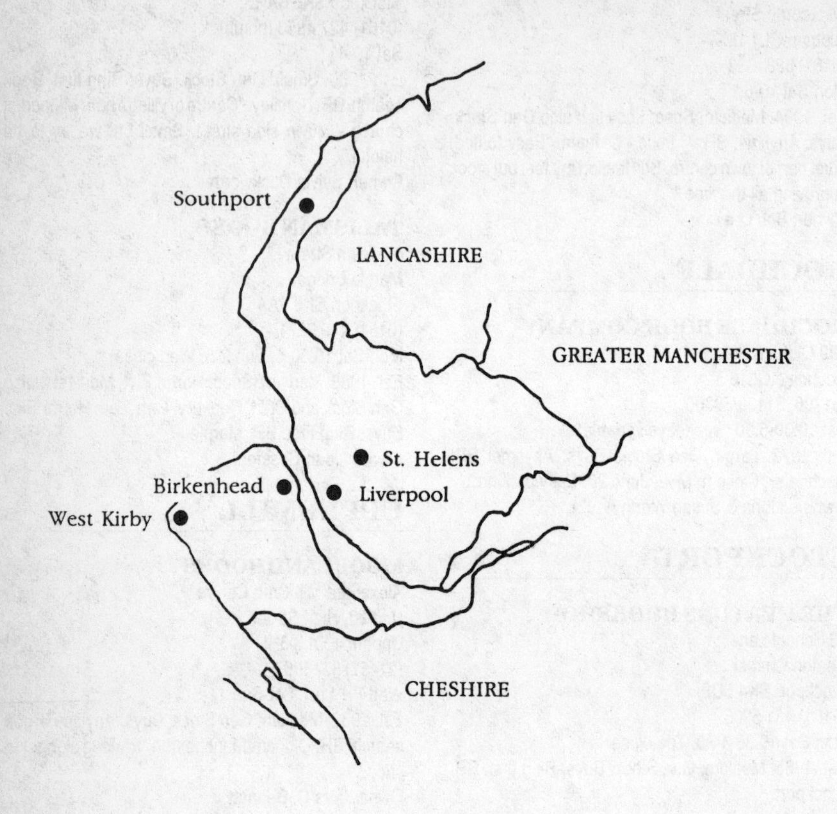

BIRKENHEAD

SPEAKS VOLUMES - WIRRAL REHAB

48-50 Grange Road West
Birkenhead L41 4DA
(0151) 647 6076
Mon-Sat 10-5
Est. 1990. Medium. Gen Stock. BR: Birkenhead Park/ Hamilton Square. "Charity shop with large selection of books. Reservation service. Good quality books always wanted."
Manager: Ken Garner

LIVERPOOL

ATTICUS

2A Hardman Street
Liverpool L1
(0151) 708 9834
Mon-Sat 10-6
Est. 1984. Small. Gen Stock and Lit, Pol, Phil. Buys: Anytime. BR: Liverpool Lime Street. "Mostly academic. Also branch in Lancaster."
Owner: Tom Flemons

HENRY BOHN BOOKS
32 Berry Street
Liverpool L1 4JQ
(0151) 709 4501
Mon-Sat 10:30-6
Small. Spec: Lit: also Gen Stock and Art. Buys: Anytime. Book search. BR: Liverpool Lime St. "Gen. stock of good quality. Large stock (over 50,000 in store room)."
Owners: Anis & Michael McCabe

NORTHWEST BOOKS
15 Seel Street
Liverpool L1
(0151) 708 7427
Mon-Sat 11-5:30
Est. 1994. Medium. Gen Stock. Buys: Anytime. BR: Liverpool Lime Street. "Good quality, general s'hand stock."
Owner: J.E. Burns

REID OF LIVERPOOL
105 Mount Pleasant
Liverpool L3 5AT
(0151) 709 2312
Mon-Fri 10:30-5:30, Sat 11:30-6
Large. Spec: SF, Eso: also Gen Stock and Review copies, Atqn, Acad. Buys: Ring first. cc: AV. BR: Liverpool Lime Street. "3 min walk from BR. Telephone, toilet and refreshments available."
Owner: Gerard Fitzpatrick

SOUTHPORT

BROADHURST OF SOUTHPORT LTD
5-7 Market Street
Southport PR8 1HD
(01704) 532064/534110
Fax (01704) 542009
Mon-Sat 9-5:30
Est. 1926. Large. Spec: Topog, Priv. Press: also Gen Stock and Mod 1sts, Art, Fine Bindings. Cat: 2 pa: Specialist, 1 pa: Gen. Buys: Anytime. Book search. BR: Southport/Chapel Street. "Situated in large Victorian building just off Lord Street."
Owner: Laurens R. Hardman

KERNAGHAN'S BOOKS
61-65 Wayfarer's Arcade
Lord Street
Southport PR8 1NT
(01704) 546329
Mon-Sat 10-5
Est. 1972. Large. Spec: Ireland: also Gen Stock and Theol, Topog, Illus. Cat: occ. Buys: Ring first. Book search. cc: AV. BR: Southport. "Delightful Victorian arcade. Fresh stock everyday. Special charity sales of cheaper collector books twice yearly. Now in much larger premises."
Owners: Bryan & Alwyn Kernaghan

ANTHONY PARKINSON
359-363 Lord Street
Southport PR8 1NH
(01704) 547016/531244 (eve)
Mon-Sun 10:30-5
Est. 1977. Large. Spec: Sci, Tech: also Gen Stock and Phil, Shells, Minerals. Buys: Anytime. Book search. BR: Southport. "Growing emphasis on Sci, Technol, Med & Phil - now in 3 floors."
Owners: K.A. & J. Parkinson

ST. HELENS

NEW CROSS GALLERY
33 New Cross Street
St. Helens WA10 2JW
(01744) 813124
Tue, Fri, Sat 9-4
Est. 1982. Small. Spec: Mil Hist: also Gen Stock. Buys: Anytime. BR: St. Helens Central. "Near Do It All Superstore. Plenty of parking nearby."
Owner: Mrs J. Bromilow

WEST KIRBY (WIRRAL)

BOOKENDS
4 Hilbre Road
West Kirby (Wirral) L48 3HD
(0151) 625 6389
Mon-Sat 10-1, 2-4, Wed close
Est. 1990. Medium. Gen Stock. Buys: Anytime. Book search. BR: West Kirby. "10 min from BR."
Owner: Mrs M. Rymill

NORFOLK

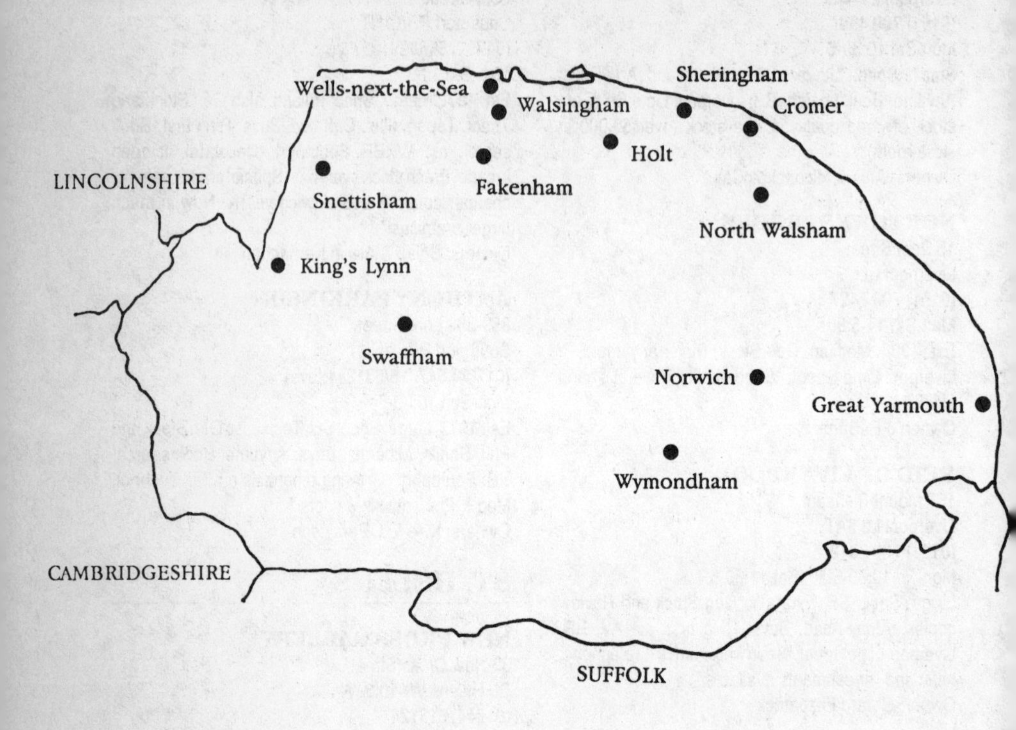

CROMER

BOOKWORMS

9 New Street
Cromer NR27 9HP
(01263) 515078
Mon-Sat 10-5, Sun 2-5, Wed close (Winter: Fri-Sun 10-5)
Est. 1988. Medium. Gen Stock. Buys: Anytime. BR: Cromer. "Shop just off seafront next to amusement arcade."
Owners: Ted & Susan Liddell

FAKENHAM

THE TIN DRUM BOOKSHOP

32/34 Oak Street
Fakenham NR21 9DY
(01328) 864937
Mon-Sat 10-6, Wed 10-1
Large. Spec: Mod 1sts, Art: also Gen Stock and Lit, Hist, Avia. Buys: Anytime. BR: Norwich/King's Lynn. "Parking available nearby. New separate stock of Mod 1sts viewable by appointment."
Owner: David Kenyon

GREAT YARMOUTH

DAVID FERROW
77 Howard Street South
Great Yarmouth NR30 1LN
(01493) 843800
Mon-Sat 9:30-5:30, Thur close
Est. 1940. Large. Spec: East Anglia: also Gen Stock and Atqn. Buys: Ring first. cc: AV. BR: Norwich/Great Yarmouth. "10 min walk from BR."
Owner: David Ferrow

HOLT

SIMON GOUGH BOOKS
5 Fish Hill
Holt NR25 0BD
(01263) 712650/712761
Fax (01263) 712276
Mon-Sat 10-5 (or by appt)
Est. 1976. Large. Spec: Cookery: also Gen Stock and Bound sets, Nat Hist, Lit. Buys: Anytime. cc: AVAm. BR: Norwich/Sheringham. "Books in fine condition on any subject."
Owner: Simon Gough

THE OLD BUTCHERS BOOKSHOP
High Street,
Cley-next-the -Sea
Holt NR25 7RB
(01263) 741212
Tue-Sat (Winter), Tue-Sun (Summer)
Est. 1993. Medium. Spec: Birds, Po, Biog: also Gen Stock and Norfolk Books, Mod 1sts edn. Cat: 2 pa: Gen. Buys: Anytime. Book search. cc: AVE. "A bookshop in a beautiful part of Norfolk."
Owner: Terry Johnson

KING'S LYNN

BOOKWORM
33-35 Tower Street
King's Lynn
(01553) 760904
Mon-Sat 10-4:30
Medium. Gen Stock and Occult, SF, Horror. Buys: Anytime. BR: King's Lynn. "On leaving BR, straight ahead bus station into Baxter's Plain to top of Tower Street. Large quantity of new and back number American comics and graphic covers in annexe."

NORTH WALSHAM

THE ANGEL BOOKSHOP
4 Aylsham Road
North Walsham NR28 0BH
(01692) 404054
Mon-Sat 10-5:30, ec Wed
Medium. Spec: Cycling: also Gen Stock and East Anglia, Occult. Buys: Anytime. Book search. BR: North Walsham. "Turn right out of BR, cross bypass and ask. Try to have small selected stock. Spec kept in bookroom."
Owner: Mr W. Green

NORWICH

ALBROWS & SONS (incorporating WESTLEGATE BOOKSHOP)
10 All Saints Green
Norwich NR1 3NA
(01603) 622569
Mon-Sat 9:30-4:30
Est. 1932. Small. Spec: Loc: also Gen Stock. Buys: Anytime. cc: AVD. BR: Norwich Thorpe. "Opp Bonds Department Store. A s'hand jewellery, silver, and small collectables shop with bookshop above."
Owner: Mr Albrow

JOY & DAVID CLARKE BOOKS
St. Michael at Plea Antique Centre
Bank Plain
Norwich NR2 4SN
(01603) 619226/624577 (eve)
Mon-Sat 9:30-5
Est. 1988. Medium. Spec: Norwich, The Broads: also Gen Stock and Topog, Chld. Buys: Anytime. BR: Norwich Thorpe. "Near cathedral. 30 min parking close by. Book and print shop in city centre medieval church. Centre also houses antique sellers and Sue Ryder coffee lounge."
Owners: Joy & David Clarke

PETER CROWE
75, 77 Upper St. Giles Street
Norwich NR21 2AB
(01603) 624800
Mon-Sat 9:30-6
Medium. Spec: Atqn, Lit: also Gen Stock and Fine bindings, Trav, Nat Hist. Cat: 2 pa: Gen, Atqn. Buys: Anytime. cc: AV. BR: Norwich. "St. Giles is a fine Georgian street shop next to church. 3 floors of books. Bargain basement, scholarly C18th room, display room of fine bindings and sets, also antique maps and prints."
Owner: Peter Crowe

J.R. & R.K. ELLIS
53 St. Giles Street
Norwich NR2 1JR
(01603) 623679
Mon-Sat 8-5:30
Est. 1960. Medium. Spec: Hist: also Gen Stock and Eng Lit, Classics. Buys: Anytime.BR: Norwich Thorpe.
Owners: J.R. & R.K. Ellis

THE MOVIE SHOP
11 St. Gregory's Alley
Norwich NR2 1ER
(01603) 615239
Mon-Sat 10-5
Est. 1985. Small. Spec: Film: also Gen Stock and Atqn, Humanities. Buys: Anytime. BR: Norwich.
Owner: Peter Crossey

S.P.C.K
19 Pottergate
Norwich NR2 1DS
(01603) 627332
Mon-Sat 9-5:30
Est. 1960. Medium. Gen Stock and Theol, Hist, Lit. Buys: Ring first. cc: AV. BR: Norwich. "Also stock new religious books."

SCIENTIFIC ANGLICAN BOOKSHOP
30-30A St. Benedict Street
Norwich NR2 4AQ
(01603) 624079
Tue-Sat 10-5:30, Mon & Thur 1-5:50 (Win: Mon-Sat 11:30-5:15)
Est. 1967. Large. Gen Stock and Biog. Buys: Ring first. BR: Norwich. "Car park 150 yards. O/S maps (when available). Fast turnover."
Owner: Norman Peake

THE TOMBLAND BOOKSHOP
8 Tombland
Norwich NR3 1HF
(01603) 760610
Fax (01508) 50747
Mon-Sat 9:30-5
Est. 1987. Large. Gen Stock and Atqn. Buys: Ring first. Book search. cc: AV. BR: Norwich. "City centre opp cathedral. 5 min walk from BR."
Owners: J.G. & A.H. Freeman

SHERINGHAM

PETER PAN
The Courtyard
Sheringham NR26
(01263) 824411
Mon-Sat 9:30-5:30, Sun 11-5:30 (Winter:Tue-Sat 9:30-5:30, Mon, Wed, Sun close)
Est. 1994. Medium. Gen Stock. Buys: Ring first. BR: Sheringham. "Newer s'hand books from within the last fifteen years."
Owners: Peter & Sue Cox

PETER'S BOOKSHOP
19 St. Peter's Road
Sheringham NR26 8QY
(01263) 823008
Mon-Sat 10-6, Sun 2-6 (Win: Tue-Sat 10-5, Wed close)
Est. 1984. Large. Gen Stock and Chld, Po, Lit. Buys: Ring first. BR: Sheringham. "We buy and sell 25,000 books a year."
Owners: Peter & Sue Cox

SNETTISHAM

TORC BOOKS
9 Hall Road
Snettisham PE31 7LU
(01485) 54118(ring)/540212(home)
Mon, Wed, Fri 10-1, Sat 10-4
Est. 1977. Medium. Gen Stock. Buys: Ring first. BR: King's Lynn. "Easy parking off market place."
Owner: Heather Shepperd

SWAFFHAM

THE OLD BOOK & PRINT SHOP

95 Market Place
Swaffham PE37 7AQ
(01760) 723151
Mon-Sat 10-5
Est. 1988. Medium. Spec: East Anglia, Eng Lit: also Gen Stock. Buys: Anytime. BR: Downham Market.
Owners: K.A. & V.J. Ward

VIth SENSE

2 Lynn Street
Swaffham PE37 7AX
(01760) 721679 (tel/fax)
Mon-Sat 9:45-4:30
Est. 1995. Medium. Spec: Hist, New Age: also Gen Stock. Cat: 4 pa: New Age/Hist (to be introduced). Buys: Ring first. Book search. BR: Downham Market. "On main A47 - oposite P.O. Sorting Yard and Budgens Supermarket. Newly established shop, but many years experience in s'hand booktrade."
Partners: Marion Hancock & Eleanor Finn

WALSINGHAM

PILGRIM'S PROGRESS BOOKSHOP

63 High Street
Walsingham NR22 6BZ
(01328) 820399
Tue-Sun 9:30-5
Est. 1984. Medium. Spec: Ecclesiology, Theol: also Gen Stock and Atec, Biog. Buys: Anytime. Book search. cc: V. BR: Norwich (26 miles). "My customers say they like it."
Owners: Howard & Mary Fears

WELLS-NEXT-THE-SEA

COOK (THE BOOKS)

65 Staithe Street
Wells-next-the-Sea NR23 1AN
(01328) 710419
Mon-Sun 9:30-5 (Winter, Tue-Sat 10-4:30, Thur close)
Est. 1986. Small. Gen Stock. Buys: Ring first. BR: King's Lynn.
Owners: Don & Dorothy Cook

WYMONDHAM

M. & A.C. THOMPSON

The Bookshop
1 Town Green
Wymondham NR18 0PN
(01953) 602244
Mon 10:45-5, Tue-Sat 10:15-5, Wed close
Est. 1975. Medium. Spec: SF: also Gen Stock and Topog. Buys: Anytime. BR: Wymondham. "Easy parking. Fast turnover."
Owner: A.C. Thompson

TURRET HOUSE

27 Middleton Street
Wymondham NR18 0AB
(01953) 603462
Mon-Sat 9-6 (ring first)
Est. 1972. Small. Spec: Sci: also Gen Stock and Atqn. Buys: Anytime. BR: Wymondham. "Also stock scientific instruments and collectables."
Owner: Dr D.H. Morgan

NORTHAMPTONSHIRE

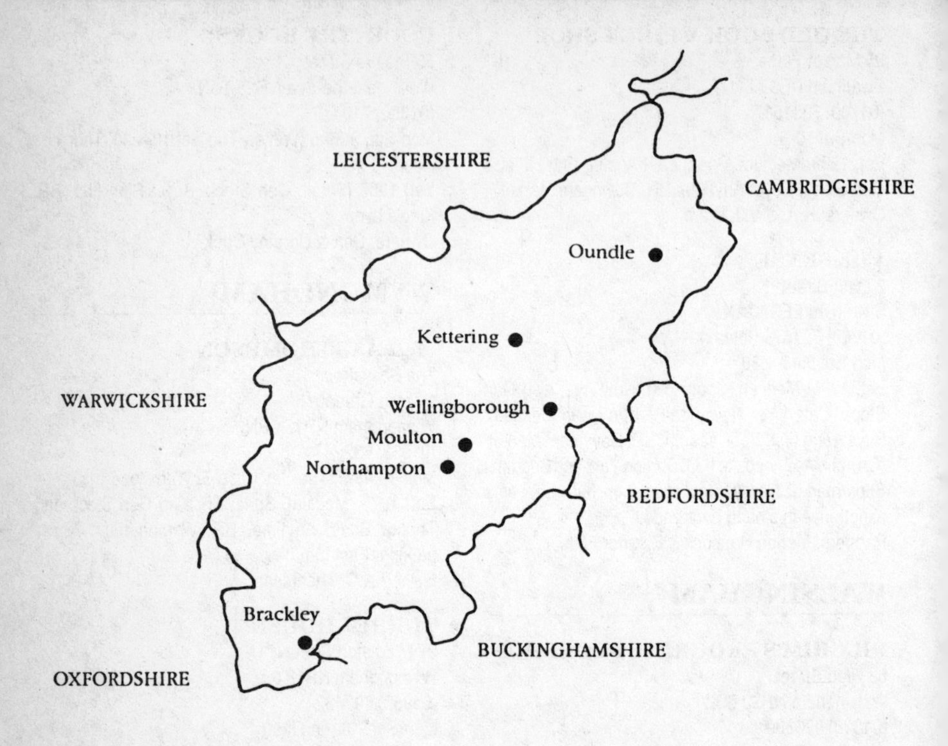

BRACKLEY

THE OLD HALL BOOKSHOP
32 Market Place
Brackley NN13 5DP
(01280) 704146
Mon-Sat 9:30-1, 2-5:30
Est. 1977. Medium. Gen Stock and Trav, Brackley, Sport. Buys: Ring first. Book search. cc: AV. BR: Banbury/Milton Keynes/Bicester. "C18th house in Brackley centre, 18 miles north of Oxford. Parking in Market Square. Large s'hand stock, plus good selection of new books & maps."
Owners: John & Lady Juliet Townsend

KETTERING

BOOKS
33 Montagu Street
Kettering NN18 8XG
(01536) 203815 (eve)
Fax (01536) 415368
Mon-Sat 9:30-5 (half-day Tue)
Est. 1967. Small. Gen Stock. Buys: Anytime. Book search."200 yards from Kettering bus station."

MOULTON

BROWSERS
2 West Street
Moulton NN3 1SB
(01604) 494620
Wed 2-8, Sat-Sun 2-6
Small. Gen Stock. Buys: Ring first. BR: Northampton. "4 miles from Northampton. Gen stock at low prices."
Owner: K. Trick

NORTHAMPTON

ABINGTON BOOKSHOP
327 Wellingborough Road
Northampton NN1 4EW
(01604) 32932
Mon-Sat 9-5
Est. 1978. Medium. Gen Stock. Buys: Ring first. cc: AV. BR: Northampton. "Good off-street parking. Also sells prints. Fairly fast turnover."
Owner: Steve James

OCCULTIQUE
73 Kettering Road
Northampton NN1 4AW
(01604) 27727
Mon-Sat 10-5
Est. 1973. Medium. Spec: Occult: also Alt Med. Cat: occ. Buys: Ring first. Book search. cc: AVAm. BR: Northampton. "75 min from Euston. Also new books."
Owner: M. John Lovett

OUNDLE

MICHAEL WATSON - BOOKSELLER
3 West Street
Oundle PE8 4EJ
(01832) 275028
Mon-Sat 10-5 Wed close
Est. 1995. Medium. Gen Stock. Buys: Ring first. Book search. BR: Peterborough. "General stock including Fict, Hist, Geog, Trav, Atec, the Arts."
Owner: Michael Watson

WELLINGBOROUGH

PARK BOOK SHOP
12 Park Road
Wellingborough NN8 4PG
(01933) 222592
Mon-Sat 10-5, Thur close
Est. 1979. Medium. Spec: Topog, Mil: also Gen Stock and Trans. Buys: Anytime. Book search. BR: Wellingborough.
Owner: J.A. Foster

NORTHUMBERLAND

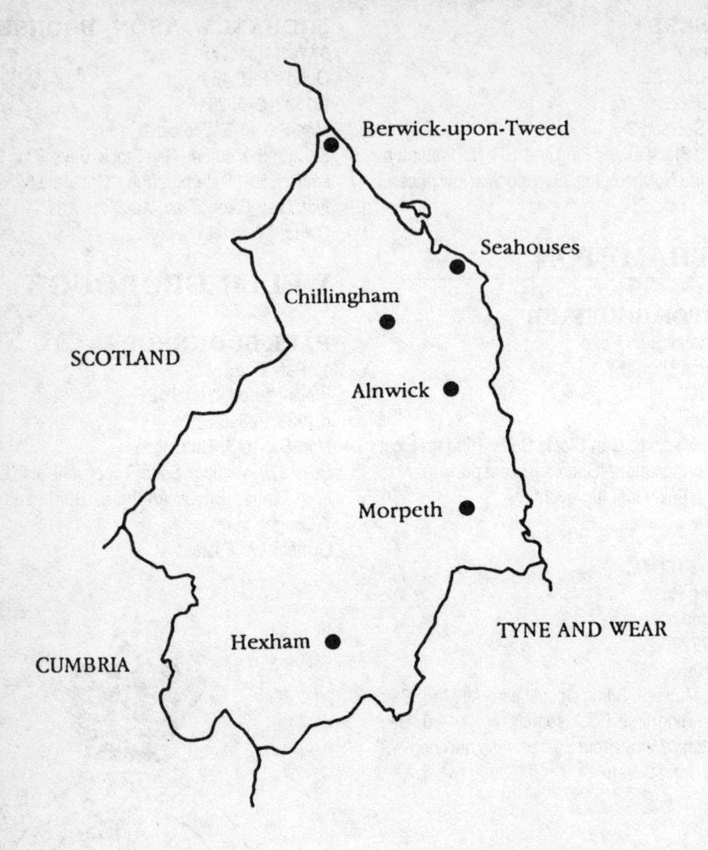

ALNWICK

BARTER BOOKS

Alnwick Station
Alnwick NE66 2NP
(01665) 604888
Mon-Sun 10-5 (Winter, Mon-Sat 10-5)
Large. Spec: Mod 1sts, Railways: also Gen Stock and Pbks. Buys: Anytime. Book search. BR: Alnmouth. "Very large shop in listed Victorian railway station on main road from A1. Free car park. Also stocks O/S maps, CDs, LPs, cassettes, videos. One of the largest shops in the country."
Owners: Stuart & Mary Manley

BERWICK-UPON-TWEED

BARTER BOOKS

Berwick Station
Berwick-upon-Tweed
(01289) 331022
Mon-Sun 10-5
Est. 1994. Medium. Gen Stock. Buys: Anytime. BR: Berwick. "Right in the station itself."
Owner: Patricia Russell

CHILLINGHAM

BARTER BOOKS
Chillingham Castle
Chillingham
(01668) 215359
Mon-Sun 12-5 (Easter-Sept; otherwise ring first)
Est. 1994. Medium. Gen Stock. Buys: Ring first. BR: Chathill/Alnmouth. "Close to Chillingham Wild Cattle Park, Ros Castle and the Cheviots. New shop with good general stock."
Owners: Stuart & Mary Manley

HEXHAM

HENCOTES BOOKS & PRINTS
8 Hencotes
Hexham NE46 4PW
(01434) 605971
Mon-Sat 10-5, Thur close
Medium. Spec: Northumberland, Lit: also Gen Stock and Nat Hist, Cookery, Gard. Buys: Ring first. Book search. BR: Hexham. "Small but well-stocked. Most subjects covered. Shop established over 20 years ago and taken over by present owners in 1992 after 10 years in Hexham antiques shop."
Owner: Penny Pearce

MORPETH

APPLEBY'S BOOKSHOP
60 Newgate Street
Morpeth NE61 1BE
(01670) 512960
Mon-Sat 9-5
Est. 1982. Small. Gen Stock and Local. Buys: Ring first. cc: AV. "Small stock of s'hand. Good range of general remainders. Large stock of new general & children's books, antique county maps & local rail photos."
Owner: W.E. Wallace

SEAHOUSES

BARTER BOOKS
67 Main Street
Seahouses
(01665) 720330
Mon-Sun 10-5
Est. 1994. Large. Gen Stock. Buys: Ring first. BR: Alnmouth. "15 miles from BR. Large, good quality gen stock."
Owners: Stuart & Mary Manley

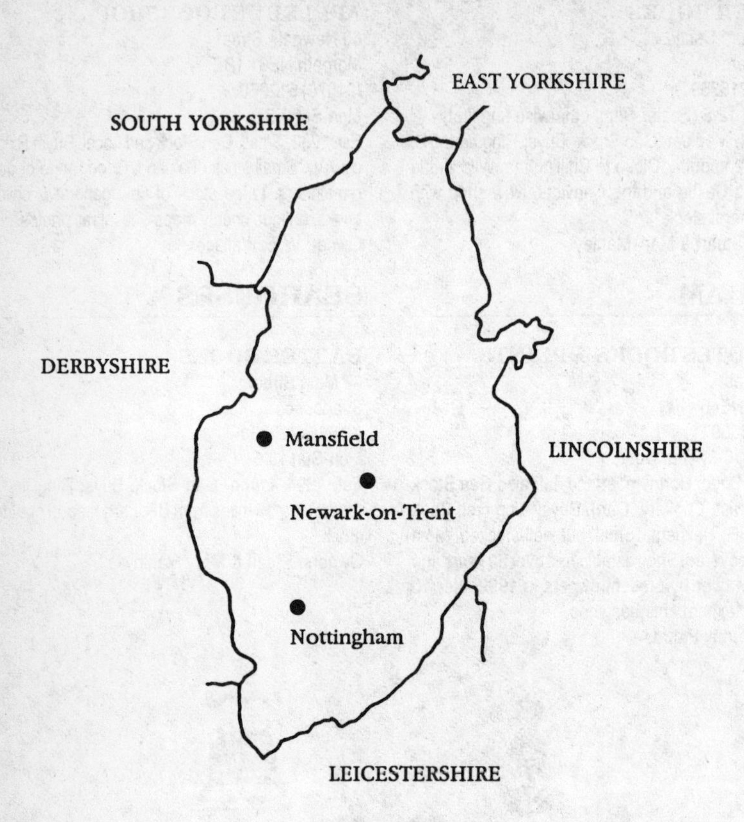

MANSFIELD

THE BOOKSHELF

7A Albert Street
Mansfield NG18 1EA
(01623) 648231
Mon-Sat 9:30-5, Wed close
Est. 1979. Large. Gen Stock and Biog, Byron, Nat Hist. Buys: Ring first. Book search. BR: Mansfield.
Owner: Mrs S. Payton

NEWARK-ON-TRENT

LAWRENCE BOOKS

Newark Antiques Centre
Lombard Street
Newark-on-Trent NG24 1XR
(01636) 605865
Fax (01636) 701619
Mon-Sat 9:30-5, Sun 11-4
Est. 1988. Small. Spec: Nautical, Nottinghamshire: also Gen Stock and Topog, Mil, Antique Ref. Buys: Ring first. Book search. BR: Newark. "Book unit in Antiques Centre. Opposite Bus Station. 200 yards from Market Square."
Owners: Arthur & Brigid Lawrence

GUY DAVIS - ANTIQUARIAN BOOKSELLER
Portland Street Antiques Centre
Newark-on-Trent NG24
(01636) 74397
Tue-Sat 10-5, Thur close (Sun by appt)
Small. Spec: Fine Bindings, Plate Books: also Gen Stock and Lit. Cat: 4 pa. Buys: Ring first. Book search. BR: Newark Northgate. "Stock ranges in price from £10-£4000."
Owner: Guy Davis

NOTTINGHAM

GEOFF BLORE'S BOOKSHOP
484 Mansfield Road
Sherwood
Nottingham NG5 2BF
(0115) 969 1441
Mon-Sat 10:30-5:30
Est. 1987. Medium. Gen Stock. Buys: Anytime. BR: Nottingham Midland. "2 miles from City Centre on A60 Nottingham-Mansfield Road. Easy parking nearby."
Owner: Geoff Blore

BOOK-A-BRAC
110 Outram Street
Sutton-in-Ashfield
Nottingham NG17 4FS
(01623) 553667
Mon-Sat 9-5, Wed close
Est. 1990. Small. Spec: Cinema, Hist: also Gen Stock. Buys: Anytime. Book search. BR: Alfreton/Mansfield Parkway. "5 min from Junc 28 of M1. Small but wide selection in 2 rooms, with music room above. Also classical records, sheet music, 78s."
Owner: S. Cooke

NICK DORIS
170 Derby Road
Nottingham NG17 1LR
(0115) 978 1194
Mon-Sat 10-5
Est. 1982. Small. Spec: Atqn: also Gen Stock and Mil, Lit. Buys: Anytime. BR: Nottingham. "Behind Val Smith's coin shop"
Owner: Nick Doris

JERMY AND WESTERMAN
203 Mansfield Road
Nottingham NG1 3FS
(0115) 947 4522
Mon-Sat 10:30-5:30
Medium. Spec: Local: also Gen Stock. Buys: Anytime. BR: Nottingham Midland. "Just up the hill (A60) from City Centre."
Owner: Geoff Blore

KYRIOS BOOKS
32B Kingsway
Kirkby-in-Ashfield
Nottingham NG17 7BD
(01623) 750966 (24 hour ansa)
Mon-Fri 9-4:30, Sat 9:30-4:30
Est. 1989. Medium. Spec: Theol, Phil: also Gen Stock and Greek, Hebrew. Cat: 6 pa: Christianity. Buys: Ring first. Book search. BR: Nottingham. "10 min from Junc 27 of M1."
Owners: C. Parr & R. Brown

MAYNARD & BRADLEY
30 Friar Lane
Nottingham NG1 6DZ
(0115) 948 4824
Mon-Fri 9:30-5:30, Sat 9-5:30
Est. 1988. Medium. Spec: Topog: also Gen Stock and Atqn, Sports. Cat: occ. Buys: Ring first. Book search. BR: Nottingham. "Also maps & prints."
Owners: David Maynard & Steven Bradley

OXFORDSHIRE

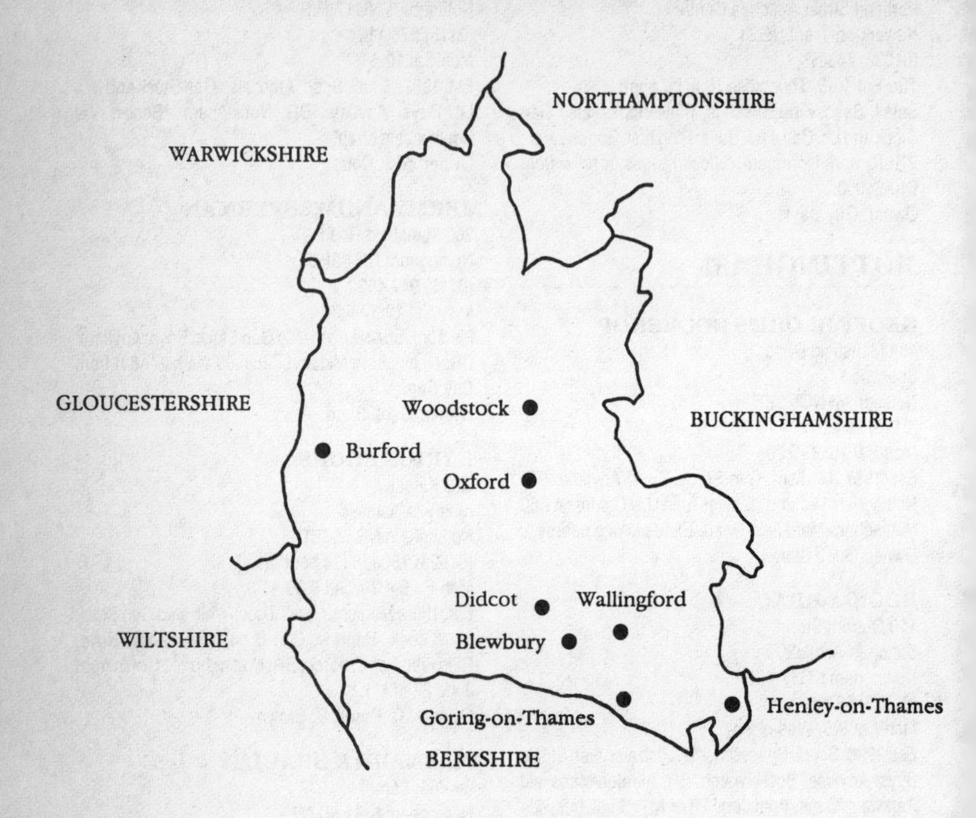

BLEWBURY

BLEWBURY ANTIQUES

Applethorpe
London Road
Blewbury OX11 9NX
(01235) 850366
Mon-Sun 10-6, Tue close
Est. 1971. Small. Gen Stock and Topog, Lit. Buys: Anytime. BR: Didcot. "Situated on Berkshire Downs. Books, prints & antiques under one roof. I am always looking for Thames and Berkshire books for my own collection."
Owners: Sheila & Eric Richardson

BURFORD

QUILL BOOKS (GILLIAN & DON PARTON)

The Old Forge
24 High Street
Burford OX18 4RR
(01993) 823594
Mon-Sun 10-1, 2-5:30, Wed close (ring first Sun)
Est. 1991. Medium. Gen Stock. Buys: Anytime. Book search. BR: Charlbury, Bus: from Oxford. "Visitors made welcome. Interesting old premises with a good general stock of s'hand and out-of-print books. Some collector's items."
Owners: Gillian & Don Parton

DIDCOT

THE BOOKSHOP
Didcot Antiques Centre
220 Broadway
Didcot OX14 8RS
(01235) 510819
Tue-Sat 10-5, Sun 11-4
Est. 1995. Small. Gen Stock. Buys: Anytime. cc: AV. BR: Didcot.
Owner: Rose Mears

GORING-ON-THAMES

BARBARA'S
The Orchard
Goring-on-Thames
(01491) 873032
Mon-Sat 10-1, 2:15-5
Small. Spec: Railways, Great Western Railways: also River Thames. Buys: Ring first. Book search. BR: Goring. "In car park behind High St., 5 min walk from BR. Small stock on all aspects of GWR."
Owner: Nevill Tiridger

HENLEY-ON-THAMES

THE ATTIC
4 Station Road
Henley-on-Thames RG9 1AY
(01491) 579107
Mon-Sat 9:30-6, Sun 12-5
Small. Gen Stock. Buys: Anytime. BR: Henley-on-Thames. "Good gen selection of good condition hbks & pbks at reasonable prices. Bric-a-brac & furniture."
Owners: G.C. & R.M. Honeyfield

RICHARD J. KINGSTON
95 Bell Street
Henley-on-Thames RG9 2BD
(01491) 574535
Mon-Fri 9-5:30, Sat 9:30-5
Est. 1974. Small. Spec: Topog: also Gen Stock and Trav. Buys: Ring first. Book search. BR: Henley-on-Thames.
Owner: R.J. Kingston

RICHARD WAY BOOKSELLER
54 Friday Street
Henley-on-Thames RG9 1AH
(01491) 576663
Mon-Sat 10-5:30
Est. 1978. Small. Spec: Rowing, River Thames: also Gen Stock. Buys: Ring first. cc: AV. BR: Henley-on-Thames. "Good turnover. Gen stock of 5,000 rare, s'hand & Atqn books, maps and prints. ABA member."
Owners: Richard Way & Diana Cook

OXFORD

ARCADIA
4 St. Michael's Street
Oxford OX1 2DU
(01865) 241757
Mon-Sat 9:30-6, Sun 1-5:30
Est. 1975. Small. Gen Stock. Buys: Anytime. BR: Oxford. "Also sell old postcards & prints."
Owner: Michael Keirs

ARTEMIS BOOKS
76 Cowley Road
Oxford OX4 1JB
(01865) 726909
Wed-Sat 10-5, close for lunch
Est. 1980. Medium. Spec: Humanities, Soc Sci: also Gen Stock. Buys: Ring first. BR: Oxford. "A wide range of reasonably priced books in good condition for students and collectors."
Owner: Diana Burfield

B.H. BLACKWELL LTD
48-51 Broad Street
Oxford OX1 3BU
(01865) 792792
Fax (01865) 794143
Mon-Sat 9-6, Tue 9:30-6
Est. 1879. Large. Spec: Academic: also Gen Stock and Fict, Everyman. Buys: Anytime. Book search. cc: AVAm. BR: Oxford. "Book search for account-holders only."
Owner: Nigel Blackwell

BLACKWELL'S MUSIC SHOP
38 Holywell Street
Oxford OX1 3SW
(01865) 792792
Mon-Sat 9-6, Tue 9:30-6
Large. Spec: Mus: also Gen Stock. Buys: Ring first. BR: Oxford. "Also CDs–mainly classical."
Owner: B.H. Blackwell Ltd

BLACKWELL'S RARE BOOKS
38 Holywell Road
Oxford OX1 3SW
(01865) 792792
Fax (01865) 248833
Mon-Sat 9-6
Medium. Spec: Atqn, Mod Lit: also Private Press, Local, Biblio. Cat: freq: classified. Buys: Ring first. Book search. cc: AVAm. BR: Oxford. "Small general Atqn section. Also chld & sets."
Owner: B.H. Blackwell Ltd

THE BOOKIES
6 Gloucester Street
Oxford OX1 2BN
Mon-Sat 10:30-5:30
Small. Spec: Academic, Phil: also Gen Stock and Trav. Cat: 2 pa: Spec subjs. Buys: Anytime. Book search. BR: Oxford. "Good academic stock on History of Ideas."
Owners: D. Whitaker, P. Butcher, et al.

THE BOOKSHOP
Oxford Antiques Centre
27 Park End Street
Oxford OX1 1HU
(01865) 251075
Mon-Sat 10-5, 1st Sun of month 11-5
Est. 1986. Small. Spec: Chld, Fr, Ger: also Gen Stock. Buys: Anytime. cc: AVAm. BR: Oxford. "Interesting varied stock, Atqn & s'hand."
Owner: Ian Sanger

THE BOOKSHOP AT THE PLAIN
11 Cowley Road
Oxford OX4 1HP
(01865) 790285
Mon-Sat 10:30-1, 2-6
Est. 1982. Medium. Spec: Hist, Chld: also Gen Stock and Detective, Trav, Lit. Cat: occ. Buys: Ring first. cc: AV. BR: Oxford. "Shop is near Magdalen College Bridge and Plain roundabout. Small car park in St.Clements. Customers courteously treated."
Owner: M.D. Watts

K.P. CLARK
Oxford Antique Trading Co
40-41 Park End Street
Oxford OX1 1JD
(01865) 793927
Mon-Sat 10-5, Sun 11-5
Est. 1989. Small. Spec: Art, Lit: also Gen Stock. Buys: Anytime. BR: Oxford. "PBFA member."
Owner: K.P. Clark

THE CLASSICS BOOKSHOP
3 Turl Street
Oxford OX1 3DQ
(01865) 726466
Mon-Sat 10-5
Medium. Spec: Latin & Greek, Arch: also Ancient Hist, Trav. Cat: occ. Buys: Ring first. BR: Oxford. "Also large selection of Oxford prints & maps. ABA."
Owners: C.V. & A.P. Powell-Jones

THE INNER BOOKSHOP
111 Magdalen Road
Oxford OX4 1RQ
(01865) 245301
Mon-Sat 10-5:45
Small. Spec: Mind, Body & Spirit, Occult: also Green, WS, Gay. Cat: new books only. Buys: Anytime. Book search. cc: AV. BR: Oxford. "Buses from BR or City Centre along Cowley Road/Iffley Road to Magdalen Road. Parking outside. Buy & exchange Mind-Body-Spirit books, not Atqn. 20% of stock s'hand. Ring first if selling boxfull."
Owners: R. Ashcroft & A. Cheke

JEREMY'S
98 Cowley Road
Oxford OX4 1JE
(01865) 241011
Mon-Sat 10-12:30, 2-5
Est. 1974. Medium. Gen Stock. Buys: Ring first. cc: AV. BR: Oxford. "Primarily dealing in stamps, old & modern postcards. Pbks only at 30p-£1.50."
Owner: Jeremy Daniel

THE LITTLE BOOKSHOP
Covered Market
Oxford
(01865) 59176 (eve)
Mon-Sat 9:30-5
Est. 1976. Medium. Spec: Pol, Hist: also Gen Stock and Eng Lit, Peng. Buys: Anytime. BR: Oxford.
Owner: Philip Gilbert

NINER & HILL
43 High Street
Oxford OX1 4AP
(01865) 726105
Fax (01865) 728750
Mon-Sat 10-5:30, Sun 1-5
Est. 1988. Medium. Spec: Trav, Art: also Gen Stock and Med, Hist, Out-of-print University Press. Buys: Anytime. cc: AV. BR: Oxford.
Owners: Peter Hill & Marcus Niner

OXBOW BOOKS
Park End Place
Oxford OX1 1HN
(01865) 241249
Fax (01865) 794449
Mon-Fri 9-5:30, Sat 9-1
Est. 1983. Medium. Spec: Arch, Ancient Hist: also Medieval, Bennett & Kerr, Med & Ren. Cat: 8 pa: Arch, Med Hist & Anc His. Buys: Anytime. cc: AVAm. BR: Oxford. "Behind Waterfields on Park End Street, 3rd floor of warehouse.Also have a comprehensive stock of new & remainder Arch titles."
Owner: Oxbow Books Ltd

OXFAM BOOKSHOP in Oxford
56 St. Giles
Oxford OX1 3LU
(01865) 310145
Mon-Sat 10-5
Large. Spec: Eng Lit: also Gen Stock also For Lang, Hist, Sci. BR: Oxford (and coach). "Wide ranging and continuously stocked. Many donations from Oxford scholarly and well-read. Welcome atmosphere."
Owner: Oxfam

SANDERS OF OXFORD LTD
104 High Street
Oxford OX1 4BW
(01865) 242590
Mon-Fri 9-1, 2:15-5:15 ec Sat
Small. Spec: Oxford. Buys: Ring first. BR: Oxford. "Prints & maps. V. small selection of Oxford books. ABA."

THORNTON'S OF OXFORD LTD
11 Broad Street
Oxford OX1 3AR
(01865) 242939
Fax (01865) 204021
Mon-Sat 9-6
Est. 1835. Large. Spec: Theol, Classics: also Gen Stock and For Lang, Biblio, Hist. Cat: 8 pa. Buys: Ring first. Book search. cc: AVAm. BR: Oxford. "New books, subscriptions, import & export worldwide inc. Middle East & Far East & Third World. 1 floor of lit in Russian language."
Owner: W.A. Meeuws

TITLES OF OXFORD
Antiquarian and Secondhand Books
15 Turl Street
Oxford OX1 3DQ
(01865) 727928 (tel/fax)
Mon-Sat 9:30-5:30
Est. 1972. Medium. Spec: Lit, Nat Hist: also Agric, Trav, Topog. Cat: occ. Buys: Anytime. Book search. cc: AVAmDEJ. BR: Oxford. "Frequent trains & coaches from London. Opposite Lincoln College in Oxford centre. Also sells maps & prints–mainly local."
Owners: G. & R. Stone

WATERFIELD'S
36 Park End Street
Oxford OX1 1HJ
(01865) 721809
Mon-Fri 9:30-5:30, Sat 9:30-6
Est. 1973. Large. Spec: Phil, Lit: also Gen Stock and Hist, Atqn. Cat: 10 pa: Phil, Lit, Hist, Atqn. Buys: Anytime. cc: AVE. BR: Oxford. "In an old warehouse, easy walking distance from BR & City centre. Large stock, mainly of academic books on the Humanities."
Owner: R. Waterfield Ltd

WALLINGFORD

TOBY ENGLISH
10 St. Mary's Street
Wallingford OX10 0EL
(01491) 836389
Mon-Sat 9:30-5
Est. 1981. Medium. Spec: Art, Atec: also Gen Stock and Topog. Cat: 4 pa: Art, Atec, Ren Studies. Buys: Anytime. Book search. cc: AVAmD. BR: Cholsey.
Owner: Toby English

WOODSTOCK

AFTERNOON BOOKSHOP
21B Oxford Street
Woodstock OX20 1TH
(01993) 813445
Mon-Sat 12-5
Small. Spec: Chld, Illus: also Gen Stock and 1890s. Cat: 1 pa: Oxford, Oxford Fict, Chld. Buys: Anytime. Book search. BR: Oxford. "20 min by road from Oxford. Exhibitions of contemporary prints."
Owner: J. Hainsworth

DAVID WHITTAKER BOOKS
1 Market Place
Woodstock OX20 1SY
(01993) 812577
Mon-Sun 10-5:30
Est. 1994. Medium. Spec: Acad, Orientalia: also Gen Stock and Hist, Art, Lit. Cat: 2 pa: History of Ideas. Buys: Ring first. "Gen stock of good quality academic books."
Owner: David Whittaker

THE WOODSTOCK BOOKSHOP
3 Market Place
Woodstock OX20 1SY
(01993) 811005
Mon-Sat 10-1, 2-5 Sun 12-5
Est. 1989. Small. Spec: Academic: also Gen Stock. Buys: Anytime. cc: AV. BR: Oxford.
Owner: Mark Wratten

SHROPSHIRE

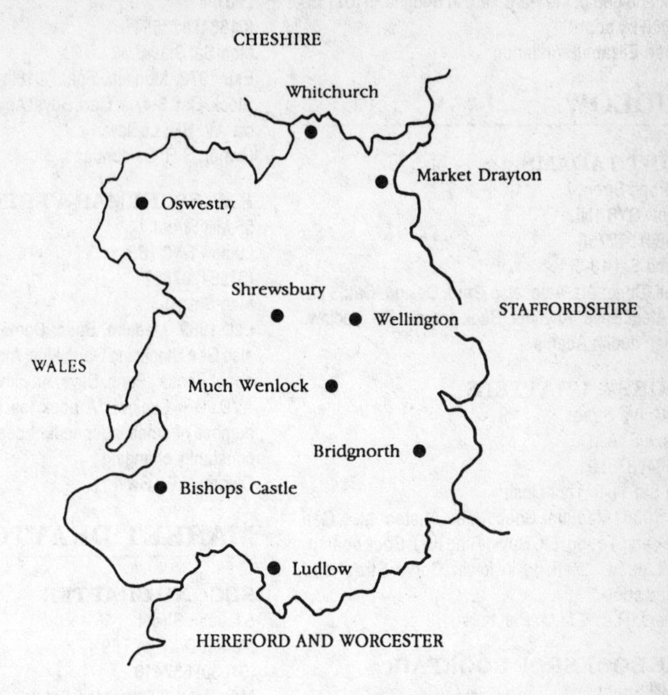

BISHOP'S CASTLE

JOHN PHEBY BOOKS
38-40 High Street
Bishop's Castle SY9 5BQ
(01588) 638301
Sat-Sun 10-5:30 (otherwise by appt)
Est. 1995. Large. Spec: Nat Hist: also Gen Stock. Buys: Ring first.
Owner: John Pheby

YARDBOROUGH HOUSE BOOKSHOP
The Square
Bishop's Castle SY9 5BN
(01588) 638318
Tue-Sun 10-5:30, Wed close
Est. 1980. Medium. Gen Stock and Penguins. Buys: Anytime. cc: A. BR: Craven Arms. "Also s'hand classical LP records, gen modern stock."
Owner: Carol Wright

BRIDGNORTH

THE BOOK PASSAGE
57A High Street
Bridgnorth WV16 4DX
(01746) 768767 (tel/fax)
Mon-Sat 8:30-5:30
Est. 1994. Medium. Gen Stock. Buys: Anytime. Book search. BR: Shrewsbury/Wolverhampton. "Stock 10,000. Fast turnover, Market Stall (permanent), 50p - £50."
Owner: J.D.W. Norris

BOOKSTACK
2A Castle Terrace
Bridgnorth WV16 4AH
(01746) 767089
Mon-Fri 11-4:30, Sat 9:30-5
Est. 1976. Medium. Spec: C17th: also Gen Stock and Loc, Chld, Illus. Cat: Request: C17th stud, Mod 1sts, Illus, Atqn. Buys: Ring first. Book search. cc: V. BR: Wolverhampton. "Shop is in Castle Terrace at top of

stoneway steps close to Castle Hill Railway. Repairs and binding service. Also store of C19th catalogue stock and gen at the Harp Yard in Bridgnorth (01746-768008 by appt)."
Owner: Elizabeth Anderton

LUDLOW

JUDITH ADAMS
41 Broad Street
Ludlow SY8 1NL
(01584) 872758
Fri and Sat 10-5
Small. Spec: Art, Atec: also Gard, Design. Cat: 3 pa: Art, Atec. Buys: Anytime. Book search. BR: Ludlow.
Owner: Judith Adams

BOOKS & CHATTELS
107 Corve Street
Ludlow SY8 1DJ
(01584) 876191
Mon-Sat 11-5, Thur close
Est. 1986. Medium. Spec: Jane Austen: also Gen Stock and Topog, Lit. Buys: Ring first. Book search. BR: Ludlow. "Parking in lower Corve Street and behind shop."
Owners: R.A. & M.M. Parkhurst

THE BOOKSHOP BOOKFAIR
56 Mill Street
Ludlow SY8 1BB
(01584) 878571
Mon-Sun 10-5 (Win, Mon-Sat 10-5)
Medium. Gen Stock. Buys: Anytime. cc: AV. BR: Ludlow. "20 booksellers display stock on 6 shelves each. 1/2 the stock of each stand is changed every month."
Owner: K.W. Swift

PETER J. HADLEY (BOOKSELLER)
132 Corve Street
Ludlow SY8 2PG
(01584) 874441
Fax (01584) 873027
Mon-Sat 10-5 (usually Tue close) or by appt
Small. Spec: Atec, Landscape Hist: also Lit, Illus. Cat: 5-6 pa. Buys: Anytime. Book search. cc: AV. BR: Ludlow. "Just down the hill from The Feathers Hotel. Carefully selected stock in collectable condition."
Owner: Peter J. Hadley

OFFA'S DYKE BOOKS
5 Bull Ring
Ludlow
(01584) 873854
Mon-Sat 9:30-5:30
Est. 1972. Medium. Spec: C18th-20th Lit: also Gen Stock. Cat: 3-4 pa: Gen. Buys: Anytime. Book search. cc: AV. BR: Ludlow.
Owner: S.R. Bainbridge

K.W. SWIFT MAP & PRINT GALLERY
56 Mill Street
Ludlow SY8 1BB
(01584) 878571
Mon-Sat 10-5
Est. 1989. Medium. Spec: Domestic Arts, Cookery: also Gen Stock and Gard, Illus, Atqn. Cat: occ: 'Books about Books', Peng. Buys: Anytime. Book search. cc: AVD. BR: Ludlow. "A book fair in a b'shop with a number of small independent dealers, 50% of stock constantly changing."
Owner: K.W. Swift

MARKET DRAYTON

SECOND CHAPTER
5 Queen Street
Market Drayton TF9 1PX
(01630) 657410
Mon-Sat 9-6 (Win, Mon-Sat 9-5, Thur close)
Est. 1982. Large. Gen Stock and Lit, Biog. Buys: Ring first. Book search. BR: Shrewsbury. "Close free parking. Pbk exchange operated (15,000). Browsers welcome."
Owner: Graham Clarke

MUCH WENLOCK

WENLOCK BOOKS
12 High Street
Much Wenlock TF13 6AE
(01952) 727877
Tue-Sat 9:30-5:30, close lunch, Wed 9:30-1, Mon 2-5:30
Est. 1987. Small. Gen Stock. Buys: Anytime. cc: AVE. BR: Shrewsbury.
Owner: Pierce Muscutt

OSWESTRY

NEWGATE BOOKS
20 Church Street
Oswestry SY11 2SP
(01691) 679786
Mon-Sat 9-5
Est. 1968. Small. Spec: Atqn: also Gen Stock and Loc Hist. Buys: Anytime. BR: Gobowen. "Watercolours, oil paintings, reproduction and antique furniture."
Owner: John Read

SHREWSBURY

CANDLE LANE BOOKS
28-29 Princess Street
Shrewsbury SY1 1LW
(01743) 365301
Mon-Sat 9:30-5
Est. 1965. Large. Gen Stock. Buys: Anytime. Book search. cc: AVAm. BR: Shrewsbury. "Pictures, prints, and framed Rackham prints."
Owner: John Thornhill

QUARRY BOOKS
24 Claremont Hill
Shrewsbury SY1 1RD
(01743) 361404
Mon-Sat 9:30-5:30
Est. 1986. Medium. Gen Stock. Buys: Ring first. Book search. BR: Shrewsbury. "Large selection on most subjects for readers and collectors."
Owner: Phil & Pat Wynne

SHREWSBURY ANTIQUE CENTRE
UNIT 19
Princess Street
Shrewsbury
(01938) 552023
Mon-Sat 9:30-5:30
Small. Gen Stock. Cat: Athletics and Olympics always. Buys: Ring first. Book search. BR: Shrewsbury.
Owner: Len Lewis

WELLINGTON nr. Telford

THE BOOK CORNER
Wellington Market
Wellington nr.Telford
(01952) 613823
Tue, Thur, Fri, Sat 9-4
Est. 1945. Small. Gen Stock. Buys: Anytime. BR: Wellington Shropshire.
Owner: Robert J. Glazzard

WHITCHURCH

BARN BOOKS
Pear Tree Farm
Norbury
Whitchurch SY13 4HZ
(01948) 663742
Fri 2-6, Sat 10-6, Sun 2-6 or by appt
Est. 1985. Medium. Spec: Gard, Loc Hist: also Gen Stock and Hist, Agri, Nat Hist. Cat: 2 pa: Gard, Loc Hist. Buys: Ring first. Book search. "Situated in rural countryside between the A49 and A525, 1 1/4 mile from Wrenbury and 3 from Cholmondeley. Hassle free parking in large cobbled yard. Although we have a Shropshire address, it's first over the border in Cheshire."
Owner: Mary Perry

SOMETHING ELSE
60 High Street
Whitchurch SY13 1BB
(01948) 664780
Mon-Sat 9:30-5
Est. 1983. Medium. Spec: Motoring: also Gen Stock. Buys: Anytime. Book search. BR: Whitchurch "20 miles from Chester, Wrexham, Shrewsbury. Also stocks ephemera, postcards, bygones."
Owners: Janet & Rod Forster

SOMERSET

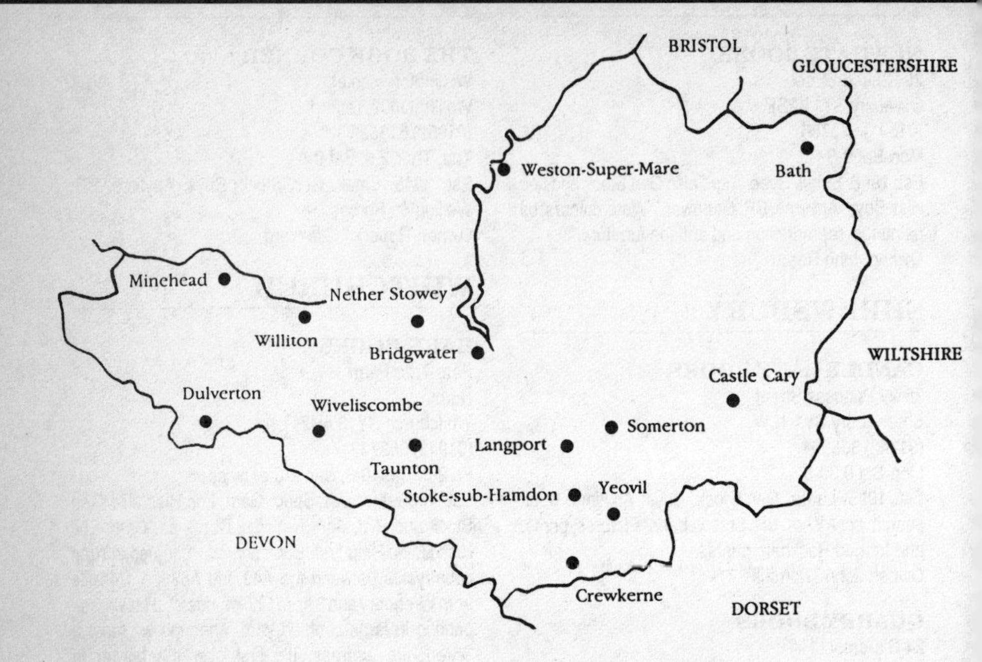

BATH

BANKES BOOKS

5 Margaret's Buildings
Bath BA1 2LP
(01225) 444580
Mon-Sat 10-5
Est. 1986. Medium. Spec: Trav, Priv Press: also Gen Stock and Chld, C18th Lit, Fine Bindings. Buys: Anytime. cc: AV. BR: Bath Spa. "Between the Circus and Royal Crescent."
Owner: Maryanne Bankes

BATH BOOK EXCHANGE

35 Broad Street
opp. Shires Yard
Bath BA1 5LP
(01225) 466214
Mon-Sat 9:30-5
Est. 1959. Small. Gen Stock and Biog, Theol, Fict. Buys: Ring first. Book search. BR: Bath Spa. "Gen stock. Inexpensive books & pbks, many as new at 1/2 price. Also classical 78 rpm records. No bulk purchases."
Owner: L.M. Turner

BATH OLD BOOKS

9C Margaret's Buildings
off Brock Street
Bath BA1 2LP
(01225) 422244
Mon-Sat 10-5
Est. 1991. Medium. Spec: Art, Fine Bindings: also Gen Stock and Erotica, Film, Gypsies. Cat: 6 pa: Gypsies, Trans & Commerce, Book Binding, Erotica; 4 pa: Gen. Buys: Anytime. Book search. cc: V. BR: Bath Spa. "Margaret's Buildings, between Royal Crescent & The Circus, is a smart pedestrianised antiques-oriented street with 2-hour free parking nearby."
Owners: A Distinguished Consortium

GEORGE BAYNTUN

21 Manvers Street
Bath BA1 1JW
(01225) 466055
Fax (01225) 482122
Mon-Fri 9-1, 2-5:30
Est. 1894. Medium. Spec: 1sts of C19th Eng Lit, Fine

bindings: also Gen Stock. Cat: 3 pa: Fine Bindings (old and new). Buys: Anytime. Book search. cc: AV. BR: Bath Spa. "Also including the book museum on craft of book binding and Bath in literature. Bayntun Riviere Bindery - binding and restoration."
Owner: H.H. Bayntun-Coward

CAMDEN BOOKS

146 Walcot Street
Bath BA1 5BL
(01225) 461606
Mon-Sat 10-5 (later in Summer)
Est. 1984. Medium. Spec: Acad, Atec: also Gen Stock and Phil, Sci, Econ. Cat: 3 pa: Atec, Phil, Sci, Econ, Hist. Buys: Anytime. cc: AV. BR: Bath Spa. "Shop located on Walcot Street amongst many antique & speciality shops. 112 hours free parking in front of shop."
Owners: Victor & Elizabeth Suchar

GEORGE GREGORY

21 Manvers Street
Bath BA1 1JW
(01225) 466055
Mon-Fri 9-1, 2-5:30 (or by appt)
Est. 1846. Medium. Gen Stock and Eng Lit, Fine bindings. Buys: Ring first. Book search. cc: AV. BR: Bath Spa. "Also prints, especially views, naval, and portraits."
Owner: H.H. Bayntun-Coward

PATHWAY BOOKS

1 Grove Street
nr Pultney Bridge
Bath BA2 6PJ
(01225) 463917
Mon-Sat 10:30-5:30
Est. 1990. Small. Spec: Mod 1sts: also Gen Stock and Topog, Eso, Biog. Buys: Anytime. Book search. BR: Bath Spa. "10 min from BR & coach station. Close to picturesque Pultney Bridge. Browsing welcome. Friendly & helpful service."
Owners: C. Chow & A. Paul

PATTERSON & LIDDLE

10 Margaret's Buildings
Brock Street
Bath BA1 2LP
(01225) 426722 (tel/fax)
Mon-Sat 10-5:30
Medium. Spec: BR Railways, Inland Waterways: also Gen Stock and Avia, Fine Bindings, Illus. Cat: occ. Buys: Anytime. Book search. cc: AV. BR: Bath. "Attractive pedestrianised street close to the Royal Crescent. An excellent gen s'hand bookshop with a full range of stock situated in the West Country's 'Street of Books'."
Owners: J.D. Patterson & S.M. Liddle

P.R. RAINSFORD

23A Manvers Street
Bath BA1 1JW
(01225) 445107
Fax (01225) 482122
Mon-Fri 10-5, Sat 10-1 (ring first)
Medium. Spec: Atec, Op. Art. Cat: 4 pa: Atec, Art, Hist. Buys: Ring first. Book search. BR: Bath Spa. "Extensive collection of out of print books on art, on 1st floor and part of basement of George Bayntun's."
Owner: P.R. Rainsford

BRIDGEWATER

BRIDGWATER BOOKS & BYGONES

Marycourt Mall Antiques Mart
St. Mary Street
Bridgwater
(01823) 451433
Fri & Sat 9:30-5
Est. 1989. Small. Spec: Crime Fict, Somerset: also Gen Stock and Peng, Pelicans. Buys: Anytime. Book search. BR: Bridgwater. "Tudor building opp St. Mary's Church, Town Centre. All corresp. to: C. Munro, Springs, Boweys Lane, Kingston St. Mary, Taunton, TA2 8HR (01823) 451433."
Owner: Colin Munro

CASTLE CARY

BAILEY HILL BOOKSHOP

Fore Street
Castle Cary BA7 7BG
(01963) 350917
Mon-Fri 9:30-6, Sat 9:30-5
Est. 1980. Medium. Spec: Local: also Gen Stock. Buys: Ring first. Book search. cc: AV. BR: Castle Cary. "Shop within easy walking distance of parking. Small, pleasant town. Also sell maps."
Owner: P.M. Booth

THE TOWER VIEW BOOKSHOP

Fore Street
Castle Cary BA7 7BG
(01963) 350929
Mon-Sat 9:30-1, 2-6 ec Thur

Est. 1983. Small. Spec: C17th and C18th Lit: also Gen Stock and Nat Hist, Topog. Buys: Anytime. Book search. cc: AV. BR: Castle Cary. "Atqn, maps of Somerset, new books as well."
Owners: J. & C. Whittaker

CREWKERNE

THE BOOKSHOP
15 Falkland Square
Crewkerne TA18 7JS
(01460) 76579
Tue-Sat 9:45-5:15, Mon 10:15-4:45
Est. 1988. Medium. Spec: Penguins, Loc Topog: also Gen Stock. Buys: Anytime. Book search. BR: Crewkerne. "On A30, 4 miles from A303. Car park nearby. New stock & books of other local dealers & their specialities, eg local hist, dogs, pbks."
Owner: Bill Lemmey

DULVERTON

ROTHWELL & DUNWORTII
2 Bridge Street
Dulverton TA22 9HJ
(01398) 323169
Fax (01398) 331161
Mon-Sat 10:30-1, 2:15-5
Est. 1983. Medium. Spec: Sport: also Gen Stock and Hunting, Shooting, Fishing. Buys: Ring first. BR: Tiverton. "1st shop in town on left hand side–on Exmoor side of river bridge. One of the biggest sporting bookshops in the SW."
Owners: C. Rothwell & M. Dunworth

LANGPORT

THE OLD BOOKSHOP
Bow Street
Langport TA10 9PQ
(01458) 252644
Mon-Sat 9-5:30
Est. 1984. Medium. Gen Stock and Nat Hist, Fict. Buys: Ring first. BR: Taunton. "Parking nearby. New local interest books. RSPB lit, maps and cassettes."
Owner: Heather Ridgway

MINEHEAD

ALCOMBE BOOKS
26 Alcombe Road
Minehead TA24 6AZ
(01643) 703452
Mon-Sat 10-5:30
Est. 1970. Medium. Gen Stock. Buys: Ring first. Book search. BR: Taunton. "Junction 24 at Bridgewater; Somerset coastal road to Minehead; on left, shortly after town centre turning at Alcombe. (Sandwich board.) Long established premises now under new ownership and with good variety of stock."
Owner: Lesley Delamont

NETHER STOWEY

COLERIDGE BOOKS
11 Castle Street
Nether Stowey TA5 1LN
(01278) 733338
Catalogue orders & appointment only
Est. 1991. Small. Spec: Coleridge, Wordsworth & circ: also Somerset. Cat: 2-3 pa: Romantics. Buys: Ring first. Book search. BR: Bridgwater. "Just off A39. Easy parking in street. Edge of Quantocks near Coleridge Cottage (N.T.)."
Owners: R. & S. Watters

SOMERTON

SIMON'S BOOKS
Broad Street
Somerton TA11 79H
(01458) 272313
Mon-Sat 10-4:30 (some Sun ring first)
Est. 1975. Large. Gen Stock. Buys: Ring first. BR: Castle Cary. "Situated between Yeovil, Glastonbury and Taunton. Fresh stock added to shelves daily-free unlimited parking outside the door."
Owner: Bryan Ives

STOKE-SUB-HAMDON

R.G. WATKINS BOOKS AND PRINTS
9 North Street Workshops
Stoke-sub-Hamdon TA14 6QR
(01935) 822891 (tel/fax)
Fri 10-5 (or by appt)

Small. Spec: Art Ref, Collecting: also Gen Stock and Topog. Cat: 4 pa: Gen. Buys: Ring first. cc: AV. BR: Crewkerne. "Workshops are converted farm buildings, 1/2 mile south of A303 near Martock, 6 miles north of Crewkerne. Atqn and gen stock including maps, prints, old master prints, and engraved portraits."
Owner: R.G. Watkins

TAUNTON

ROTHWELL & DUNWORTH
14 Paul Street
Taunton TA1 3PF
(01823) 282476
Mon-Sat 11-5:15 (Cricket season, ec Sat)
Est. 1979. Medium. Spec: Cricket: also Atqn. Buys: Ring first. BR: Taunton. "Fast turnover, constantly changing stock."
Owners: C. Rothwell & M. Dunworth

WESTON-SUPER-MARE

MANNA BOOKS
30 Orchard Street
Weston-super-Mare BS23 1RQ
(01934) 636228
Mon-Sat 10-5
Est. 1987. Medium. Gen Stock and Eso, Lit, Biog. Buys: Ring first. BR: Weston-super-Mare. "General family bookshop."
Owner: Peter Fairnington

SEVERN BOOKS
48 Severn Road
Weston-super-Mare BS23 1DT
(01934) 635389
Mon-Sat 9-5:30
Est. 1985. Medium. Gen Stock and Lit, Chld, Crime, Cricket. Buys: Ring first. Book search. BR: Weston-super-Mare. "Some prints, cigarette cards & postcards."
Owners: Brian & S.J. Alford

STERLING BOOKS
43A Locking Road
Weston-super-Mare BS23 3DG
(01934) 625056
Mon-Sat 9-6
Est. 1965. Large. Gen Stock and Topog, Atqn, Hist. Cat: occ: Gen. Buys: Anytime. Book search. cc: AV. BR: Weston-super-Mare. "Good for parking, picture-framing, book binding."
Owner: Mr D.R.J. Nisbet

TUDOR BOOKS
Tudor Mall
116 High Street
Weston-super-Mare BS23 1HP
(01934) 643374
Mon-Sat 9:30-5:30, Sun 11-5 (in season)
Est. 1992. Medium. Spec: Chld Annuals: also Gen Stock and US Comics. Buys: Ring first. Book search. BR: Weston-super-Mare. "End of High Street nr. Playhouse. Gen stock, wheelchair access, friendly reception."
Owners: Nigel & Julie Andrews

WILLITON

BLACKMORES BOOKSHOP
6 High Street
Williton TA4 4NW
(01984) 632227
Mon-Fri 9-5:30, Sat 9-1
Small. Gen Stock. Buys: Anytime. Book search. "Also sell greeting cards, maps & local books. Egon Ronay listed tearoom."
Owner: Mrs Lintott

WIVELISCOMBE

WIVEY BOOKS
1 High Street
Wiveliscombe TA4 2JX
(01984) 623506
Mon-Fri 6:30-1, 2-5:30, Thur close, Sat 7-4, Sun 8-12
Est. 1983. Small. Spec: Cookery: also Gen Stock and Sports, Handicrafts. Buys: Anytime. BR: Taunton.
Owners: Mr & Mrs J. Manley

YEOVIL

YEOVIL BOOKSHOP
44 Princes Street
Yeovil BA20 1EQ
(01935) 73638
Mon-Sat 9-5:30
Small. Gen Stock. Buys: Ring first. cc: AV. BR: Yeovil Junction/Yeovil Pen Mill. "Shop is mainly new books with small s'hand section upstairs."
Owner: D.V. Buckley

STAFFORDSHIRE

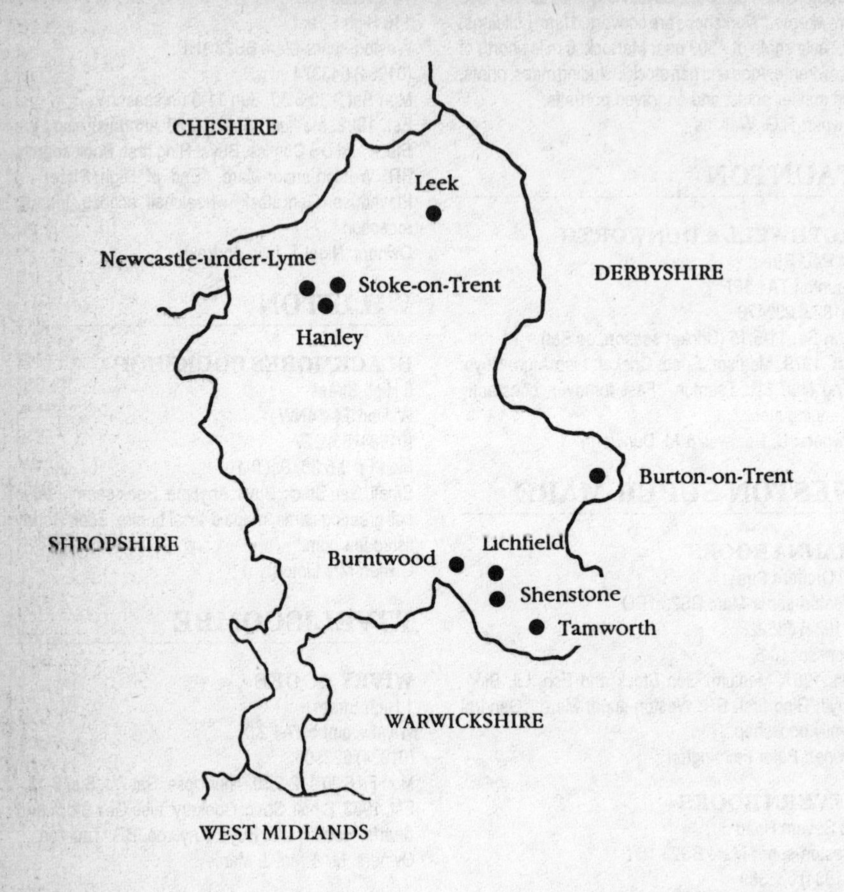

BURNTWOOD

BURNTWOOD BOOKSHOP

Church View
St. Mathews Road
Burntwood WS7 9DP
(01543) 682217
Wed & Sat 10-4:30
Est. 1973. Large. Gen Stock. Buys: Ring first. BR: Lichfield. "Easy parking. 3 miles from Lichfield. Large gen stock in country shop with an old fashioned atmosphere. Prices reasonable. Also antiques and curios."
Owners: Ken Hayward & Royden Smith

BURTON-ON-TRENT

THE NEEDWOOD BOOKSHOP

55 New Street
Burton-on-Trent DE14 3QY
(01283) 541641
Tue-Sat 10-5
Est. 1974. Medium. Spec: Railways, Theol: also Gen Stock and Classics. Cat: 3 pa: Railways, 2 pa: Theol. Buys: Ring first. BR: Burton-on-Trent. "2 min walk from Safeway/Sainsbury car parks. General bookshop with 6 rooms of stock on 2 floors."
Owner: Elaine Brown

HANLEY

THE SENSIBLE BOOKSHOP
30-32 Hope Street
Hanley ST1 5BS
(01782) 261352
Mon-Sat 10-5:30
Est. 1970. Medium. Gen Stock and Ceramics, Arnold Bennett. Buys: Anytime. BR: Stoke-on-Trent.
Owner: David Lees

LEEK

LEEK OLD BOOKS
43 Bath Street
Leek ST13 6JQ
(01538) 399033
Fax (01538) 399696
Tue-Fri 9:45-5:15, Sat 9-4:30
Medium. Spec: Ornithology, Loc Hist: also Gen Stock. Buys: Ring first. Book search. cc: AV.
Owner: B. Richardson

THE VILLAGE BOOKSHOP
17 Russell Street
Leek ST13 5JF
(01538) 372092
Wed, Fri & Sat 9:30-4:30, Thur 9:30-1
Medium. Spec: Local: also Gen Stock. Buys: Ring first. Book search. "Also a branch in Stoke-on-Trent."
Owners: David & Margaret Mycock

LICHFIELD

THE STAFFS BOOKSHOP
4-6 Dam Street
Lichfield WS13 6AA
(01543) 264093
Mon-Sat 9:30-5:30
Est. 1938. Large. Spec: C18th, Samuel Johnson: also Illus, Chld, Biog. Cat: 4 pa: Dolls, Chld, S. Johnson, Illus. Buys: Ring first. Book search. BR: Lichfield. "Inc. Images and Newbery and Johnson. Unusual new books, esp biblio, dolls, art, fine printing. Art gallery opened. Also run a consultancy for booksellers and publishers."
Man. Dir.: Peter Stockham

NEWCASTLE-UNDER-LYME

POMES PENYEACH
63 High Street
Wolstanton
Newcastle-under-Lyme ST5 0ER
(01782) 630729
Mon-Sat 9:30-5:30
Est. 1985. Medium. Spec: Mod 1sts: also Gen Stock and Perf Arts, Lit, Chld. Cat: occ. Buys: Ring first. Book search. cc: AV. BR: Stoke-on-Trent. "10 min from Junc 16 on M6. Easy parking outside entrance."
Owners: Paul & Shelagh Robinson

SHENSTONE

COLIN SHAKESPEARE BOOKS
3 Chestnut Drive
Shenstone WS14 0JH
(01543) 480978
Mon-Sun 9-9
Small. Gen Stock. Cat: irreg: as necessary. Buys: Ring first. Book search. BR: Shenstone.
Owner: Colin Shakespeare

STOKE-ON-TRENT

BERNARD TAYLOR

337 Newcastle Street
Longport
Stoke-on-Trent ST6 3RP
(01782) 824682
Wed-Fri 10-6, Sat 10-3
Est. 1983. Medium. Spec: Football: also Gen Stock and Film, Railways, Mus. Buys: Anytime. BR: Longport. "Very easy to find off A500. Take A52 to Tunstall. Opposite Price & Kensington's carpark. Also stock cigarette cards."
Owner: B. Taylor

THE VILLAGE BOOKSHOP

56 Millrise Road
Milton
Stoke-on-Trent
(01782) 543005
Mon-Sat 9-5
Small. Spec: Loc Hist: also Gen Stock. Buys: Ring first. Book search. BR: Stoke on-Trent. "3 miles from BR. Small shop, predominantly local - new local Hist books, local videos, cards. More extensive stock found at Leek Branch, 7 miles away."
Owners: David & Margaret Mycock

TAMWORTH

G. & J. CHESTERS

19 Bridge Street
Polesworth
Tamworth B78 1DR
(01827) 894743
Mon-Sat 9:30-5:30, Wed 9:30-9
Medium. Spec: Acad: also Gen Stock and Br Topog, Atqn. Cat: 6 pa. Buys: Ring first. BR: Polesworth. "Leave M42 at Junc 10, go south along A5 to first roundabout. Turn left into Long Street, continue for 1 mile. Go straight across crossroads in Polesworth. Take 1st left into Private Road. Stocks maps & prints. Also at Crewe Market Bookstall, Sat 9-4."
Owners: G. & J. Chesters

SUFFOLK

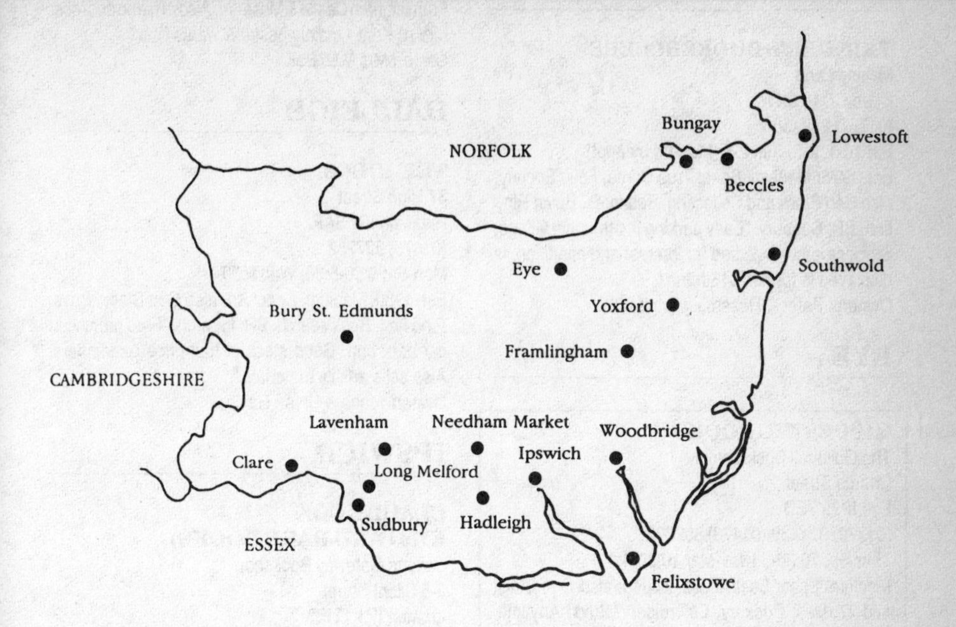

BECCLES

BESLEYS BOOKS

4 Blyburgate
Beccles NR34 9TA
(01502) 715762
Mon-Sat 9:30-1, 2-5, Wed close
Est. 1980. Medium. Spec: Gard, Nat Hist: also Gen Stock. Cat: 2-4 pa. Buys: Anytime. Book search. cc: AV. BR: Beccles. "Although shop is open 5 days a week, much of our catalogue is at a different venue. Please phone and make an appointment to view this."
Owners: Piers & Gabby Besley

BUNGAY

SCORPIO BOOKS

1 Nethergate Street
Bungay NR35 1HE
(01986) 895743
Tue, Thur-Sat 10-1, 2-5 (or by appt)
Est. 1989. Medium. Spec: Mil: also Gen Stock and Avia, Jazz. Buys: Anytime. Book search. BR: Norwich. "Near Town Centre, parking available in street. Hourly bus service from Norwich."
Owners: Lorna & Patrick Quorn

BURY ST. EDMUNDS

THE BURY BOOKSHOP

28A Hatter Street
Bury St. Edmunds IP33 1NE
(01284) 703107
Mon-Sat 9-5:30
Est. 1979. Large. Gen Stock. Buys: Ring first. cc: AVAm. BR: Bury St. Edmunds.
Owner: Joe Wakerley

NEW SAXON BOOKSHOP

2 Hatter Street
Bury St. Edmunds IP33 1LZ
(01284) 764312
Mon-Sat 9-5:30
Small. Gen Stock and Fict, Po. Buys: Ring first. Book search. cc: AV. "Mainly new books, but small s'hand section."
Owner: S. Du Sautoy

CLARE

TRINDER'S BOOKSELLERS
Malting Lane
Clare CO10 8NW
(01787) 277130
Sat 10-1, 2-5, Sun 2-5 (Mon-Fri by appt)
Est. 1975. Medium. Spec: True Crime, Folio Society: also Gen Stock and Collecting, Batsfords. Buys: Ring first. BR: Sudbury. "Easy parking in attractive village. Stock carefully selected for interest and condition, is displayed in former C16th Inn."
Owners: Peter & Rosemary Trinder

EYE

GIPPESWIC BOOKS
The Guildhall Bookroom
Church Street
Eye IP23 7BD
(01379) 871439/(01473) 682302
Thur-Sat 10:30-5 (Nov-Mar 10:30-4.30)
Medium. Spec: East Anglia, Topog: also Gen Stock and Textiles, Cookery, Embroidery. Buys: Anytime. Book search. BR: Diss (Norfolk). "Shop located in historic Guildhall (next to beautiful church). Easy parking & tearoom nearby."
Owner: Martin Crook

FELIXSTOWE

TREASURE CHEST
78 Hamilton Road
Felixstowe IP11 7AF
(01394) 270717
Mon-Sat 9:30-5:30
Est. 1982. Large. Gen Stock. Buys: Ring first. Book search. cc: AV. BR: Felixstowe.
Owner: Robert Green

FRAMLINGHAM

MRS V.S. BELL (BOOKS)
19 Market Hill
Framlingham IP13 9BB
(01728) 723046
Mon-Sat 10-1, 2-4 Wed close pm
Est. 1974. Medium. Spec: Det Fict: also Gen Stock. Buys: Ring first. Book search. BR: Campsea Ashe. "5 miles from A12, 2 miles from A1120. Free car parking, Framlingham Castle & Museum. Also at same address: Mrs A. Kent - mainly postal & wants lists."
Owner: Mrs V.S. Bell

HADLEIGH

THE IDLER
37 High Street
Hadleigh IP7 5AF
(01473) 827752
Mon-Sat 9:30-5:30, Wed 9:30-1
Est. 1980. Medium. Spec: Art: also Gen Stock. Buys: Ring first. Book search. BR: Ipswich. "Free parking in car park opp. Good stock of half-price remainders. Also sells artist's materials."
Owners: Jane & Bryan Haylock

IPSWICH

CLAUDE COX (OLD AND RARE BOOKS)
College Gateway Bookshop
3-5 Silent Street
Ipswich IP1 1TF
(01473) 254776
Mon-Sat 10-5, Wed close
Est. 1944. Large. Spec: Printing, Art of the Book: also Gen Stock and Art, Private Press, Illus. Cat: 3 pa: Printing; 3 pa: Atqn. Buys: Anytime. Book search. cc: AV. BR: Ipswich. "Parking in Cromwell Square & Buttermarket. Small stock of remainders, esp, Art & Illus, Also sells maps & prints."
Owner: A.B. Cox

LAVENHAM

R.G. ARCHER
7 Water Street
Lavenham CO10 9RW
(01787) 247229
Mon-Sat 9-5, Sun 10-5
Est. 1970. Medium. Gen Stock. Buys: Anytime. Book search. BR: Sudbury. "Opp. the Priory."
Owner: R.G. Archer

LONG MELFORD

LIME TREE BOOKS
Hall Street
Long Melford CO10 9JF
(01787) 311532
Mon-Sun 9-5:30
Est. 1992. Medium. Spec: Atqn, Folio Society, Art: also Gen Stock and Colour Plate, Fict & Mod 1sts, Hist. Buys: Anytime. Book search. cc: AVAmE. BR: Sudbury. "3 miles north of Sudbury. Pleasant shop, well-presented & lit, with plenty of room."
Owner: Bryan Marsh

LOWESTOFT

JOHN ROLPH
Manor House
Pakefield Street
Lowestoft NR33 0JT
(01502) 572039
Tue-Sat 11-1, 2:30-5, Thur close
Est. 1948. Medium. Gen Stock and Fict, Chld, Mod 1sts. Buys: Ring first. BR: Lowestoft. "Shop lies behind private house. Ample parking with no restrictions. Stock old magazines."
Owner: John Rolph

NEEDHAM MARKET

ROY ARNOLD
77 High Street
Needham Market IP6 8AN
(01449) 720110 (tel/fax)
Mon-Sat 9:30-5:30 (or by appt)
Est. 1974. Small. Spec: Tools, Trade: Cat: 3-4 pa: also old catalogues on above subjects. Buys: Anytime. Book search. cc: AVAm. BR: Needham Market. "Highly specialised. Only deals in books on these & allied subjects. Also new books."
Owner: Roy Arnold

SOUTHWOLD

DRUNKEN BOAT BOOKSHOP
9 Pinkney's Lane
Southwold IP18 6EW
(01502) 722224
Mon-Sat 10-5 (ring first)
Est. 1995. Small. Gen Stock and Art, Lit. Buys: Ring first. BR: Halesworth/Darsham. "New shop. Also have a private bookroom in Yoxford."
Owner: Richard Hamburger

SUDBURY

SUFFOLK RARE BOOKS
7 New Street
Sudbury CO10 6JB
(01787) 372075
Tue-Sat 10:30-4:30, Wed close (phone first)
Est. 1975. Medium. Gen Stock and Topog, Hist, Mil. Buys: Anytime. BR: Sudbury. "Into North Street car park, then ask for direction to shop or pub opp. (Prince of Wales). Good turnover, reasonable selection of Atqn & rare books."
Owner: T.M. Cawthorn

WOODBRIDGE

BLAKES BOOKS
88 Thoroughfare
Woodbridge IP12 1AL
(01394) 380302
Mon-Sat 9:30-5
Est. 1983. Medium. Spec: Maritime: also Gen Stock and Lit, The Arts, Woodbridge. Buys: Ring first. cc: V. BR: Woodbridge.
Owner: Robert Green

WORDS & MUSIC
3A Cumberland Street
Woodbridge IP12 4AH
(01394) 383098
Mon-Sat 10-5
Est. 1992. Medium. Spec: Lit, Fine Art: also Gen Stock and Mus. Buys: Ring first. cc: AV. BR: Woodbridge via Ipswich. "Pleasant town on River Deben noted for sailing, antiques & walks. Also site of Sutton Hoo - Saxon ship burial. Also sell classical CDs."
Owner: P.J. Freeman

YOXFORD

THE BOOKSHOP
High Street
Yoxford IP17 3JQ
Mon-Sun 10-6 (Winter, Sat & Sun 10-4 or by appt)
Est. 1973. Medium. Gen Stock. Buys: Anytime. BR: Darsham, Bus: Yoxford. "Off A12. Phone at home (eves) (01728) 668309."
Owners: Mrs P. Packer & Mrs J. Hanson

SURREY

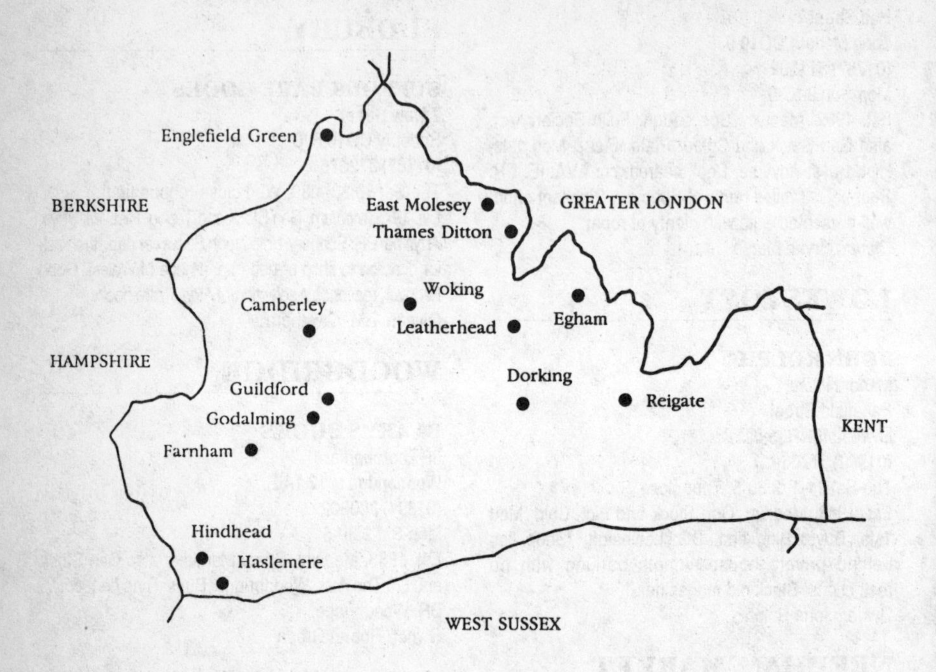

CAMBERLEY

BYGONE BOOKS
149 London Road
Camberley GU15
(01276) 686583
Mon-Fri 10-5, Sat 9-6, Sun 12-4
Medium. Spec: Atqn: also Gen Stock and Mil, Chld, Trav. Buys: Ring first. cc: AVAm. BR: Blackwater/ Camberley. "On A30."
Owner: G.P. Griffiths

DORKING

T.S. HILL BOOKS
122 South Street
Dorking RH4 2EU
(01306) 886468
Tue, Thur, Fri, Sat 9:30-1, 2-5
Est. 1987. Medium. Spec: Atec: also Gen Stock and Art, Hist, Nat Hist. Buys: Ring first. BR: Dorking North. "On the right-hand side of a one-way street; can stop right outside the door."
Owner: T.S. Hill

DONALD WENDON BOOKS
Dorking Emporium Antiques Centre
1A West Street
Dorking
(01306) 876646/881010 (eve)
Mon-Sat 10-5
Medium. Spec: Chld, Illus: also Gen Stock and Trav, Cookery, Gard. Buys: Ring first. BR: Dorking/Dorking Deep Dene. "Please make all enquiries to D. Wendon, Ennisdene, 16 St. Paul's Road West, Dorking, Surrey, RH4 2HU."
Owner: Donald Wendon

EAST MOLESEY

BOOKS BOUGHT & SOLD
68 Walton Road
East Molesey KT8 0DL
(0181) 224 3232
Fax (0181) 224 3576
Tue-Fri 10-5, Sat 9:30-5:30
Est. 1994. Medium. Spec: Chld, Motoring: also Gen Stock and Avia. Buys: Ring first. Book search. BR: Hampton Court. "From Hampton Court follow B369 to Walton. Large free car park near shop. Bright spacious shop. Large sections on most subjects."
Owners: P. Sheridan & W.J. Collyer

MOLE BOOKSHOP
81 Walton Road
East Molesey KT12 0DP
(01784) 483467
Fax (01784) 483076
Fri & Sat 9-5
Small. Spec: Mil, Mount: also Gen Stock and Trav. Cat: 1 pa: Mount. Buys: Ring first. Book search. BR: Hampton Court. "Car park opposite."
Owner: Keith Langford

EGHAM

BLACKLOCK'S
8 Victoria Street
Englefield Green
Egham TW20 0JJ
(01784) 438025
Mon-Sat 9-1, 2-5
Est. 1988. Small. Spec: Local: also Gen Stock and Biog, Classics, 1sts. Buys: Anytime. Book search. BR: Egham. "Browsers welcome. We order new books & take book tokens. Also have Philatelic dept. supplying stamps & albums."
Owner: Graham Dennis

FARNHAM

COBWEB BOOKS
29 The Woolmead
East Street
Farnham GU9 7TT
(01252) 734531
Mon-Sat 9-5:30
Est. 1990. Large. Spec: Mod 1sts, Trans: also Gen Stock. Buys: Anytime. Book search. cc: AVAmDEJ. BR: Farnham.
Partner: R. Buckler

GODALMING

THE EUREKA BOOKROOM
19A Church Street
Godalming GU7 1EL
(01483) 426968
Mon-Sat 10-5
Est. 1973. Medium. Gen Stock. Buys: Anytime. BR: Godalming.
Owner: Peter Fennymore

N.S.F. BOOKSHOP
9 Queen Street
Godalming GU7 1BA
(01483) 415950
Mon-Sat 10-4
Est. 1985. Medium. Gen Stock. BR: Godalming. "600 yards from BR, through Church Street and High Street as far as King's Arms. Charity shop relying on donated books and run by volunteers including work placements for the recovering mentally ill."
Owner: NSF West Surrey Group

GUILDFORD

THOMAS THORP
170 High Street
Guildford GU1 3HP
(01483) 62770
Mon-Sat 9-5
Est. 1983. Small. Gen Stock. Cat: 4 pa: Remainders. Book search. BR: Guildford. "Large stock of new books with small s'hand section. Also St. Albans office (01727) 865576."
Owner: Thomas Thorp

CHARLES W. TRAYLEN
49-50 Quarry Street
Guildford GU1 3UA
(01483) 572424
Fax (01483) 450048
Tue-Sat 9-1, 2-5
Est. 1946. Large. Spec: Lit: also Gen Stock and Hist, Art, Econ. Cat: 2-3 pa: Atqn. Buys: Ring first. Book search. BR: Guildford. "Also prints and a book binding & repair service."
Owner: Charles Traylen

HASLEMERE

THE HASLEMERE BOOKSHOP
2 Causewayside
High Street
Haslemere GU27 2JZ
(01428) 652952
Mon-Sat 9-5:15
Est. 1980. Medium. Gen Stock and Trav, Topog, Hist. Buys: Anytime. Book search. cc: AV. BR: Haslemere. "New, s'hand & Atqn booksellers."
Owner: R.G. Timms

HINDHEAD

BEACON HILL BOOKSHOP
Beacon Hill Road
Hindhead GU26 6QL
(01428) 606783
Mon-Sat 9-5, Wed close
Est. 1978. Large. Gen Stock. Cat: 1 pa: the Book Trade. Buys: Ring first. BR: Haslemere. "Easy parking. Low prices, very fast turnover."
Owners: S.F. & C.M. Jenks

LEATHERHEAD

BOOKWORM
22 & 30 North Street
Leatherhead KT22 7AT
(01372) 377443/376925
Fax (01372) 812674/386424
Mon-Sat 9:30-5:30
Est. 1948. Large. Gen Stock. Buys: Ring first. Book search. cc: AV. BR: Leatherhead. "Located between station & centre of town. New maps. Whittaker Book Bank."
Owner: R. Starr

REIGATE

REIGATE GALLERIES LTD
45A Bell Street
Reigate RH12 7AQ
(01737) 246055
Mon-Sat 9-5:30
Est. 1948. Medium. Gen Stock and Trav, Topog, Nat Hist. Buys: Anytime. cc: AV. BR: Reigate. "Also about 5,000 prints & engravings."
Owners: K. & J. Morrish

THAMES DITTON

ELISABETH GANT
52 High Street
Thames Ditton KT7 0SA
(0181) 398 0962
Mon-Sat 11-5, Wed close
Est. 1982. Medium. Spec: Chld, Illus: also Gen Stock. Cat: 2 pa: Chld, Illus. Buys: Anytime. cc: AV. BR: Thames Ditton. "Free parking. Nice village. 2 bookshops, antiques & pubs. ABA & PBFA."
Owner: Elisabeth Gant

WOKING

GOLDSWORTH BOOKS & PRINTS
47 Goldsworth Road
Woking GU21 1JY
(01483) 767670
Tue-Sat 10-5:30
Est. 1988. Medium. Spec: Atqn, Illus: also Gen Stock. Buys: Anytime. Book search. cc: AV. BR: Woking. "3 min walk from 'Peacock'. BR 5 min. Parking outside shop usually. Maps & prints also stocked."
Owner: D.B. Hartles

East Sussex

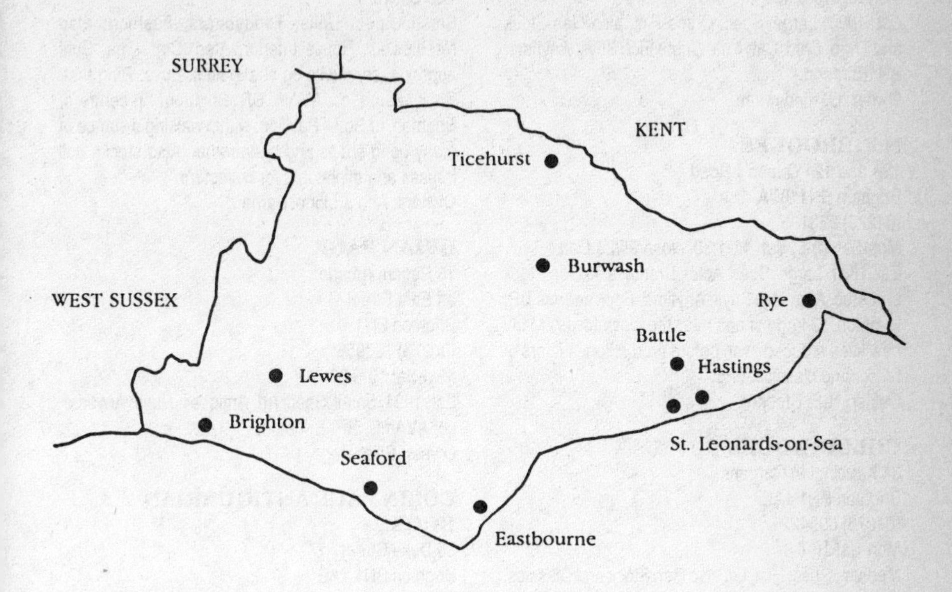

BATTLE

J.E.D. SAUNDERS AT BATTLE ANTIQUES

91A High Street
Battle TN33 0AQ
(01424) 773364
Mon-Sat 10-5
Est. 1989. Small. Gen Stock. Buys: Ring first. Book search. BR: Battle. "Close to Abbey Gateway. Stall in Antiques Centre. Prices 50p. - £25. Shop also includes postcard dealers."

BRIGHTON

THE BOOKMARK

91 Duke Road
Brighton BN1 3JE
(01273) 735577
Mon-Sat 10-6
Est. 1994. Small. Gen Stock and Art, Film, Contemporary Fict. Buys: Anytime. Book search. BR: Brighton. "Head for the Seven Dials - I am on the south side. Friendly. Very wide range of stock."
Owner: Sally May

BRIMSTONES
33 St. James Street
Brighton BN2 1RF
(01273) 571099
Mon-Sat 10-5:30
Est. 1990. Large. Spec: Crime Fict: also Gen Stock and Theo, Chld. Cat: 4 pa: Crime Fict. Buys: Anytime. BR: Brighton.
Owner: G. Kinderman

N.F. BROOKES
12A and 124 Queen's Road
Brighton BN1 3WA
(01273) 323105
Mon-Sat 10-5, Sun 11-1:30, close 25/26 Dec
Est. 1981. Large. Spec: Acad, Drama: also Gen Stock and Atec, Atqn, Art. Buys: Anytime. Book search. BR: Brighton. "2 large shops near the clock tower. Many new titles reduced even before production. 4 floors of books and classical LPs."
Owner: N.F. Brookes

COLLIE BOOKS
34 Kensington Gardens
Brighton BN1 4AL
(01273) 605422
Mon-Sat 10-6
Medium. Spec: Hist, Lit: also Gen Stock and Classics, Phil, Sci. Buys: Ring first. cc: AV. BR: Brighton.
Owner: Collie Books Ltd

HOLLEYMAN AND TREACHER LTD
21A-22 Duke Street
Brighton BN1 1AH
(01273) 328007
Tue-Sat 9-5
Est. 1939. Large. Gen Stock and Atqn. Buys: Anytime. cc: AVAm. BR: Brighton. "Also Sheet Music maps and prints."
Owners: M. Kadwell & D. Plumtree

KEMP TOWN BOOKS
91 St. George's Road
Brighton BN2 1EE
(01273) 682110
Mon-Sat 10-5:30
Est. 1973. Medium. Spec: Psy: also Gen Stock. Buys: Ring first. Book search. BR: Brighton. "New books, cards."
Owner: Mr. D. Goodwin

THE MULBERRY BUSH
Brighton BN2
(01273) 493781/600471
Fax (01273) 495138
Tue-Sat 10-5
Small. Spec: Dolls, Teddybears, Fashion: also Needlework, House Interior, Atec. Cat: 1 pa: Supl approx every 6 wks on above subj. Buys: Ring first. Book search. cc: AVAm. BR: Brighton. "In centre of Brighton, nr Royal Pavilion, within walking distance of many good shops and restaurants. Also stocks doll houses and miniatures for collectors."
Owners: Ann & Lionel Barnard

BRIAN PAGE
18 Regent Arcade
off East Street
Brighton BN1
(01273) 723956
Mon-Sat 10-5:30
Est. 1994. Small. Spec: Art, Antiques. Buys: Anytime. cc: AVAmD. BR: Brighton.
Owner: Brian Page

COLIN PAGE ANTIQUARIAN BOOKS
36 Duke Street
Brighton BN1 1AG
(01273) 325954
Mon-Sat 10-5:30
Est. 1969. Medium. Gen Stock and Atqn, Trav, Nat Hist. Buys: Anytime. cc: AVAmD. BR: Brighton. "Large selection of bindings, illus."
Owner: Colin Page

PUBLIC HOUSE BOOKSHOP
21 Little Preston Street
Brighton BN1 2QH
(01273) 328357
Mon-Sat 10-5:30
Medium. Spec: North American Indians: Cat: 1 pa: N.American Indians, Crit Theo. Buys: Ring first. cc: AV. BR: Brighton. "Best in contemporary fiction and theory. Only s'hand stock concerns North American Indians. This supports our new titles and books in print - the largest collection in Europe."
Owner: Richard Cupidi

TALL STOREYS BOOKSHOP
88 St. James's Street
Brighton BN2 1TP
(01273) 697381
Fax (01273) 692982
Mon-Sat 10-6, Sun 12-5 (Winter, Mon-Sat 10-5:30, Sun 1-4)
Large. Spec: 1sts: also Gen Stock and Theol, Art, Mysticism. Cat: occ: Hist, Pol, Mod 1sts. Buys: Ring first. Book search. cc: AVAm. BR: Brighton. "5 min east of the Steyne opp bottom of North Street. Large s'hand stock in all subject areas, plus pbk basement and rare book rooms."
Owner: J. Dodds

TALL STOREYS TOO
30 Kensington Gardens
Brighton BN1 4AL
(01273) 683748
Mon-Sat 10:30-5:30
Est. 1994. Small. Spec: Acad, Collectables. Buys: Ring first. cc: AV. BR: Brighton.
Owner: J. Dodds

THE TRAFALGAR BOOKSHOP
44 Trafalgar Street
Brighton BN1 4ED
(01273) 684300
Mon-Fri 10-6, Sat 10-5, Wed close
Est. 1979. Medium. Spec: Sport: also Gen Stock and Lit, Art. Buys: Ring first. Book search. BR: Brighton. "Situated 50 yds from BR."
Owner: David Boland

WAX FACTOR
24 Trafalgar Street
Brighton BN1 4EQ
(01273) 673744
Mon-Fri 10-5, Sat 9:30-5:30
Est. 1982. Medium. Gen Stock and Lit, Occult, Mus, Media. Buys: Anytime. BR: Brighton. "Competitive prices."
Owners: A. Berwick & M. Driver

BURWASH

ANTHONY WHITTAKER CHATEAUBRIAND ANTIQUES
Hight Street
Burwash TN19 7BN
(01435) 882535
Fax (01892) 723494
Mon-Sat 10-5, Sun 12-5
Small. Spec: Lit, Fine and Applied Art: also Gen Stock and Kent and Sussex Topog. Buys: Anytime. cc: AVAmD. BR: Etchingham. "Superb tea shop opp, open Sun pm. Also stocks maps, prints, and watercolors."
Owner: Anthony Whittaker

EASTBOURNE

CAMILLA'S BOOKSHOP
57 Grove Road
Eastbourne BN21 4TX
(01323) 736001
Mon-Sat 10-6
Est. 1975. Large. Spec: Avia: also Gen Stock and Mil, Fict, Needlework. Buys: Anytime. Book search. cc: AVAm. BR: Eastbourne. "3 min. from BR. Very large stock on 3 floors - a whole day's browsing. Also maps and postcards."
Owners: Camilla Francombe & S. Broad

A & T GIBBARD (was RAYMOND SMITH)
30 South Street
Eastbourne BN21 4XB
(01323) 734128 (tel/fax)
Mon-Sat 9:30-5:30
Est. 1993. Large. Spec: Travel, Nat Hist, Sussex Top: also Gen Stock and Transport, Lit. Buys: Anytime. BR: Eastbourne.
Partners: Alan and Tania Gibbard

HASTINGS

HOWES BOOKSHOP
Trinity Hall, Braybrooke Terrace
Hastings TN34 1HQ
(01424) 423437
Fax (01424) 460620
Mon-Fri 9:30-1, 2:15-5, Sat 9:30-1
Est. 1920. Large. Gen Stock and Lit, Biblio, Theol. Cat: 4 pa. Buys: Anytime. cc: AV. BR: Hastings. "Converted Victorian school building, customer's car park. Appointed agents to the Bibliographical Society."
Owners: R. Kilgarriff & M. Bartley

OLD HASTINGS BOOKSHOP
15 George Street
Hastings TN34 3EG
(01424) 425989
Mon-Sat 10-4, Wed close
Est. 1976. Small. Spec: Mil: also Gen Stock and Lit, Nat Hist, Gard. Buys: Ring first. BR: Hastings.
Owner: Brian Riches

THE PAPERBACK READER
82 Queens Road
Hastings TN34 1RL
(01424) 446749
Mon-Sat 9-5:30
Est. 1972. Medium. Gen Stock and Romance, SF, Classics. Buys: Ring first. BR: Hastings. "Large stock of Marvel and D.C. Comics. All types of pbks bought and sold and exchanged. A warm welcome assured."
Owner: Mr Read

JOHN WILBRAHAM
16 George Street
Old Town
Hastings TN34 3EG
(01424) 446413
Mon-Sat 10-1, 2-5, Wed close
Est. 1980. Small. Spec: Atqn: also Gen Stock and Illus, Mus. Cat: 4 pa. Buys: Ring first. BR: Hastings.
Owner: John Wilbraham

LEWES

BOW WINDOWS BOOKSHOP
128 High Street
Lewes BN7 1XL
(01273) 480780
Mon-Sat 9-5
Est. 1962. Medium. Gen Stock and Nat Hist, Lit, Geol. Cat: 5 pa. Buys: Ring first. cc: AV. BR: Lewes.
Owners: Allan & Jennifer Shelley

A.J. CUMMING
84 High Street
Lewes BN7 1XN
(01273) 472319
Fax (01273) 486364
Mon-Fri 10-5, Sat 10-5:30
Est. 1976. Large. Gen Stock and Trav, Topog, The Arts. Buys: Anytime. cc: AVAm. BR: Lewes. "Fast turnover (new stock added regularly), large reserve stock of leather bindings, sets, etc."
Owner: A.J. Cumming

DISJECTA BOOKS
Pipe Passage
151A High Street
Lewes BN7 1XU
(01273) 480744
Mon-Sat 10-4
Est. 1991. Small. Spec: Cookery, Po: also Gen Stock and Cycling, Art, Schools. Cat: 3 pa: Cookery, Gard. Buys: Anytime. BR: Lewes. "Opp. Bull House. Eclectic."
Owner: Peter Carter

FIFTEENTH CENTURY BOOKSHOP
99-100 High Street
Lewes BN7 1XH
(01273) 474160
Mon-Sat 10-5:30
Est. 1936. Large. Spec: Chld: also Gen Stock and Lit, Fr, Trav. Buys: Ring first. Book search. cc: AV. BR: Lewes. "C15th bldg. operating as b'shop for over 50 years. Fast moving stock. Also limited editions, etchings, prints."
Owner: S. Mirabaud

THE LEWES BOOK CENTRE
38 Cliffe High Street
Lewes BN7 2AN
(01273) 487053
Mon-Sat 10-5
Est. 1993. Medium. Gen Stock. Buys: Anytime. Book search. BR: Lewes. "Easy to browse. Connected with the Fifteenth Century Bookshop."
Owner: Susan Mirabaud

RYE

LANDGATE BOOKS
Hilder's Cliff
Rye
(01797) 222280
Mon-Sun 10-4:30 (Win, Wed-Sat 10-3:30)
Est. 1985. Medium. Gen Stock and Illus, Chld. Cat: 1 pa. Buys: Ring first. Book search. BR: Hastings/Rye. "Also Atqn, maps, and prints."
Owner: Graham Kirkham

THE MEADS BOOK SERVICE
5 Lion Street
Rye TN31 7LB
(01323) 734361
Mon-Sat 10:15-5:30, Sun 11:15-5:30
Est. 1988. Small. Spec: EF Benson, Doctor Syn Titles: also Gen Stock and Rye and Loc -Topog-Sussex, Kent & Smuggling. Cat: 1 pa: EF Benson, etc. Buys: Ring first. Book search. BR: Rye. "Bookshop near Rye Parish Church. Small. Good s'hand selection of books in period listed premises."
Owner: Clive Ogden

RYE OLD BOOKSHOP
7 Lion Street
Rye TN31 7LB
(01797) 225410
Mon-Sat 10:30-5:30, Thur close, Sun 2-5
Est. 1993. Medium. Spec: Irish Lit: also Gen Stock and Nat Hist, Topog, Po. Buys: Ring first. cc: AVE. BR: Rye. "Within Rye citadel a few hundred yards from St. Mary's Church. Jan-Feb shop will only be open Fri-Mon inclusive only."
Owner: Ms Aoife Coleman

SEAFORD

BARN COLLECTORS MARKET AND STUDIO BOOKSHOP
Church Lane
Seaford BN25 1HL
(01323) 890010
Tue, Thur, Sat 10-5
Est. 1968. Large. Gen Stock. Buys: Anytime. BR: Seaford. "Shop is just off Seaford High St. Also stocks collector's items, postcards, cigarette cards, and all categories of ephemera."
Owner: Miss L. Price

ST. LEONARDS-ON-SEA

BOOK JUNGLE
24 North Street (off London Road)
St. Leonards-on-Sea TN38 0EX
(01424) 421187
Mon-Sat 10-5, Wed close
Medium. Gen Stock. Buys: Ring first. BR: St. Leonards/Warrior Sq.
Owner: Michael Gowen

HELGATO ANTIQUES
121 Bohemia Road
St. Leonards-on-Sea TN37 6RL
(01424) 423049
Mon-Sat 2-5 (ring first or by appt)
Small. Spec: Illus, Graphic Art: also Atec. Buys: Ring first. BR: St. Leonards/Hastings. "Situated on the A21. Also stocks Atqn prints, maps, porcelain, glass, and objets d'art."
Owners: R.J. & H. Nicholls

SPRINGFIELD BOOKSHOP
269 London Road
St. Leonards-on-Sea TN38 0TR
(01424) 718848
Fax (01797) 252960
Thur-Fri 10-5:30, Sat 10-12:30 (or by appt)
Medium. Gen Stock and Penguins, Sports, C20th History. Buys: Anytime. BR: St. Leonards/Warrior Sq. "About 1/2 mile from BR on main road opp Buchanan Hospital. Reasonably close parking. Gen. Stock inexpensive but some good 1sts and old books. About 10-12,000 books available."
Owner: Stephen Cockhill

West Sussex

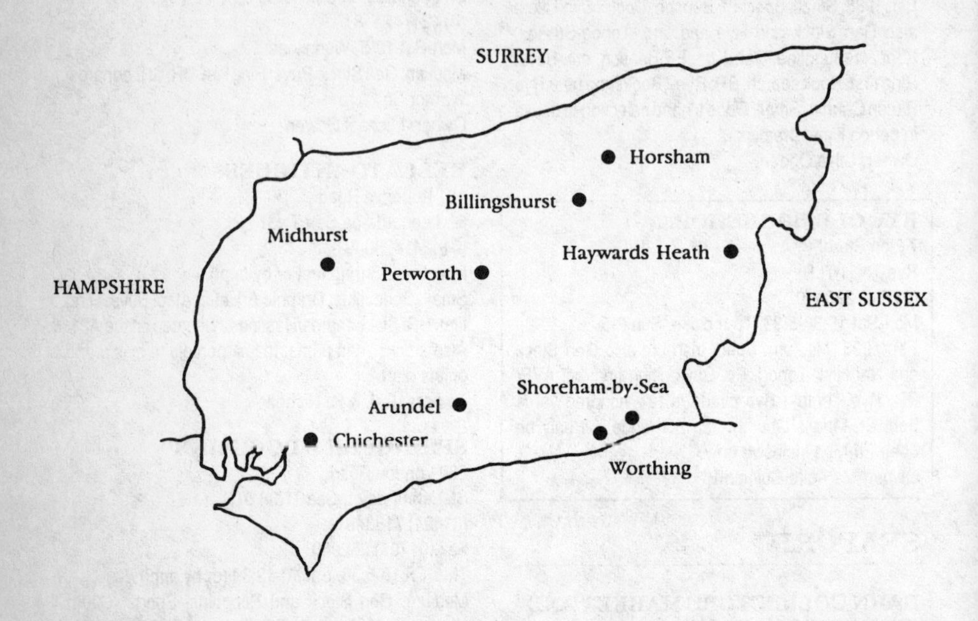

ARUNDEL

ARUNDEL BOOKSHOP

10 High Street
Arundel BN18 9AB
(01903) 882620
Mon-Sat 9:30-1, 2:15-5:30; Sun 11:45-1, 2:15-5:30 (Summer)
Est. 1978. Large. Gen Stock. Buys: Ring first. BR: Arundel.
Owners: G. & A. Shephard

BILLINGHURST

BOOKS AND THINGS

58 High Street
Billinghurst RH14 9NY
(01403) 785131
Mon-Sat 9:30-5
Est. 1976. Small. Gen Stock. Buys: Anytime. Book search. cc: AVAmD. BR: Billinghurst.
Manageress: Jill Dennis

CHICHESTER

JOHN DENT'S BOOKSHOP

39 Southgate
Chichester PO19 1DP
(01243) 785473
Mon-Sat 9-5:30
Est. 1966. Medium. Gen Stock. Buys: Ring first. BR: Chichester. "Near BR and bus station. Large car park nearby. Constantly changing stock, also sheet music, postcards, and ephemera."
Owner: John Dent

PETER HANCOCK

40 West Street
Chichester PO19 1KP
(01243) 786173
Mon-Sat 10:30-1, 2:30-5:30
Est. 1960. Small. Spec: Non-Fict, 1sts: also Travel. Buys: Ring first. cc: AVAm. BR: Chichester. "Small but good selection. Various dealers and collectors must apply for entry to the inner sanctum."
Owner: Peter Hancock

ST. PETER'S BOOKSHOP

St. Peter's Arcade, West Street
Chichester PO19 1QI
(01243) 778477
Mon-Sun 10-5 (Winter, Tue-Sat, 10:30-5:30)
Est. 1986. Small. Spec: Phil: also Gen Stock and Mysticism. BR: Chichester. "Good condition, interesting stock."
Owners: Phil & Wendy Pegler

HAYWARDS HEATH

THE HALCYON BOOKSHOP

11 The Broadway
Haywards Heath RH16 3AQ
(01444) 412785
Mon-Sat 9:30-5:30, Wed 9:30-1
Est. 1987. Small. Gen Stock. Buys: Ring first. Book search. BR: Hay. "Independent new b'shop with varied stock and a s'hand section upstairs - several out of print titles. Many subjects, many bargains."
Owners: Mrs Farley & Miss Kennedy

HORSHAM

THE HORSHAM BOOKSHOP

4 Park Street
Horsham RH12 1DG
(01403) 252187
Tue-Sat 9:30-5:15
Medium. Spec: Cricket, Avia: also Gen Stock and Mil, Chld, Local. Buys: Ring first. Book search. BR: Horsham.
Owners: Christine & Tom Costin

MERLIN BOOKS

P.O. Box 153
Horsham RH12 2JG
(01403) 257626 (tel/fax)
Mon-Sat 9-6
Est. 1990. Small. Spec: Motorcycling: Cat: 12 pa: Revised Motoring. Buys: Ring first. Book search. cc: AVEJ. BR: Horsham. "Motorcycle books specialist, both new and secondhand/out of print."
Owner: Mike Husband

MURRAY & KENNETT

102 Bishopric
Horsham RH12 1QN
(01403) 254847
Mon-Sat 9-1:30, 2:15-5:15 ec Thur
Est. 1980. Medium. Spec: Mus, Lit: also Gen Stock and Theol, Fict. Buys: Anytime. cc: AV. BR: Horsham. "Situated out of main shopping area on A281 going west out of Horsham. Also LPs, cassettes, and CDs."
Owner: J.C.W. Murray

MIDHURST

BROWSE AWHILE

Mint Market
Grange Road
Midhurst GU29 9LT
(01730) 815425
Tue-Fri 11-4, Sat 9:30-5, Wed close
Est. 1980. Small. Spec: Topog: also Gen Stock and Lit, Sport. Buys: Ring first. BR: Haslemere. "Next to free car park. Also sells maps, postcards, cigarette cards."
Owner: Mrs. D. Taylor

THE CAMEO BOOKSHOP
2 Knockhundred Market
Midhurst GU29 9DQ
(01730) 815221
Mon-Sat 9:15-5
Est. 1991. Medium. Gen Stock. Buys: Anytime. Book search. BR: Petersfield. "Midhurst has free car park. Coffee shop upstairs."
Owners: M. & K. Tanner

PETWORTH

BOOKROOM
Petworth Antique Market, East Street
Petworth GU28 0AB
(01798) 342073
Mon-Sat 10-5:30
Est. 1968. Small. Spec: Atqn: also Gen Stock. Buys: Anytime. cc: AVAm. BR: Pulborough.
Owner: Doris Rayment

PETWORTH BOOKSHOP
Middle Street
Petworth GU28 0BE
(01798) 343314
Fax (01798) 867618
Mon-Sat 10-5 (Sun 11-4, Easter to Sept)
Est. 1995. Medium. Spec: Russia, China: also Gen Stock and Central Asia, Fine Fict, Sussex. Cat: 2 pa: varies. Buys: Anytime. Book search. BR: Pulborough. "A283/A272/A285 for Petworth. B'shop is on way to public library/Cottage Museum. Free parking in centre of town."
Owner: Andrew Railing

SHOREHAM-BY-SEA

BOOKWORMS OF SHOREHAM
14A High Street
Shoreham-by-Sea BN43 5DA
(01273) 465665
Tue-Sat 10-5, Wed 10-1
Est. 1992. Small. Gen Stock. Buys: Anytime. BR: Shoreham-by-Sea.
Owner: Mrs P. Liddell

WORTHING

BADGERS BOOKS
8-10 Gratwicke Road
Worthing BN11 4BH
(01903) 211816
Mon-Sat 9-6
Est. 1982. Medium. Gen Stock and Trans, Avia, Occult. Buys: Anytime. Book search. cc: AVAmD. BR: Worthing Central. "Easy parking."
Owner: Ray Potter

KIM'S BOOKSHOP
19 Crescent Road
Worthing BN11 1RL
(01903) 206282
Mon-Sat 9:30-5:30
Est. 1971. Large. Gen Stock and Sheet Music. Buys: Anytime. Book search. BR: Worthing Central. "Very large interesting stock. Always keen to purchase all types of books and music. Good range on all subjects."
Owners: Mrs Francombe & Mrs Flowers

THE STEYNE BOOKSHOP
5 High Street
Worthing BN11 1NY
(01903) 206216
Mon-Sat 9:15-5:30
Est. 1981. Medium. Spec: Motoring: also Gen Stock and Tran, Mil. Buys: Anytime. Book search. cc: A. BR: Worthing Central. "Go east from clock on roundabout in town center."
Owner: Mrs Jenny Bennett

TYNE AND WEAR

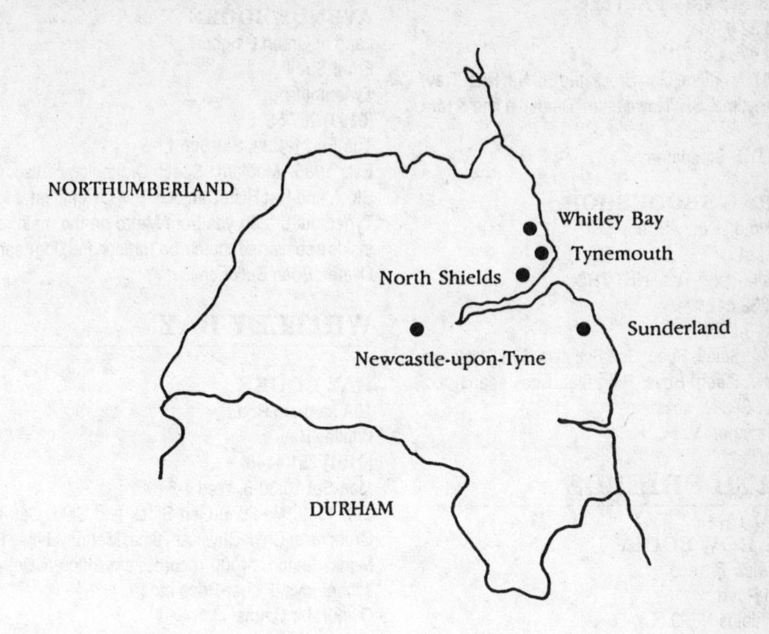

NEWCASTLE-UPON-TYNE

BOOKWORMS PARADISE

Greenmarket
Eldon Square
Newcastle-upon-Tyne NE1 7YA
(0191) 232 3196
Mon-Sat 10-5:30
Small. Spec: Romance: "We only sell pbks, mainly Mills & Boon, modern popular Fict, Non-Fict, magazines & children's annuals."
Owner: Peter Cleyland

NEWCASTLE BOOKSHOP

9 Side
Newcastle-upon-Tyne NE1 3JE
(0191) 261 5380
Mon-Sat 10-5, Sun 11-3
Est. 1975. Medium. Spec: Art, Des: also Lit. BR: Newcastle. "Not city centre, so parking reasonable. Also large selection of prints."
Owner: Valerie Levitt

W. ROBINSON (NEWCASTLE) LTD

49-53 Grainger Market
Newcastle-upon-Tyne NE1 5QQ
(0191) 232 2978
Mon-Sat 9:30-5
Est. 1881. Medium. Gen Stock. Buys: Anytime. BR: Newcastle. "Also 1/2 price remainders."
Owner: Mr W. Cornish

FRANK SMITH MARITIME AVIATION BOOKS

98/100 Heaton Road
Newcastle-upon-Tyne NE6 5HL
(0191) 265 6333
Fax (0191) 224 2620
Mon-Fri 10-4, Sat 10-1 (or by appt)
Est. 1981. Large. Spec: Maritime, Naval: also Avia, Motoring, Mil. Cat: 12 pa: Maritime; 12 pa: Avia; Motoring stocklist (as req). Buys: Ring first. cc: AVAmEJS. Metro: Byker. "On the east side of Newcastle, off the A1058."
Owner: Frank Smith

ROBERT D. STEEDMAN
9 Grey Street
Newcastle-upon-Tyne NE1 6EE
(0191) 232 6561
Mon-Fri 9-5, Sat 9-12:30
Est. 1907. Medium. Gen Stock and Lit, Nat Hist, Trav. Buys: Anytime. BR: Newcastle. "Dealer in fine & rare books."
Owner: D.J. Steedman

THORNE'S BOOKSHOP
Grand Hotel, Percy Street
Haymarket
Newcastle-upon-Tyne NE1 7RS
(0191) 232 6421
Mon-Sat 9-5:30
Est. 1944. Small. Spec: Soc Sci: also Gen Stock and Hist, Law, Geog. Buys: Ring first. Book search. cc: AVAmD. BR: Newcastle.
Gen. Manager: Mrs C. Kelly

NORTH SHIELDS

KEEL ROW BOOKS
11 Fenwick Terrace
Preston Road
North Shields NE29 0LY
(0191) 296 0664
Mon-Fri 10:30-5, Sat 10-5, Wed close
Est. 1980. Large. Gen Stock. Buys: Ring first. BR: North Shields.
Owners: Robert & Brenda Cook

SUNDERLAND

DURHAM BOOK CENTRE
Vine Place
Sunderland
(0191) 567 4389
Mon-Sat 10-5, Wed close
Est. 1968. Medium. Gen Stock. cc: AV. BR: Sunderland. "Atqn books kept at Alston, Cumbria - open at weekend or by appt.; tel. (01434) 381066."
Owner: Mrs A. Dumble

TYNEMOUTH

AVENUE BOOKS
Land of Green Ginger
Front Street
Tynemouth
(0191) 257 5836
Tue-Fri 11-4:30, Sat-Sun 11-5
Est. 1985. Medium. Spec: Ornithology: also Gen Stock and Nat Hist. Cat: occ. Buys: Ring first. Metro: Tynemouth. "200 yds from Metro on the main road. Inside a converted church, on 1st floor. Parking nearby."
Owner: Brian Bullough

WHITLEY BAY

BAY BOOKS
10A Morham Road
Whitley Bay
(0191) 251 4448
Mon-Sat 10:30-5, Wed 1-5
Est. 1989. Medium. Gen Stock and Chld. Cat: Mail Order lists: Chld. Buys: Anytime. Metro: Whitley Bay/ Monk Seaton. "4000 records, cassettes, CDs, pre-school toys (Fisher-Price etc.)"
Owner: Mr Cairns

OLIVERS BOOKSHOP
48A Whitley Road
Whitley Bay NE26 2NF
(0191) 251 3552
Mon-Sat 11-5, Wed close, occ Tue close
Est. 1987. Medium. Gen Stock and Art, Nat Hist, Illus. Buys: Ring first. Book search. Metro: Whitley Bay. "Parking no problem. A bit of everything stocked. Pbks, printed collectables."
Owner: John Oliver

WARWICKSHIRE

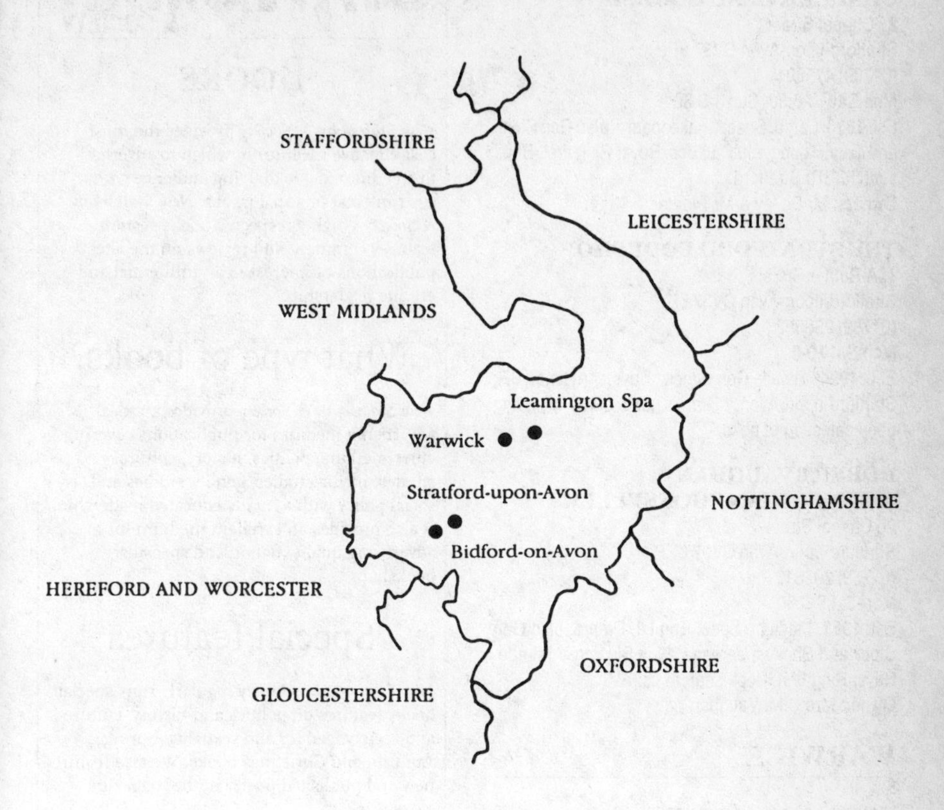

BIDFORD-ON-AVON nr. Alcester

JULIA'S SECONDHAND BOOKS

39 High Street
Bidford-on-Avon nr. Alcester BS0 ABQ
(01789) 772108 (tel/fax)
Tue-Sat 9:30-1, 2:30-5:15
Est. 1994. Medium. Gen Stock. Buys: Ring first. BR: Stratford/Evesham/Honeybourne. "Gen s'hand stock including a selection of pbks."
Owner: Julia Montanjees

LEAMINGTON SPA

PORTLAND BOOKS

5 Spencer Street
Leamington Spa CV31 3NE
(01926) 338793
Mon-Sat 10-5:30
Est. 1974. Medium. Spec: Eng Lit, Lit Crit: also Gen Stock and Art, Acad, Hist. Buys: Anytime. BR: Leamington Spa. "Close to BR and town library."
Owner: Jan Weddup

STRATFORD-UPON-AVON

CHAUCER HEAD BOOKSHOP

21 Chapel Street
Stratford-upon-Avon CV37 6EP
(01789) 415691
Mon-Sat 10-5:30, Sun 1-5:30
Est. 1830. Large. Spec: Shakespeare: also Gen Stock and Trav, Topog, Lit. Cat: occ. Buys: Ring first. Book search. BR: Stratford.
Owners: Mr Bailey & Mr Pierce

THE STRATFORD BOOKSHOP

45A Rother Street
Stratford-upon-Avon CV37 6LY
(01789) 298362
Mon-Sat 10-6
Est. 1994. Small. Gen Stock. Buys: Anytime. BR: Startford-upon-Avon. "Gen. s'hand stock including good selection of pbks."

ROBERT VAUGHAN ANTIQUARIAN BOOKSELLERS

20 Chapel Street
Stratford-upon-Avon CV37 6EP
(01789) 205312
Mon-Sat 9-5:30
Est. 1953. Medium. Spec: Eng Lit, Drama: also Gen Stock and Shakespeareana, Fine Bindings, 1st edn. Buys: Ring first. Book search. cc: AV.
Owner: Mrs C.M. Vaughan

WARWICK

DUNCAN M. ALLSOP

26 Smith Street
Warwick CV34 4HS
(01926) 493266
Mon-Sat 9:30-5:30
Est. 1966. Large. Spec: Local: also Gen Stock. Cat: 2 pa: Gen. Buys: Ring first. BR: Warwick. "Situated in centre of busy tourist town. Conveniently placed for access to motorways."
Owner: D.M. Allsop

WEST MIDLANDS

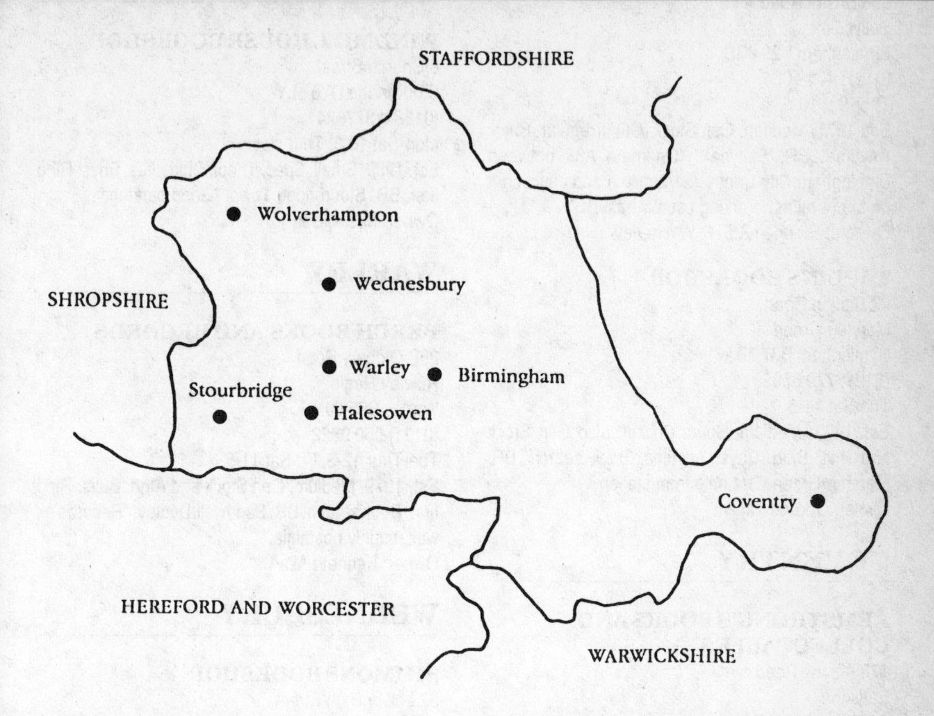

BIRMINGHAM

ANDROMEDA BOOKSHOP

84 Suffolk St
Birmingham B1 1TA
(0121) 643 1999
Mon-Sat 9:30-5:30
Est. 1971. Medium. Spec: SF: also Fantasy, Horror. Cat: 4 pa. Buys: Ring first. cc: AVAmD. BR: Birmingham. "World's oldest SF bookshop. SF magazines available."
Owner: Mr Peyton

BIRMINGHAM BOOKSHOP

567 Bristol Road
Birmingham B29 6AF
(0121) 472 8556
Varied
Est. 1976. Large. Gen Stock. Buys: Anytime. Book search. BR: Selly Oak. "On A38."
Owner: I.K. Watson

READER'S WORLD

11 St. Martin's House Parade
Bullring (opp. church)
Birmingham B5 5DL
(0121) 643 8664
Tue-Sat 10-6
Est. 1969. Medium. Gen Stock and Comics, Pbks, SF. Buys: Anytime. Book search. BR: Moor Street. "Also sells magazines and video. Always wanted - SF, Horror, Crime, Penguin Pbks, US Comics - cash paid. Also at stall No.6, Rag Market, Edgbaston Street."
Owners: R. Teague & G. Eastwood

READER'S WORLD

16 Hurst Street
Queensway
Birmingham B5
(0121) 643 7151
Mon-Sat 10-5:30, Thur 10-7
Est. 1994. Small. Gen Stock. Buys: Anytime. BR: Birmingham/Moor St. "Large stock of magazines."
Owners: R. Teague & G. Eastwood

STEPHEN WYCHERLEY
508 Bristol Road
Sellyoak
Birmingham B29 6BD
(0121) 471 1006
Thur-Sat 10-5
Est. 1971. Medium. Gen Stock. Cat: Irregular. Buys: Anytime. BR: Sellyoak. "On main A38 between Birmingham City Centre (21/2 miles) and Junction 4 on M5 (4 miles). Parking usually easy."
Owners: Stephen & E.A. Wycherley

TAPLINS BOOKSHOP
62 Station Road
Marston Green
Birmingham B37 7BA
(0121) 779 6505
Tue-Sat 11-5
Est. 1990. Medium. Spec: Cricket: also Gen Stock and Hist, Biog. Buys: Anytime. Book search. BR: Marston Green. "1/4 mile from station."
Owner: George Taplin

COVENTRY

ARMSTRONG'S BOOKS AND COLLECTABLES
178 Albany Road
Earlsdon
Coventry CV5 6NG
(01203) 714344
Est. 1983. Medium. Spec: Annuals, SF: also Gen Stock and Penguins, 1st, Comics. Buys: Ring first. BR: Coventry. "Easy parking, buses 15 min from city centre. Good area for antiques and good pubs."
Owner: Colin R. Armstrong

HALESOWEN

CLENT BOOKS
52 Summer Hill
Halesowen
(0121) 550 0309
Mon-Sat 10-4
Est. 1977. Small. Spec: Topog, Hist, Countryside. Buys: Ring first. BR: Birmingham. "Waverley Fairs organiser."
Owner: Ivor Simpson

STOURBRIDGE

WINDMILL HOUSE BOOKSHOP
8 Church Street
Stourbridge DY8 1LY
(01384) 377824
Mon-Sat 10-5, Thur close
Est. 1982. Small. Spec: Theol, Chld, Illus. Buys: Ring first. BR: Stourbridge Town. "Good parking."
Owner: Mrs Allison

WARLEY

BEECH BOOKS AND RECORDS
28B Oldbury Road
Rowley Regis
Warley B65 0JN
(0121) 559 9822
Tue-Thur 12-5, Fri-Sat 11-5
Est. 1979. Medium. Gen Stock and Atqn. Buys: Ring first. Book search. BR: Sandwell/Dudley. "Records as well, mainly nostalgia."
Owner: Kenneth Allen

WEDNESBURY

SIMMONS BOOKSHOP
37 Lower High Street
Wednesbury WS10 7AQ
(0121) 502 4622
Mon-Sat 9-5, Thur 10:30-2
Est. 1989. Medium. Spec: Black Country Topog: also Gen Stock. Buys: Ring first. Book search. cc:AVAmEJ. BR: Bescot Walsall. "Wednesbury has a wide selection of mainly privately owned shops. Famed for its connection with John Wesley. Well worth a visit. Ample free parking."
Owners: R. and J. Simmons

WOLVERHAMPTON

BERRY STREET BOOKSHOP
35 Berry Street
Wolverhampton WV3 7HA
(01902) 28939
Mon-Sat 9:15-5:15
Medium. Spec: Railways, Occult, Erotica: also Gen Stock and SF, Mil, Film. Buys: Anytime. BR: Wolverhampton. "Within 300 yards of BR and bus stations, rear of Grand Theatre."
Owner: Mr G. Lambert

BOOKSTACK
53 Bath Road
Wolverhampton WV1 4EL
(01902) 21055 (tel/fax)
Mon-11-3, Tue-Sat 10-5
Est. 1979. Large. Spec: Mod 1sts, Bookbinding: also Gen Stock and Acad, Lit, Hist. Cat: 2-3 pa: Mod 1sts. Buys: Ring first. Book search. BR: Wolverhampton. "Easy parking in Park Road east and west. Corner house at junction of Bath Road and Southgate, nr swimming baths, just off Ring Road."
Owner: Elizabeth Anderton

WILTSHIRE

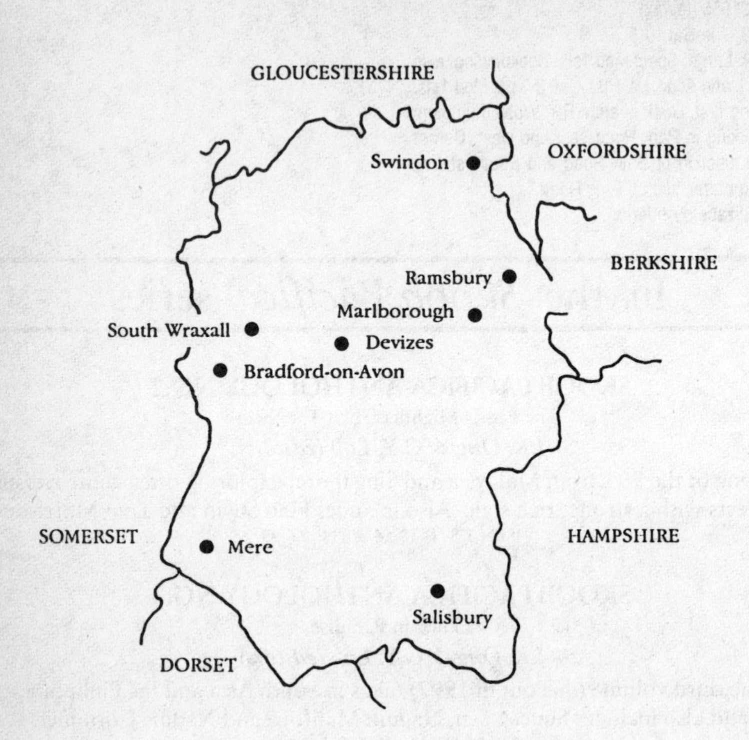

BRADFORD-ON-AVON

THE CANAL BOOKSHOP

Avoncliff
Bradford-on-Avon BA15 2HB
(01225) 723812
Mon-Sun 11-4 (Oct-Easter, fine weekends only)
Est. 1985. Small. Spec: Canals: also Rolt (LTC). Cat: 2 pa: Inland waterways, Fict, Non-Fict. Buys: Ring first. Book search. cc: AV. BR: Bradford-on-Avon. "Located by Avoncliff aquaduct on Kennett & Avon Canal. Access from Upper West Wood or from Bradford on Turleigh Road. Easy parking. Pleasant townpath walk, pub and cafe."
Owners: M. & R.B. Porter

EX-LIBRIS

1 The Shambles
Bradford-on-Avon BA15 1JS
(01225) 863595/866495 (home)
Fax (01225) 863595
Mon-Sat 9-5:30
Est. 1980. Buys: Ring first. cc: AVAm. BR: Bradford-on-Avon. "New books in shop. S'hand stock in old book barn publisher (Ex-Libris Press)."
Owner: Roger Jones

DEVIZES

D'ARCY BOOKS
The Chequers
High Street
Devizes SN10 1AT
(01380) 726922/850319
Fax (01380) 850319
Mon-Sat 10-5:30
Est. 1977. Medium. Gen Stock and Loc Topog. Buys: Ring first. Book search. BR: Trowbridge. "Also bookbinding and repairs service."
Owners: C. & J. MacGregor

MARLBOROUGH

ANTIQUE AND BOOK COLLECTOR
Katherine House, The Parade
Marlborough SN8 1NE
(01635) 200507
Mon-Sat 10-5 (close 1-2:15)
Est. 1987. Medium. Spec: Railways (5,000 titles): also Gen Stock and Railway, Ephemera, Photos (15,000), Mags. Buys: Ring first. Book search. BR: Swindon. "8 miles south of Swindon Junction 15 of M4. Railway Room in large general bookshop. Ephemera."
Owner: N. Bridger

THE ANTIQUE AND BOOK COLLECTOR
Katharine House
Marlborough SN8 1NE
(01672) 514040
Mon-Sat 10-1, 2:15-5
Est. 1983. Medium. Gen Stock and Trav, Art, Illus. Buys: Ring first. Book search. cc: AVAm. BR: Swindon. "8 miles south of Swindon, Junc 15 of M4. Good selec of modern British engravings and drawings as well as antiques."
Owner: Christopher Gange

MILITARY PARADE BOOKSHOP
The Parade
Marlborough SN8 1NE
(01672) 515470
Mon-Sat 10-1, 2:15-5
Est. 1988. Small. Spec: Mil Hist: Cat: 4 pa: Mil Hist. Buys: Anytime. Book search. cc: A. BR: Swindon. "Shop is off High Street, below town hall and between Lamb and Crown Inns. If shop is closed, chances are we're in the Lamb, hunched over the DT Crossword."
Owners: P. & G. Kent

PRINCIPIA
5 London Road
Marlborough SN8 1PH
(01672) 512072
Mon-Sat 9:30-5:30
Est. 1985. Small. Spec: Sci: also Gen Stock and Atqn. Buys: Anytime. cc: AVAmD. BR: Swindon.
Owners: Mr Forrer & N. Acheson

ANTHONY SPRANGER
6 Kingsbury Street
Marlborough SN8 1HU
(01672) 514105
Wed-Sat 10-6
Est. 1994. Medium. Gen Stock and Perf Arts, Mount, Sheet Music. Buys: Anytime. Book search. BR: Swindon or Bedwyn. "PBFA."
Owner: Anthony Spranger

MERE

BLUE RIDER BOOKSHOP
Salisbury Street
Mere BA12 6HE
(01747) 860593
Mon-Sat 9:30-1, 2:30-5, Tue-Wed close
Est. 1976. Medium. Spec: Mod 1sts, Chld: also Gen Stock and Illus, Trav, Topog. Buys: Anytime. BR: Gillingham. "Just off A303. Very attractive."
Owner: Christopher Richards

RAMSBURY

HERALDRY TODAY
Parliament Piece
Ramsbury SN8 2QH
(01672) 520617
Fax (01672) 520183
Mon-Fri 9:30-4:30
Est. 1954. Large. Spec: Heraldry Peerage: also Hist, Genealogy. Cat: 3 pa. Buys: Ring first. Book search. cc: AV. BR: Swindon. "Publishers of books on Heraldry and Genealogy."
Owner: Mrs Rosemary Pinches

SALISBURY

BADGER BOOKS
37 Catherine Street
Salisbury SP1 2DN
(01722) 338487
Mon-Sat 9:30-5
Est. 1987. Small. Spec: Atqn, S'hand: also Gen Stock. Buys: Anytime. Book search. cc: AVAmDS. BR: Salisbury. "Brown St. car park - town centre."
Owner: Peter Bletsoe

D.M. BEACH
52 High Street
Salisbury SP1 2PG
(01722) 333801
Fax (01722) 333720
Mon-Sat 9-5:30
Est. 1931. Large. Gen Stock and Atqn. Buys: Ring first. Book search. cc: AVAm. BR: Salisbury. "Probably the oldest building in the world to house an Atqn bookshop. Also stocks maps and prints."
Owner: Anthony Beach

JOHN AND JUDITH HEAD
The Barn Book Supply
88 Crane Street
Salisbury SP1 2QD
(01722) 327767
Fax (01722) 339888
Mon-Fri 9:30-5
Medium. Spec: Angling, Field Sports: Cat: 4 pa. Buys: Anytime. Book search. cc: AVAmD. Salisbury. "Shop is in town centre, 50 yards from cross roads of High Street and Crane Street, 10 min walk from BR."
Owners: J. & J. Head

SOUTH WRAXALL

VIRGO BOOKS
Little Court
South Wraxall BA15 2SE
(01225) 862040
Fax (0181) 560 2751
Mon-Fri 10-5
Small. Spec: Mod 1sts: also Autobiog, Bloomsbury, US Expat Authors in Paris. Cat: 4 pa: Mod 1sts. Buys: Ring first. Book search. BR: Bath. "We are about 7 miles from Bath or Chippenham, 4 miles south of Corsham. House is immediately behind church."
Owners: A.B., V. & J. Mason

SWINDON

VICTORIA BOOKSHOP
30 Wood Street
Old Town
Swindon SN1 4AB
(01793) 527364
Mon-Sat 9-5:30
Large. Gen Stock and Mil, Myst, Occult, Alt Rel. BR: Swindon. "Large stock of new books and maps, old postcards."
Owner: Mr S. Austin

East Yorkshire

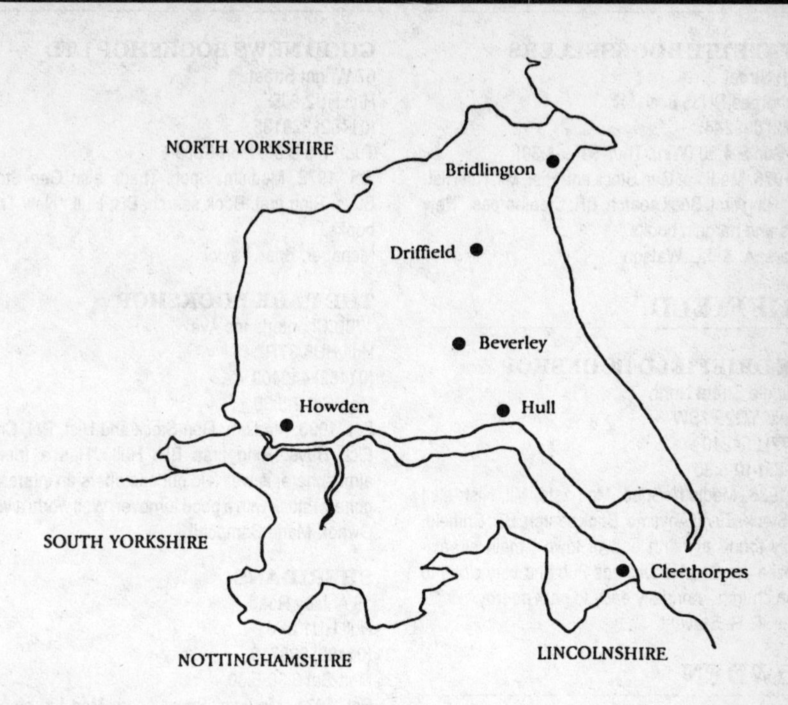

BEVERLEY

EASTGATE BOOKSHOP

11 Eastgate
Beverley HU17 0DR
(01482) 868579
Mon-Sat 10-5
Est. 1983. Medium. Spec: SE Asia, Yorkshire: also Gen Stock and Loc Hist, Mil, Fict. Cat: 2 pa: SE Asia. Buys: Ring first. Book search. BR: Beverley. "Free parking good in Beverley. Eastgate runs north from Beverley Minster, near BR and Mil Museum. Incorp. Sarawak books."
Owner: Barry Roper

BRIDLINGTON

J.L. BOOK EXCHANGE

72 Hilderthorpe Road
Bridlington YO15 2BQ
(01262) 601285
Mon-Sun 8:30-6:30 (Win., Mon-Sat 9:30-5:30)
Est. 1971. Medium. Gen Stock. Buys: Ring first. BR: Bridlington.
Owner: John Ledraw

CLEETHORPES

LAFAYETTE BOOKSELLERS
6 High Street
Cleethorpes DN35 8JN
(01472) 699244
Thur-Sun 9-4:30 (Win., Thur-Sat 9-4:30)
Est. 1976. Medium. Gen Stock and Hist, Mil, Nat Hist. Buys: Ring first. Book search. BR: Cleethorpes. "New books and bargain books."
Owners: A. & J.L. Watson

DRIFFIELD

THE DRIFFIELD BOOKSHOP
21 Middle Street North
Driffield YO25 7SW
(01377) 254210
Mon-Sat 10-5:30
Est. 1986. Medium. Spec: Mod 1sts, Mil, Hist: also Gen Stock. Buys: Anytime. Book search. BR: Driffield. "Easily found at north end of town's main street - opposite the Charles Dickens Pub and very close to parish church - normally easy to park nearby."
Owner: G.R. Stevens

HOWDEN

HOWDEN BOOKSHOP
5B Vicar Lane
Howden DN14 7BP
(01430) 432071 (tel/fax)
Mon-Sat 9-5
Est. 1989. Medium. Spec: SF: also Gen Stock and Mod 1sts. Buys: Ring first. BR: Howden/Goole.
Owners: E.J. & M.S. Kemp

HULL

GOOD NEWS BOOKSHOP LTD
67 Wright Street
Hull HU2 8JD
(01482) 328135
Tue-Fri 9-5:30, Mon-Sat 9-5
Est. 1972. Medium. Spec: Theol: also Gen Stock. Buys: Ring first. Book search. BR: Hull. "New Theol books."
Manager: Brian Taylor

THE PARK BOOKSHOP
178B Chanterlands Ave
Hull HU5 3TR
(01482) 442409
Mon-Sat 9-5:30
Est. 1993. Medium. Gen Stock and Hist, Pol, Crime Fict. Buys: Ring first. BR: Hull. "Has a friendly atmosphere, is well laid out and offers an interesting general stock with a good turnover. Well worth a visit."
Owner: Marie Campbell

SHERIDANS
19 Anlaby Road
Hull HU1 2PJ
(01482) 328759
Mon-Sat 9:30-5:30
Est. 1971. Medium. Spec: Acad, Mod Lit: also Lit. Buys: Anytime. BR: Hull. "2 min from main bus station and BR. Hull's largest s'hand b'shop. Also s'hand LPs, CDs, tapes - classical, folk, blues and general."
Owner: Richard Duffy

NORTH YORKSHIRE

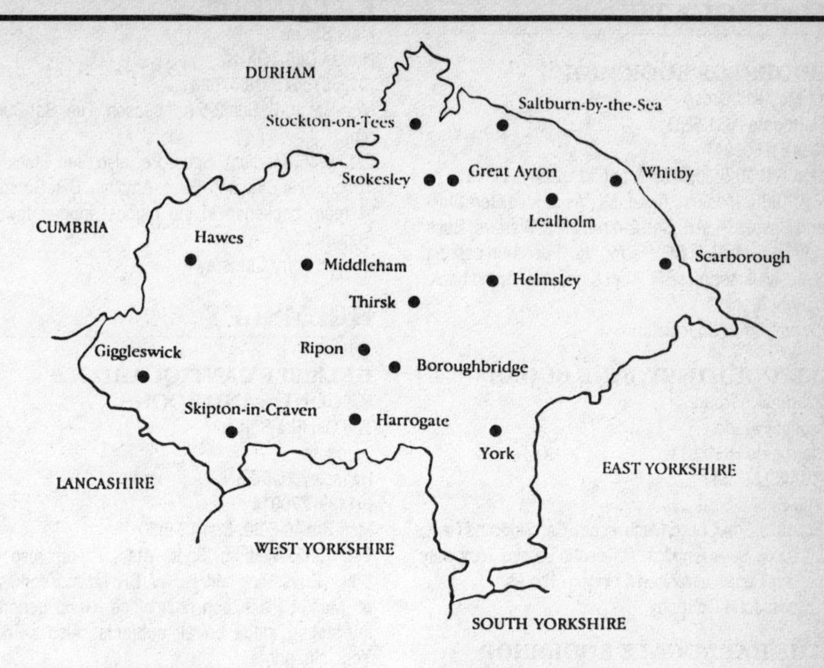

BOROUGHBRIDGE

BATES & HINDMARCH (Also PEPPIATT, GARBUTT & WALKINGAME at BATES & HINDMARCH)

Bridge Street
Boroughbridge YO5 9LA
(01423) 324258 (tel/fax)
Mon-Sat 10:30-5, Thur close
Small. Spec: Asia/India Trav: also Atqn. Cat: 5-6 pa: Trav. Buys: Ring first. cc: AVAm. BR: Thirsk/ Knaresborough. "Spec bookshop with emphasis on Trav & Exploration in India & Central Asia. Also Peppiatt, Garbutt & Walkingame."
Owners: J. Bates & Prof I. Hindmarch

GIGGLESWICK

POST HORN BOOKS

Giggleswick BD24 0BA
(01729) 823438
Wed-Sat 10:30-2, 2-6
Est. 1976. Medium. Spec: Mount: also Gen Stock and Nat Hist, Yorks. BR: Settle. "Parking outside shop. Big selection of O/S maps, also prints. PBFA."
Owner: Mrs B.H. Panton

GREAT AYTON

THE GREAT AYTON BOOKSHOP

47 & 53 High Street
Great Ayton TS9 6NH
(01642) 723358
Tue, Thur, Fri, Sat 10-5:30, Wed 10-2, Sun 2-5:30
Est. 1979. Medium. Spec: Sculpture (by appt): also Gen Stock. Buys: Ring first. Book search. BR: Middlesbrough. "7 miles south of Middlesbrough on the Stokesley Road. Situated in a pretty village on edge of N. Yorks Moors."
Owner: Madalyn Sinnett-Jones

HARROGATE

BOOKSTOP BOOKSHOP
11 Mayfield Grove
Harrogate HG1 5HD
(01423) 505817
Mon-Sat 10-5:30, Wed & public holidays close
Est. 1986. Medium. Spec: Mil, Avia: also Gen Stock and Naval, SF, Art. Cat: 2-4 pa: Mil & Warfare. Buys: Anytime. cc: AVE. BR: Harrogate. "Forecourt parking. 3 min walk north of BR. Atqn & general s'hand books bought & sold."
Owner: Mr J. Shackleton

J.E. COURTNEY, FINE BOOKS
2 Granville Road
Mount Parade
Harrogate HG1 1BX
(01423) 500341
Tue-Sat 10-5:30
Est. 1979. Small. Spec: Maritime: also Gen Stock and Trans, Lit, Topog. Buys: Ring first. "Adjacent to Theatre. Temporary parking. Repair, restoration & binding of books."
Owner: John Courtney

THE HARROGATE BOOKSHOP
29 Cheltenham Crescent
Harrogate HG1 1DH
(01423) 500479
Mon-Sat 10-5:30
Est. 1978. Large. Spec: Mus: also Gen Stock and Art, Atec, Nat Hist. Buys: Anytime. BR: Harrogate. "Situated near the Conference Centre & Exhibition Halls."
Owner: Ian Linford

HAWES

JIGAJOG TOYS AND PENNYPOST BOOKS
The Penn House
off Market Place
Hawes DL8 3QX
(01969) 667008/667298
Mon-Sat 10:30-5 (restricted hours out of season)
Est. 1994. Small. Spec: Chld, JRR Tolkien: also Gen Stock and Hist. Cat: 2-4 pa: Chld, Illus. Buys: Ring first. Book search. cc: AV. BR: Garsdale. "The shop is in the Market Hall Yard behind the Spar supermarket. Also makers/retailers of hand-made wooden toys."
Partner: Martin Cluderay

KIT CALVERT'S
Main Street
Hawes DL8 3QX
(01969) 667667/667523
Mon-Sat 10-5, Sun 2-5 (off-season, Tue, Sat-Sun pm)
Est. 1946. Medium. Spec: Po: also Gen Stock and Topog, Fine Bindings. Buys: Anytime. BR: Garsdale. "4 room bookshop in the highest market town in England."
Owner: Terry Cluderay

HELMSLEY

HELMSLEY ANTIQUARIAN & SECONDHAND BOOKS
The Old Fire Station
Borogate
Helmsley YO6 5BN
(01439) 770014
Mon-Sat 10-5:30, Sun 12-5:30
Est. 1985. Medium. Spec: Atec, Topog: also Gen Stock. Buys: Ring first. cc: AV. BR: Malton/York. "Just off Market Place opp post office. Good general & interesting stock on all subjects. Also selected Yorkshire prints."
Owner: Myles Moorby

RIEVAULX BOOKS
18 High Street
Helmsley YO6 5AG
(01439) 770912
Tue-Fri 10:30-5, Sat-Sun 1-5
Est. 1987. Medium. Gen Stock and Art, Atec, Nat Hist. Buys: Ring first. BR: York. "Quality general stock."
Owner: Catherine Howard

LEALHOLM nr. Whitby

STEPPING STONES BOOKSHOP
Lealholm nr. Whitby
(01947) 897382
Mon-Sun 10-5
Est. 1970. Medium. Gen Stock. Buys: Ring first. BR: Lealholm. "Deal in mainly cheap volumes."
Owners: L. & J. Davies

MIDDLEHAM nr. Leyburn

WHITE BOAR BOOKSHOP (& ANTIQUES)
Kirkgate
Middleham nr. Leyburn DL8 4PF
(01969) 623901
Mon-Sun 10-5:30 (or by appt)
Est. 1984. Medium. Spec: Theol, Biog: also Gen Stock and Eng Lit. Buys: Ring first. BR: Northallerton. "Parking opp. shop. New books of local interest. Engravings, maps & prints. Stock continually changing."
Owners: Gerald & Jeanne Armstrong

RIPON

ST. MARGARET'S BOOKSHOP
10-11 Kirkgate
Ripon HG4 1PA
(01765) 602877
Mon-Sat 9-5, Wed 9-12:30
Est. 1958. Medium. Gen Stock. Buys: Anytime. BR: Harrogate. "New bookshop with a s'hand dept."
Owner: Mrs Sanderson

SALTBURN-BY-THE-SEA

SALTBURN BOOKSHOP
3 Amber Street
Saltburn-by-the-Sea TS12 1DT
(01287) 623335
Mon-Sat 11-2, 2-5 (Mar-Oct); 11-1, 2-4 (Nov-Feb)
Est. 1978. Large. Spec: Penguin-type Fict, Crime: also Gen Stock. Buys: Ring first. Book search. BR: Saltburn. "Ring first before travelling from a long distance. 5 min from BR. Enquiries welcome, dealers with trade cards welcome."
Owner: Jeff Thompson

SCARBOROUGH

THE BAR BOOKSTORE (THE ANTIQUARY LTD)
4 Swan Hill Road
Scarborough YO11 1BW
(01723) 500141/(01262) 679468 (home)
Tue-Sat 10-5
Est. 1976. Medium. Spec: AE Housman: also Gen Stock and Atqn, Eng Lit, Po. Cat: occ. Buys: Ring first. BR: Scarborough.
Directors: M. Chaddock & D. Clarke

SCARBOROUGH BOOKS
55 Castle Road
Scarborough YO11 5BH
(01723) 368813
Mon-Sat 10-5 (Sun in high season)
Est. 1978. Medium. Spec: Lit: also Gen Stock and Nostalgia, Leo Walmsley (local author). Buys: Ring first. Book search. cc: AVAm. BR: Scarborough. "Adjacent to main Town Centre car park in North Street."
Owner: J. Owen

SKIPTON-IN-CRAVEN

THE BOX OF DELIGHTS
25 Otley Street
Skipton-in-Craven BD23 1DY
(01756) 790111
Mon, Wed, Fri, Sat 11-5:30 (ring first)
Est. 1976. Small. Spec: Chld: also Gen Stock and Cookery, Soc Hist, Mod 1sts. Cat: 3 p. BR: Skipton. "Catalogues vary in rotation covering Cookery, Chld, C19th Life, Lit & Mod 1sts."
Owners: Sheila & Peter Coe

CRAVEN BOOKS
23 New Market Street
Skipton-in-Craven BD23 2JE
(01756) 792677
Mon-Fri 9:30-12:30, 1:30-5, Sat 9:30-4, Tue close, 1st & last Mon of each month
Est. 1961. Small. Spec: Atqn: also Gen Stock. Buys: Ring first. Book search. BR: Skipton. "Also sells antique maps."
Owners: Miss K. Farey & Miss M. Fluck

EMBSAY STATION BOOKSHOP
Embsay Station
Embsay
Skipton-in-Craven BD23 6AX
(01756) 794727
Mon-Sun 10:30-5
Small. Spec: Rail, Trans: also Mining, Industry. Cat: 1-4 addenda pa. Buys: Ring first. Book search. cc: AV. BR: Skipton. "Situated 11/4 miles out of Skipton off the A54 trunk road. Shop is situated on a working steam railway."
Owner: Mr Keavey

STOCKTON-ON-TEES

BARNARD GALLERY
2 Theatre Yard
off Green Dragon Yard
Stockton-on-Tees TS18 1NZ
(01642) 616203
Tue-Sat 10-4:30, Thur close
Est. 1973. Small. Gen Stock. Buys: Ring first. BR: Darlington. "Original paintings, engravings & old prints."
Owner: David Barnard Wilson

STOKESLEY

THE STOKESLEY BOOKSHOP
63 High Street
Stokesley TS9 5BQ
(01642) 712514
Mon, Tue, Thur 10-5 (April-Sept) 10-4 (Oct-Mar), Fri & Sat 10-5, Wed close
Est. 1987. Medium. Spec: Northern Hist & Topog: also Gen Stock and Atqn. Buys: Ring first. BR: Middlesbrough. "Mostly Non-Fict."
Owner: Tom Quinn

THIRSK

HAMBLETON BOOKS
43 Market Place
Thirsk YO7 1HA
(01845) 522343
Mon-Fri 9:30-5, Sat 9:30-4:30 (Jan-Mar Wed close)
Est. 1978. Medium. Spec: Nat Hist: also Gen Stock and Geol, Topog, Fict. Buys: Anytime. cc: AV. BR: Thirsk. "Mainly new books. Sometimes worth a trade call to exploit our numerous and vast areas of ignorance".
Owner: Anne Turner

YORK

BARBICAN BOOKSHOP
24 Fossgate
York YO1 2TA
(01904) 653643/644878
Mon-Sat 9-5:30
Est. 1962. Large. Spec: Yorkshire, Theol: also Gen Stock and Lit, Topog, Sport. Cat: occ. cc: AV. BR: York. "12 rooms of books, new & old, including many bargains. S'hand books on most subjects, constantly replenished by purchase of large and small libraries."
Owner: H. Bingham

CADUCEUS BOOKS
Unit 2, The Fishergate Centre
4 Fishergate
York YO1 4AB
(01904) 628021
Fax (01904) 613696
Mon-Sat 2-5 (ring first, or by appt)
Est. 1989. Small. Spec: Crowley, Eso: also Magic, Occult, Witchcraft. Cat: occ: Occult, Eso. Buys: Ring first. Book search. cc: AV. BR: York. "Bookroom open more by chance. Also Alt. Health & Yoga books. Visitors very welcome."
Owner: Ben Fernee

JACK DUNCAN BOOKS
36 Fossgate
York YO1 2TF
(01904) 641389
Fax (01904) 672184
Mon-Sat 10-5:30 (often shut lunchtime)
Est. 1978. Medium. Spec: Lit, Medieval Hist: also Gen Stock and Nat Hist, Byzantine, WS. Cat: 10 pa: Med Hist, Byzantine, WS, Folio Society. Buys: Ring first. Book search. cc: AV. BR: York.
Owner: Jack Duncan

INCH'S BOOKSHOP
82 The Mount
York YO2 2AR
(01904) 627082/629770
Fax (01904) 635821
Mon-Fri 10-5 (or by appt)
Est. 1980. Medium. Spec: Atec, Des: also Gen Stock and Photo, Art. Cat: 8 pa: Hist, Photo, C20th Atec. Buys: Ring first. Book search. BR: York. "Close to BR. On-street parking nearby. PBFA member."
Owners: Peter Inch & Janette Ray

PHILIP MARTIN MUSIC BOOKS
38 Fossgate
York
(01904) 670323
Tue-Sat 10-5:30
Large. Spec: Mus: also Scores. Cat: 4 pa: Mus. Buys: Ring first. BR: York. "S'hand & Atqn Music, books, scores. Also new 'serious' music books."
Owners: Martin & Eleanor Dreyer

MINSTER GATES BOOKSHOP
8 Minster Gates
York YO1 2HL
(01904) 621812
Mon-Sun 10-5:30
Est. 1970. Medium. Spec: Chld, Lit: also Gen Stock and Illus, Folklore, Occult. Cat: occ. Buys: Ring first. Book search. cc: AV. BR: York. "3 floors of s'hand & Atqn stock."
Owner: Nigel Wallace

O'FLYNN ANTIQUARIAN BOOKS
35 Micklegate
York YO1 1JH
(01904) 641404
Fax (01904) 611872
Mon-Sat 9-6
Est. 1969. Large. Spec: Atqn: also Gen Stock and Printing, Hist, Illus. Cat: 4+ pa: Misc. Buys: Ring first. cc: AV. BR: York. "Large stock of maps & prints covering most areas of the UK and the world, as well as most subjects - Topog, Costume, Floral, Birds, etc."
Owner: Francis O'Flynn

OBLONG BOOKS
91 Micklegate
York YO1 1LE
(01904) 631375
Mon-Sat 10:30-5:30
Small. Gen Stock. Buys: Anytime. Book search. BR: York. "Follow A64 through Walls into York. Very near BR. Same street as Ken Spelman's Bookshop. Gen s'hand quality stock. Most subject areas covered."
Owner: Mr Alex Helstrip

PASSAGEWAY BOOK ROOM
33C Fossgate
York YO1 2TA
(01274) 392685
Thur-Sat 10:30-4
Medium. Spec: Lit, the Arts: also Gen Stock. Buys: Ring first. BR: York. "Passageway leading to bookroom is near bridge behind restaurant. More specialised section at Jack Duncan, 36 Fossgate."
Owner: John Hepworth

PICKERING & CO. BOOKSELLERS
42 The Shambles
York YO1 2LX
(01904) 627888
Mon-Sat 9-5:30
Est. 1858. Medium. Spec: WW2: also Gen Stock and Avia. Cat: 1 pa: Avia. Buys: Anytime. Book search. cc: AV. BR: York. "We have developed and maintained a large stock of s'hand, out-of-print and rare Avia. Catalogues: apply enclosing £1 (no cheques) or £4 (overseas Airmail)."
Owner: Mr D. Reed

ROSE FINE ART & GOODRAMGATE BOOK CENTRE
58C Goodramgate
York YO1 2LF
(01904) 641841/690118
Mon-Sat 9:30-5, Wed close
Est. 1987. Small. Spec: Topog, Company Hist: also Gen Stock. Buys: Anytime. cc: AV. BR: York. "Situated in Passageway adjacent to Newcastle Building Society. Also stocks paintings."
Owner: Stephen Rose

KEN SPELMAN
70 Micklegate
York YO1 1LF
(01904) 624414
Fax (01904) 626276
Mon-Sat 9-5:30
Est. 1948. Large. Spec: Art, Arch: also Gen Stock and C18th, Atqn. Cat: 2 pa: Recent Acquisitions. Buys: Anytime. Book search. cc: AVAmE. BR: York. "On-street parking. Large s'hand & fine Atqn shop. Also maps, prints & watercolours. ABA, PBFA."
Owners: A. Fothergill & P. Miller

STONE TROUGH BOOKS
38 Fossgate
York YO1 2TF
(01904) 670323
Mon-Sat 10-5:30
Small. Spec: Lit (Association Copies): also Gen Stock. Cat: 3 pa: Lit, Letters. Buys: Anytime. Book search. BR: York. "3 other bookshops within 50 yards."
Owner: George Ramsden

TAIKOO BOOKS LTD
46 Bootham
York YO3 7BZ
(01904) 641213
Mon-Fri 10-5 (phone first)
Medium. Spec: Africa, Orient: also Mid E, Central Asia. Cat: occ. Buys: Ring first. BR: York. "Fine Atqn, scholarly & out-of-print stock. Appointment advised if travelling from a distance."
Owner: David Chilton

SOUTH YORKSHIRE

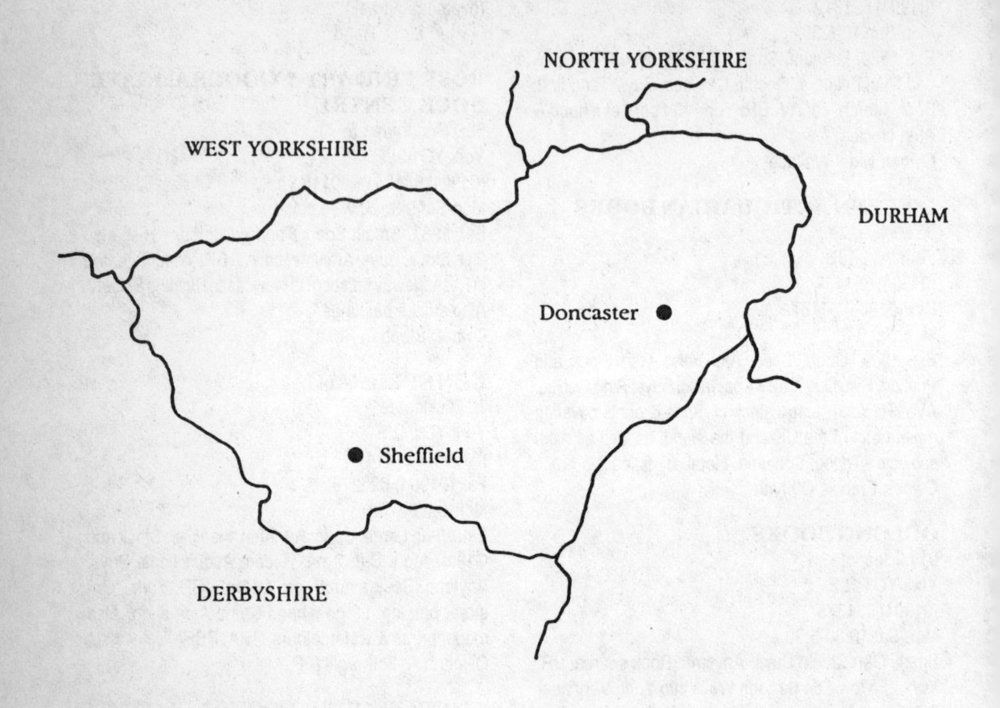

DONCASTER

ATHENA BOOKS
34 Imperial Crescent
Town Moor
Doncaster DN2 5BU
(01302) 322913
Fax (01302) 730531
Mon-Sat 9-5
Est. 1970. Large. Spec: Mil: also Maritime, Avia, Atqn. Cat: 8 pa: Mil, Marit, Avia. Buys: Anytime. cc: AVAm. BR: Doncaster. "Off Town Moor Ave. No parking restrictions."
Owner: L.A. Thomas

SHEFFIELD

BIFF BOOKS AND RECORDS
11 Commonside
Sheffield S10 1GA
Mon 2:30-5:30, Tue-Fri 11-5:30, Sat 10-5:30
Est. 1984. Medium. Spec: Lit, Humanities: also Gen Stock and Science Fict, S/H Records. Buys: Anytime. BR: Sheffield. "95 bus route, mainly pbks."
Owner: Mr B. Andrews

THE BOOK AND ART SHOP
204 West Street
Sheffield S1 4EU
(0114) 275 7576
Mon-Sat 10-5:30
Est. 1966. Medium. Gen Stock and Art, Lit. Buys: Anytime. BR: Sheffield Midland. "Also sells water colours, oil paintings and etchings."
Owner: Georgina Purse

ALAN HILL BOOKS
261 Glossop Road
Sheffield S10 2GZ
(0114) 278 0594
Mon-Sat 10-5:30
Est. 1980. Medium. Spec: Local: also Gen Stock and Cricket, Acad. Buys: Ring first. cc: AVAmE. BR: Sheffield. "Also shop on Bakewell."
Owner: A.D. Hill

THE PORTER BOOKSHOP
227 Sharrowvale Road
Sheffield S11 8ZE
(0114) 266 7762
Mon-Fri 11-5:30, Sat 10-5:30
Medium. Gen Stock. Buys: Anytime. BR: Sheffield Midland. "Off Ecclesall Road and Hickmott Road. Mainly pbk, Art, Humanities, and gen stock."
Owner: S. Everson

RARE & RACY
164-166 Devonshire Street
Sheffield S3 7SG
(0114) 270 1916
Mon-Sat 10-6
Est. 1969. Large. Gen Stock. Buys: Ring first. BR: Sheffield. "Also sells maps, prints, and records and at 278 South Road, Walkley, (0114) 232 0465."
Owners: J. Capes, J. Mhlongo & A. Capes

TILLEY'S VINTAGE MAGAZINE SHOP
281 Shoreham Street
Sheffield S1
(0114) 275 2442 (tel/fax)
Est. 1989. Medium. Spec: Comics, Mags: also Gen Stock. Buys: Ring first. Book search. BR: Sheffield. "Opp. Sheffield United FC, 10 min walk from BR and buses. Hourly train from London. 15 min from M1 and Peak District. Unique shop. Also programmes, postcards, prints, cigarette cards, newspapers, ephemera. Magazine valuation service."
Owners: A.G. & A.A. Tilley

Y.S.F. BOOKS
365 Sharrowvale Road
Hunters Bar
Sheffield S11 8SG
(0114) 268 0687
Mon-Sat 8-6
Large. Spec: Avia, Art: also Gen Stock and Mount, Angling, Car Manuals. Buys: Anytime. BR: Sheffield. "Indescribable - has to be seen to be appreciated, also sells sheet music and at 81 Junction Road, Hunters Bar."
Owner: J. Eldridge

WEST YORKSHIRE

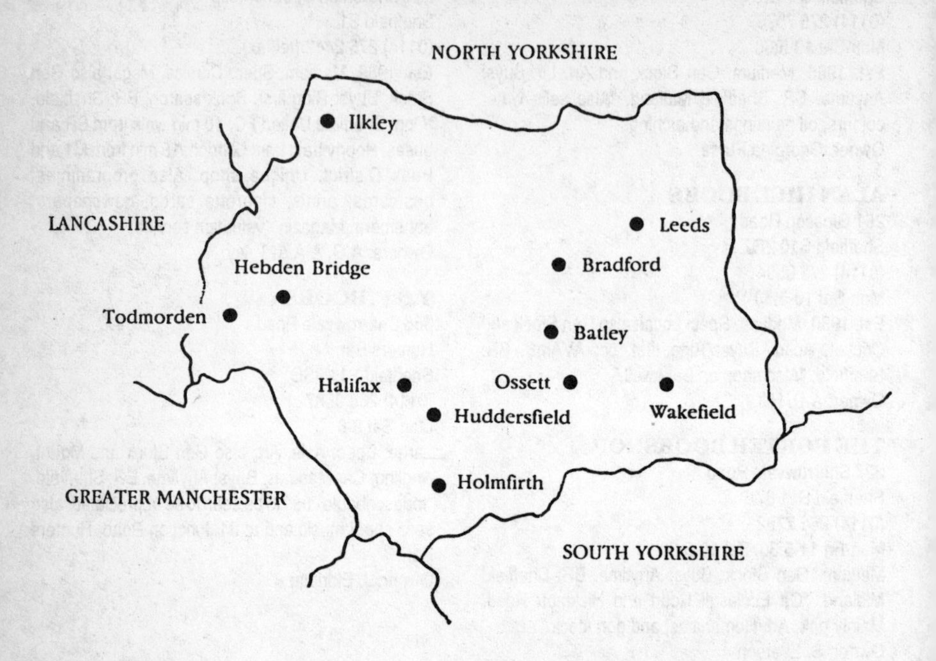

BATLEY

VINTAGE MOTORSHOP

749 Bradford Road
Batley WF17 8HZ
(01924) 470773
Thur-Sat 11-5
Est. 1978. Medium. Spec: Trans. Buys: Ring first. Book search. BR: Batley. "Trans Lit bought, sold & exchanged. Large stock of new & s'hand Motoring, Technical books & magazines."
Owner: Richard Hunt

BRADFORD

THE BODHRAN

9 Victoria Road
Saltaire
Bradford BD18 3LA
(01274) 530102
Mon-Sun 10-6
Est. 1990. Medium. Spec: Ireland: also Gen Stock and C20th Novels, Topog, Lit. Cat: occ. Buys: Anytime. cc: AV. BR: Saltaire. "Shop opp. 1853 Gallery - the only permanent display of Hockney's work in the country. We sell Irish music (tapes, CDs) & wooden crafts."
Owners: Mandy Farrar & Mark Killingray

FALCON BOOKS OF SALTAIRE

13-13A Victoria Road
Saltaire
Bradford BD18 3LQ
(01274) 584275
Mon-Fri 2-5, Sat 11-5, Sun 1-5
Large. Spec: Eng Lit, Hist: also Gen Stock and Art, Lit Crit. Buys: Ring first. BR: Saltaire. "Saltaire is the most complete model village in UK, housing David Hockney Gallery, Victorian Reed Organ Museum & Shipley Glen Tramway."
Owner: Clive Woods

S.P.C.K. BOOKSHOP
14 North Parade
Bradford BD1 3HY
(01274) 728669
Mon-Fri 9-5:30, Tue 9:30-5:30, Sat 9-5
Est. 1936. Medium. Spec: Theol: also Gen Stock. Buys: Ring first. cc: AV. BR: Bradford. "New books, s'hand Theol books & Religious remainders. Shop on 3 floors."
Owner: Robert Purvis

HALIFAX

THE COLLECTOR
36 The Collonade
Piece Hall
Halifax HX1 1RS
(01422) 363895
Mon-Sat 10-5:30, Sun 12-4:30 Thur close
Est. 1982. Medium. Spec: Mil, Avia, Naval: also Espionage, Holocaust, magazines on above. Cat: 9-10 pa: as above. Buys: Ring first. Book search. cc: AVAmDEJ. BR: Halifax.
Owner: Ian Wilkinson

WEST RIDING BOOKS & PICTURES
11-12 The Piece Hall
Halifax HX1 1RE
(01850) 163425
Thur-Sun 10:30-5
Large. Spec: Lit, Trav: also Gen Stock and Topog, Nat Hist, Yorkshire. Buys: Ring first. BR: Halifax. "Central Halifax, 5 min from BR. V. large, long-established bookshop. Regular purchaser of private collections - ever-changing stock in all main areas of collectable books."
Owner: R. Forbes

HEBDEN BRIDGE

ELIZABETH DOBSON
Dunkley House
9-11 Albert Street
Hebden Bridge HX7 8AH
(01422) 844232
Thur 10-4 (later in Summer) (or by appt Ring first)
Small. Spec: Atec, Des: also Railways, Nat Hist, Food & Wine. Buys: Ring first. BR: Hebden Bridge. "PBFA member."
Owner: E. Dobson

HATCHARD & DAUGHTERS
56 Market Street
Hebden Bridge
(01422) 845717
Thur & Fri 1-5, Sat 10:30-5, Sun 12-5
Est. 1989. Medium. Gen Stock and Art, Nat Hist, Topog. Buys: Anytime. cc: AV. BR: Hebden Bridge.
Owner: Miss Hatchard

NEPTUNE BOOKS
54 Market Street
Hebden Bridge HX7 6HA
(01422) 845567
Wed-Sun 11-4:30, Sat 11-5
Small. Spec: Crime, Lit: also Gen Stock and Po, Drama, Mod 1sts. Cat: occ. Book search. "Good general s'hand & Atqn stock."

HOLMFIRTH

DAISY LANE BOOKS
Towngate
Holmfirth HD7 1HA
(01484) 688409
Mon-Sun 9-5:30 (Winter 10-4:30)
Est. 1983. Large. Gen Stock. Buys: Anytime. BR: Huddersfield.
Owners: J. & B. Townsend Cardew

THE TOLL HOUSE BOOKSHOP
32-34 Huddersfield Road
Holmfirth HO7 1JS
(01484) 686541
Fax (01484) 688406
Mon-Sat 9-5
Est. 1977. Large. Spec: Hist, Art: also Gen Stock and Topog, Lit, Chld. Buys: Ring first. cc: AV. BR: Huddersfield. "6 rooms of new, s'hand & Atqn books in a building of great charm which has been quite recently renovated."
Owner: Mrs E. Beardsel

HUDDERSFIELD

CHILDREN'S BOOKSHOP
37-39 Lidget Street
Lindley
Huddersfield HD3 3JF
(01484) 658013
Fax (01484) 460020
Mon-Sat 10-5

Est. 1973. Medium. Spec: Chld, Dickens: also Gen Stock and Biog. Buys: Ring first. cc: AV. BR: Huddersfield. "Between Huddersfield & Halifax, close to Junc. 24 of M62. Spec Chld b'shop recently expanded into quality s'hand & Atqn."
Owners: Sonia & Barry Benster

ROBLYN'S SECONDHAND BOOKSHOP

18 Westgate
Huddersfield HD1 1NN
(01484) 516793
Mon-Sat 9:15-5:30
Est. 1983. Medium. Gen Stock and Acad, Penguins. Buys: Ring first. BR: Huddersfield. "Good cross-section."
Owners: R. & L. Wood

ILKLEY

THE GROVE BOOKSHOP

10 The Grove
Ilkley
(01943) 609335
Fax (01943) 817086
Mon-Sat 9-5:30
Small. Spec: Yorkshire Topog: also Gen Stock. Buys: Ring first. cc: AV. BR: Ilkley.
Owners: Andrew & Janet Sharpe

LEEDS

THE BOOK BARN

Antique City, Christopher Road
off Woodhouse Street
Leeds LS6 2JX
(0113) 243 9212 (tel/fax)
Sat (or by appt)
Est. 1996. Large. Gen Stock. Buys: Ring first. BR: Leeds. "Buy, browse, sell or swap. Thousands of rare books, comics, LP records and collectables. Trade by arrangement. Used to be Bury Place Rare Books in London."
Owner: David Fairbairn

THE BOOKSHOP

10 Commercial Road
Kirkstall
Leeds LS5 3AQ
(0113) 278 0937
Mon-Sat 10:15-5:30
Est. 1975. Medium. Gen Stock and Atqn, Fict, Art. Buys: Anytime. BR: Leeds, Metro: Headingley. "Very good selection of books - good condition & reasonable prices. Some 1/2 price review copies. Accepts BNU cards."
Owner: Mr Roy Brook

BOOKSIDE

off Midland Road
Nr. Hyde Park Corner
Leeds LS6 1BQ
(0113) 274 4021
Mon-Sat 10-6
Est. 1987. Large. Spec: Pbk Lit: also Gen Stock and SF, Mod 1sts, The Arts. Buys: Ring first. Book search. BR: Leeds. "From Hyde Park Corner walk down Hyde Park Terrace, take 2nd left into Midland Road then 1st right. 20,000 books on display (20p-£100). Most subjects covered."
Owners: Tom Cadbury & Gill Cooksey

MR MILES OF LEEDS (James Miles (Leeds) Ltd)

12 Great George Street
Leeds LS1 3DW
(0113) 245 5327
Fax (0113) 243 0661
Mon-Sat 9-5:30
Est. 1870. Large. Spec: Hist, Biog: also Gen Stock and Atqn, Trav. Cat: £20+ new acquisitions monthly. Buys: Ring first. cc: AV. BR: Leeds City. "Large community-based City-centre bookshop within walking distance of public transport & parking, close to Town & Civic Halls. Gen stock, fully classified. Collectors items listed for reference. Phone, post, trade & fax orders welcome. Trade cards welcome."
Directors: D. & P.F. Austick

UBIK

5A The Crescent
Hyde Park Corner
Leeds LS6 2NW
(0113) 230 4585
Mon-Sat 10-6, Sun 12-4
Est. 1992. Small. Spec: Occult & Fortean, SF: also Gen Stock. Cat: 3 pa: Occult, Fortean. Buys: Anytime. Book search. BR: Leeds.
Owners: Simon Michael & Jake Kirkwood

OSSETT

ZOAR BOOKS
Old 21A Queen Street
Ossett WF5 8AS
(01924) 260502
Mon-Sat 9:30-5, Wed 9:30-12
Est. 1989. Small. Spec: Theol: also Gen Stock and Atqn, Biog, Hist. Cat: 4-5 pa: Rel. Buys: Ring first. BR: Dewsbury. "4 min from exit 40 of M1."
Owner: Mr J. Pollard

TODMORDEN

BORDER BOOKSHOP
61A-63 Halifax Road
Todmorden OL14 5BB
(01706) 814721/875646 (home)
Mon-Sat 10-5, Tue close (or by appt)
Est. 1979. Medium. Spec: Cricket: also Gen Stock and Chld, Comics, C20th. Buys: Anytime. BR: Todmorden. "Easy parking. New books & remainders. MBA & PBFA."
Owner: Victor Collinge

PANGOLIN
17 Water Street
Todmorden OL14 5AB
(01706) 817945
Mon 12:30-5, Tue-Sat 10-5
Medium. Gen Stock and Railways, Trans, Hist. Buys: Anytime. BR: Todmorden.
Owners: Robin & Sally Pennie

WAKEFIELD

LEO BOOKS
4 & 8 Vicarage Street
Wakefield WF1 1QX
(01924) 365109
Mon-Sat 9:30-5:30, Wed close
Est. 1986. Medium. Spec: New Age, UFOs: also Gen Stock and Occult, Paranormal, SF. Buys: Ring first. BR: Westgate/Kirkgate. "Situated in Market area of Town Centre, 2 min from main Bus station, off main shopping area. Only s'hand bookshop in Wakefield."
Owner: George Wild

Helmsdale
Lossiemouth
Dingwall
Black Isle
Dufftown
Inverness
Strathcarron
Aberdeen
Ballater
Blair Atholl
Montrose
Dunkeld
Dundee
Perth
Newport-on-Tay
Isle of Iona
St. Andrews
Bridge of Allan
Kirkcaldy
Stirling
Gullane
Helensburgh
Edinburgh
Greenock
Glasgow
Paisley
West Linton
Haddington
Kelso
Hawick
Tynron
Dumfries
Wigtown
Castle Douglas
Gatehouse of Fleet
Kirkcudbright
CUMBRIA

ABERDEEN

WINRAM'S BOOKSHOP

32-36 Rosemount Place
Aberdeen
(01224) 630673
Mon-Sat 10-5:30 (Jan-Mar ring first)
Est. 1977. Medium. Spec: Loc Hist, Scot: also Gen Stock. Buys: Anytime. BR: Aberdeen. "From Rosemount viaduct go up South Mount Street to traffic lights. Turn right. Shop is 60 yds on left. Warm, friendly atmosphere with surprisingly interesting selection on many subjects."
Owner: Mrs M. Davidson

BALLATER

McEWEN FINE BOOKS

Glengarden
Ballater AB55 5UB
(013397) 55429
Mon-Sat 10-5
Small. Spec: Golf, Country Sports: also Scot, Angling, Birds. Cat: 3 pa: Golf, 3 pa: listed subjects. Buys: Anytime. Book search. cc: AVAm. "On A939. Private premises. Easy parking."
Owners: Peter & Rhod McEwen

BLACK ISLE

HILDA HESLING BOOKS

The Old Post Office
Avoch
Black Isle
(01381) 621000/ (01463) 772250 (home)
Mon-Sat 10:30-5, Thur close
Est. 1982. Small. Spec: Scot: also Gen Stock. Buys: Ring first. BR: Inverness. "Stock of Atqn prints. Bookshop is part of an antique shop, so we may well have antique items of interest. PBFA."
Owner: Hilda Hesling

BLAIR ATHOLL

ATHOLL BROWSE

By the Old Filling Station
Tayside
Blair Atholl PH18 5SG
(01796) 473470
Fax (01796) 473030
Mon-Sun 12-8 (Apr-Oct)
Est. 1989. Medium. Gen Stock and Crafts, Nat Hist, Fishing. Cat: 1 pa. Buys: Anytime. cc: AV. BR: Blair Atholl. "Publishers of local history."
Owner: Nancy Cameron

BRIDGE OF ALLAN

BRIDGE OF ALLAN BOOKS

2 Henderson Street
Bridge of Allan FK9 4HT
(01786) 834483
Mon-Sat 9:30-5:30
Est. 1985. Medium. Spec: Scot: also Gen Stock. Buys: Anytime. Book search. cc: AV. BR: Bridge of Allan. "Near Stirling and motorway."
Owner: Mrs Virginia Wills

CASTLE DOUGLAS

BENNY GILLIES

31-33 Victoria Street
Kirkpatrick Durham
Castle Douglas DG7 3HQ
(01556) 650412
Mon-Sat 10-5 (or by appt)
Est. 1979. Medium. Spec: Scot Topog & Hist: also Gen Stock and Non-Fict. Cat: occ: Scot. Buys: Anytime. BR: Dumfries. "Kirkpatrick Durham is 1 mile off A75 road. Choice selection covering wide subject area. Quality rather than quantity. Also Atqn prints & maps. Single items or libraries purchased. PBFA."
Owner: Benny Gillies

DINGWALL

MERCAT ANTIQUES & BOOKS
6 Church Street
Dingwall IV15 9SB
(01349) 865593
Mon-Sat 10:30-4:30
Medium. Gen Stock and Nat Hist, Gard, Mount. Buys: Anytime. Book search. cc: AV. BR: Dingwall. "Easy parking. Also sells antiques."
Owner: Hazel MacMillan

THE OLD STORE
10 Inchvannie Court
Dingwall IV15 9SE
(01349) 866061
Mon-Sat 10-5
Small. Spec: Fishing, Stalking: also Hunting. Buys: Ring first. Book search. BR: Dingwall. "Very specialised stock."
Owner: Hazel MacMillan

DUFFTOWN

THE DUFFTOWN BOOKSHOP
5 Balvenie Street
Grampian
Dufftown
(01340) 820027
Mon-Sat 10-5 (Nov-Feb, Fri-Sat 10-5)
Est. 1985. Medium. Spec: Scot: also Gen Stock and Hist, Lit, Sport. Buys: Ring first. BR: Elgin. "Shop has a good quality gen stock of approx. 10,000 plus, a substantial reserve on many subjects. Well worth a visit."
Owner: N. Peardon-Cook

DUMFRIES

BOOKS AT MIDSTEEPLE
1 Midsteeple
Dumfries
(01387) 74215
Mon-Sat 10:30-5 (often earlier, occ Suns)
Small. Spec: Pbks: also Gen Stock. BR: Dumfries. "At very heart of town. Mass market pbks to Classics/Ref. Additional stock at home incl. sci-fi. Fast turnover."
Owners: Richard & Jo Batley

CRESCENT BOOKS
32 Church Street
Dumfries PO1 1DF
(01387) 261137
Tue-Sat 10:30-5
Est. 1994. Small. Gen Stock. Buys: Anytime. Book search. BR: Dumfries. "Also sell s'hand records."
Owner: M. Close

HEN HOOSE
Tynron nr. Thornhill
Dumfries DG3 4LB
(01848) 200418/330810 (eve)
Wed-Sun 11-5
Est. 1994. Medium. Spec: Art Reference: also Gen Stock and Po, Medical, Anthroposophy. Buys: Anytime. Book search. "Off A76, near Thornhill. Bookshop in building with Antique Centre & tearoom."
Owner: Ann Willows

DUNDEE

MEADOWSIDE BOOKSHOP
75 Meadowside
Dundee
(01382) 223510
Mon-Sat 10:30-5:30
Est. 1985. Small. Gen Stock and Trav. Buys: Ring first. Book search. BR: Dundee Taybridge. "Small shop, but something for everyone. 104 shelves divided into all major categories."
Owner: David Shepherd

DUNKELD

DUNKELD ANTIQUES
Tay Terrace
Dunkeld PH8 0AQ
(01350) 728832
Mon-Sat 10-5:30, Sun 12-5 (or by appt)
Est. 1986. Small. Spec: Fishing: also Shooting, Sport, Mount. Buys: Ring first. cc: AV. BR: Dunkeld. "Easily found adjacent to 2 rivers. Just off A9. Good parking. Coffee at all times. Small select stock."
Owner: David Dytch

EDINBURGH

ARCHWAYS SPORTS BOOKS
50 Lochrin Buildings
Gilmore Place
Edinburgh EH3 9ND
(0131) 228 8182
Mon, Tue, Fri 10:30-7, Wed 1-7, Thur 10:30-5:30, Sat 9-5:30
Est. 1992. Medium. Spec: Sport: Cat: 4+ pa: Sport. Buys: Ring first. cc: AV. BR: Edinburgh. "Also new sports books, programmes, cigarette cards, tradecards, tickets, handbooks & associated memorabilia."
Owner: Iain Murray

ARMCHAIR BOOKS
72 West Port (off Grassmarket)
Edinburgh EH1 2LE
(0131) 229 5927
Mon-Sat 10:30-5:30
Est. 1989. Medium. Spec: Victorian and early C20th Lit: also Gen Stock and Occult, SF, Golf. Buys: Anytime. BR: Edinburgh Waverley. "1 mile from BR. Five other s'hand bookshops within the area."
Owner: David Govan

PETER BELL
68 West Port
Edinburgh EH1 2LD
(0131) 229 0562
Fax (0131) 556 5525
Mon-Sat 10-5
Est. 1975. Small. Spec: Academic Hist, Lit: also Gen Stock and Phil, Scottish, Small C19th Atqn. Cat: 12 pa: Gen Atqn, Acad. Buys: Ring first. Book search. cc: AVAm. BR: Edinburgh Waverley. "West Port is the road out of the Grassmarket to the West, in the Old Town. 4 other shops in immediate vicinity."
Owner: Peter Bell

BROUGHTON BOOKS
2A Broughton Place
Edinburgh EH1 3RX
(0131) 557 8010/553 1925
Tue-Fri 12-6, Sat 10:30-5:30
Est. 1971. Medium. Gen Stock and Lit, Hum, Hist. Buys: Anytime. Book search. BR: Edinburgh Waverley. "Emphasis on the Arts. Also some prints."
Owner: Peter Galinsky

CASTLE BOOKS
204 Canongate
Royal Mile
Edinburgh EH8 8DQ
(0131) 556 0624
Mon-Sat 12-5 (July & Aug, Mon-Sat 11-6)
Medium. Gen Stock and Art, Lit, Trav. Cat: occ. Buys: Ring first. cc: V. BR: Edinburgh Waverley.
Owner: Kathleen Choucha

JAMES A. DICKSON BOOKS
12 Forrest Road
Edinburgh EH1 2QN
(0131) 225 6937
Mon-Sat 9:30-5:30
Est. 1982. Medium. Spec: Theol. Cat: 6-8 pa: Theol. Buys: Anytime. Book search. BR: Edinburgh. "5 min from BR. We carry a good stock of s'hand, Atqn, conservative theol."
Owner: James Dickson

MARGARET DUNCAN BOOKS under DUNCAN & REID
5 Tanfield
Edinburgh EH3 5JS
(0131) 556 4591
Tue-Fri 12-5:30, Sat 11:30-5:30
Est. 1977. Medium. Spec: Scot: also Gen Stock. Buys: Ring first. Book search. BR: Edinburgh Waverley. "Parking possible at door (with caution!). Also sells, antiques, postcards & prints."
Owner: Margaret Duncan

McNAUGHTAN'S BOOKSHOP
3A-4A Haddington Place
Edinburgh EH7 4AE
(0131) 556 5897
Fax (0131) 556 8220
Tue-Sat 9:30-5:30
Est. 1957. Medium. Gen Stock and Trav, Topog, Art. Buys: Ring first. Book search. BR: Edinburgh Waverley.
Owner: Elizabeth Strong

OLD GRINDLES BOOKSHOP
Corner of Bread Street & Spittal Street
Edinburgh EH3 9DY
(0131) 229 7252
Mon-Sat 10-9
Large. Spec: Scot: also Gen Stock and Atqn, Po, Tech. Cat: occ. Buys: Ring first. BR: Edinburgh Waverley. "Die Hard publishers."
Owner: Ian King

THE OLD TOWN BOOKSHOP
8 Victoria Street
Edinburgh EH1 2HG
(0131) 225 9237
Mon-Sat 10:30-5:45 (Aug, also Sun 1-5)
Medium. Spec: Eng Lit, Fine Art: also Gen Stock and Scot, Theol, Chld. Cat: 2 pa: Art, Scot. Buys: Ring first. cc: AV. BR: Edinburgh Waverley. "5 min walk from Princes St. & Edinburgh Castle. Also Scottish prints."
Owners: Ronald Wilson & Isobel Kiltie

ANDREW PRINGLE BOOKSELLERS
7 Dundas Street
Edinburgh EH3 6QG
(0131) 556 9698 (tel/fax)
Mon-Fri 10-5:30, Sat 10:30-4
Est. 1988. Medium. Spec: Scot, Hist: also Gen Stock and Lit, Atqn. Cat: 3 pa: Scot. Buys: Ring first. BR: Edinburgh Waverley.
Owner: Andrew Pringle

REID AND REID
134 St. Stephen Street
Edinburgh EH3 5AA
(0131) 225 9660
Tue-Sat 11-5:30
Est. 1984. Small. Spec: Scot: also Gen Stock and Lit, Sport. Buys: Ring first. BR: Edinburgh Waverley. "Also antique prints."
Owner: Mr W.B. Reid

SECOND EDITION
9 Howard Street
Edinburgh EH3 5JP
(0131) 556 9403
Mon-Fri 12-5:30, Sat 9:30-5:30
Est. 1979. Large. Gen Stock and Mod 1sts, Lit, Art. Buys: Ring first. BR: Edinburgh Waverley. "Parking possible. Adjacent to Royal Botanic Gardens. Stock added daily. Some maps & prints."
Owner: Mrs Maureen Smith

JAMES THIN LTD
53 South Bridge
Edinburgh EH1 1YS
(0131) 556 6743
Fax (0131) 557 8149
Mon-Sat 9-5:30
Est. 1884. Medium. Spec: Scot Hist and Topog: also Gen Stock and Atqn. Cat: 3 pa: Gen. Buys: Ring first. cc: AVAm. BR: Edinburgh Waverley. " New, Atqn and s'hand, general academic."
Owner: James Thin

TILL'S BOOKSHOP
1 Hope Park Crescent
Behind Buccleuch Street
Edinburgh EH8 9NA
(0131) 667 0895
Mon-Fri 12-7:30, Sat 11-6
Est. 1986. Medium. Spec: Lit: also Gen Stock and Crime, SF, 1sts. Buys: Ring first. BR: Edinburgh Waverley. "Lots of old film posters as well."
Owners: Rick & Ann Till

TOLBOOTH BOOKS
175 Canongate
Royal Mile
Edinburgh EH8 8BN
(0131) 558 3411
Mon-Sat 12-5
Est. 1992. Small. Spec: Illus, Chld: also Gen Stock and Scot, Soc Hist. Cat: 1 pa: Chld, Illus. Buys: Anytime. cc: AVAm.
Owner: Margaret Jameson

JOHN UPDIKE RARE BOOKS
7 St. Bernard's Row
Edinburgh EH4 1HW
(0131) 332 1650
Fax (0131) 332 1345
Ring first for appt
Est. 1965. Medium. Spec: C19th & C20th 1sts: also Gen Stock and Illus, Private Press. Cat: occ: as above. Buys: Ring first. BR: Edinburgh Waverley. "5 min by taxi from station. Prior phone call advised."
Owners: E.G. Nairn & J.S. Watson

WEST PORT BOOKS
145-7 West Port
Edinburgh EH3 9DP
(0131) 229 4431
Mon-Fri 10-5:30, Sat 11-5
Est. 1978. Medium. Spec: Art, Class Mus: also Gen Stock and Lit, Topog. Cat: 1 pa: Indian Books. Buys: Anytime. BR: Edinburgh Waverley. "New imported books on Indian Art, travel and Phil. Also fine arts, classical records, and sheet music."
Owner: Mr H. Barrott

GATEHOUSE OF FLEET

ANWOTH BOOKS
Rutherford Hall
High Street
Gatehouse of Fleet DG7 4HS
Apr-Oct: Mon-Sat 10:30-5, Sun 1-5 (Winter, ring first)
Medium. Gen Stock. Buys: Anytime. "Former church beside car park. Wheelchair access. Comprehensive quick-changing stock. Also records, new books, maps, genuine remainders. Children's corner."
Owner: Anwoth Books Community Business

GLASGOW

ADAM BOOKS
47 Parnie Street
Glasgow G1
(0141) 552 2665
Mon-Sat 10-5:30
Est. 1991. Small. Spec: Scot: also Gen Stock. Cat: 6 pa: Scot, Gen. Buys: Anytime. Book search. BR: Mount Florida. "New books & remainders."
Owner: Adam T. McNaughtan

ALBA SECONDHAND MUSIC
61 Otago Street
Glasgow G12 8PQ
(01389) 875996 (home)
(0141) 334 9663
Mon-Sat 10:30-6
Est. 1994. Large. Spec: Printed Music. Buys: Ring first. Book search. Underground: Kelvinbridge. "Situated in basement of Alba Cafe. Proprietor usually in attendance Sat pm or by appt. Please phone before 9am or page on (01426) 977225. No phone in shop."
Owner: Robert Lay

CALEDONIA BOOKSHOP
483 Great Western Road
Glasgow G12 8HL
(0141) 334 9663
Mon-Sat 10:30-6
Est. 1986. Large. Spec: Scot: also Gen Stock and Art, Hist, Lit. Buys: Anytime. Book search. Tube: Kelvinbridge.
Owner: Maureen Smillie

DOWANSIDE BOOKS
Dowanside Lane
Glasgow G12 9BZ
(0141) 334 3245
Mon-Sat 10:15-6
Est. 1991. Medium. Spec: Scot, Po: also Gen Stock and Drama, Hist, Pol. Buys: Anytime. cc: AVE. Tube: Hillhead.
Owner: Miss L. Welsh

FREE PRESBYTERIAN BOOKROOM
133 Woodlands Road
Glasgow G3 6LE
(0141) 332 1760
Mon-Fri 9:30-5, Sat 10:30-4
Est. 1961. Small. Spec: Theol: Cat: 6 pa: Theol. Buys: Anytime. cc: AV. BR: Glasgow Central. "New books as well."
Manager: M. Morrison

GILMOREHILL BOOKS
43 Bank Street
Glasgow G12 6NE
(0141) 339 7504
Mon-Sat 10-6
Est. 1982. Medium. Spec: Humanities: also Gen Stock. Buys: Anytime. Tube: Kelvinbridge. "V. near Glasgow University, off Gibson St. & Great Western Road, North-West City."
Owner: Mr G. McGonigle

COOPER HAY RARE BOOKS
203 Bath Street
Glasgow G2 4HZ
(0141) 226 3074 (tel/fax)
Mon-Fri 10-5, Sat 10-1
Small. Spec: Scot: also Gen Stock and Art, Atqn. Cat: 6 pa. Buys: Ring first. Book search. BR: Glasgow Central. "Maps and prints."
Owner: Cooper Hay

VOLTAIRE & ROUSSEAU
12-14 Otago Lane
Glasgow G11 7QY
(0141) 339 1811
Mon-Sat 11-6:30
Est. 1972. Medium. Spec: Scot: also Gen Stock and Lit, Art. Buys: Anytime. BR: Glasgow Central.
Owner: Joseph McGonigle

GREENOCK

WESTWORDS
14 Newton Street
Strathclyde
Greenock
(01475) 892467
Mon-Sat 9:30-5:30
Est. 1982. Large. Gen Stock. Buys: Ring first. BR: Greenock West.
Owner: Olav Dennison

HADDINGTON

T.B. & J.N. GRAY
3 Lodge Street
Haddington EH14 3PX
(0162082) 5851 (tel/fax)
Mon-Sat 10-5
Medium. Spec: Mid E, Russia & E. Eur: also Gen Stock and Nat Hist, Biog, Hist. Cat: 3 pa: Mid E, Nat Hist, Gen. Buys: Anytime. Book search. cc: AV. BR: Drem. "Just off High Street next to Jane Welsh Carlyle Museum. Haddington is 1/4 mile off A1."
Owner: Mrs J.N. Gray

HAWICK

WATERSPADE SECONDHAND BOOKSHOP
23A Buccleuch Street
Hawick TD9 0HH
(01450) 378566
Mon-Fri 10-4, Tue close, Sat 10-1
Est. 1991. Small. Spec: Scot Borders, Nat Hist: also Gen Stock and Railway. Cat: occ. Buys: Anytime. Book search. BR: Carlisle. "On A7. Opp Hawick High School. Ample parking. Small general s'hand bookshop on A7. Also open on request outside hours. Please phone first."
Owner: David A. Hill

HELENSBURGH

McLAREN BOOKS
91 West Clyde Street
Strathclyde
Helensburgh G84 8BB
(01436) 676453
Fax (01436) 820487
Mon-Sat 9:30-1, 2-5:30 (Oct-Mar, Wed close)
Est. 1976. Medium. Spec: Yachting, Naval: also Gen Stock and Maritime, Scot. Cat: 4-5 pa: Nautical, 1-2 pa: Scot, Gen. Buys: Ring first. cc: AVAmE. BR: Helensburgh. "Easy parking. Good gen. stock, largest maritime selections in Scotland."
Owner: George Newlands

HELMSDALE

KILDONAN BOOKS & ANTIQUES
11 Dunrobin Street
Helmsdale KW8 6JA
(01431) 821412
March-Oct
Small. Gen Stock and Scot Topog, Po, 1sts. Buys: Anytime. Book search. BR: Helmsdale. "Good broad base of stock on various subjects."
Owner: Hazel MacMillan

INVERNESS

BOOKS ETCETERA
8 Market Hall
Highland
Inverness IV1 4JP
(01463) 712040 (tel/fax)
Mon-Sat 9:30-5:30
Est. 1990. Medium. Gen Stock. Buys: Anytime. cc: AVAmE. BR: Inverness. "Opp. BR, at back of market. Also chess sets, bric-a-brac, & games."
Owner: Mrs D. Mackenzie

THE INVERNESS SECONDHAND BOOKSHOP
Greyfriars Hall
Church Street, Highlands
Inverness IV1 1EA
(01463) 239947
Mon-Sat 10-5:30
Est. 1979. Large. Spec: Scot: also Gen Stock and Lit, Hist. Buys: Anytime. BR: Inverness. "2 min from town centre. Large turnover of interesting books, also large stock of maps and prints."
Owner: Charles Leakey

ISLE OF IONA

THE IONA BOOKSHOP
Old Printing Press Building
Strathclyde
Isle of Iona PA76 6SL
(01681) 700304/700335
Mon-Sun 10:30-4:30 (Winter by appt)
Est. 1978. Small. Spec: Scot: also Gen Stock. Buys: Anytime. BR: Oban.
Owners: Angus & Alison Johnston

KELSO

BORDER BOOKS
The Bookshop
47-51 Horsemarket, Borders
Kelso TD5 7BT
(01573) 225861
Mon-Sat 10-4:30
Medium. Spec: Scot Borders, Field Sports: also Gen Stock and Trav, Nat Hist, Trans. Buys: Anytime. Book search. cc: AV. BR: Berwick on Tweed.
Owner: Ronald Hodges

KIRKCALDY

BOOK-ENDS
449 High Street
Kirkcaldy KY1 2SN
(01592) 205294
Tue-Sat 10-5
Est. 1990. Medium. Gen Stock. Buys: Ring first. Book search. BR: Kirkcaldy. "Housed in the oldest building in town– Sailor's Walk- a National Trust property. Opposite inner dock of the harbour."
Owner: Mrs A. Anthony

KIRKCUDBRIGHT

THE STUDIO BOOKSHOP
Gas Lane
Kirkcudbright DG7 4HX
Tue-Sat 10-12:30, 2-4:30
Small. Gen Stock and Pbks, Scot. BR: Dumfries. "Near to car park in pleasant town. By the Post Office. Small to medium-sized gen stock."
Owner: Jean M. Terry

MONTROSE

S. JORDAN (BOOKSELLER)
91 Murray Street
Montrose DD10 8JZ
(01674) 672252
Tue 10:30-12:30, Thur-Fri 10:30-3:45, Sat 10:30-4:30
Est. 1981. Medium. Spec: NE Scot, Violet Jacob: also Gen Stock. Buys: Ring first. BR: Montrose. "On A92, Dundee to Aberdeen. Small selection of remainders."
Owner: Susan Jordan

NEWPORT-ON-TAY

MAIR WILKES BOOKS
3 St. Mary's Lane
Newport-on-Tay DD6 8AH
(01382) 542260 (tel/fax)
Sat 10-5:30
Est. 1969. Medium. Spec: Scot, Psy: also Gen Stock. Cat: 3 pa: Scot, Psy. Buys: Anytime. Book search.
Owners: J. Mair & A. Wilkes

PAISLEY

ABBEY BOOKS
16 Gordon Street
Paisley PA1 1XD
(0141) 887 7303
Mon-Sat 10:15- 5:45
Est. 1984. Medium. Spec: Scot: also Gen Stock and Lit, Fict. Buys: Ring first. Book search. BR: Paisley Central. "Parking possible. General readers' mixed stock & fine art greeting cards."
Owner: Susan Dennison

PERTH

PERTH BOOKSHOP
3A Abbot Street
Craigie
Perth PH2 0EB
(01738) 633970
Mon-Sat 10-5, Wed close (Jan-Mar, Thur-Sat 10-5) (or by appt)
Est. 1976. Medium. Gen Stock and Islands. Buys: Anytime. BR: Perth. "Free parking available. Near BR and bus station. BR 5 min. With emphasis on non-fict (especially man's influence on his environment) - Loc Hist, Atec, Soc Hist, Tech, etc."
Owner: Leslie Fraser

ST. ANDREWS

BILLSON OF ST. ANDREWS
15 Greyfriar's Garden
St. Andrews KY16 9HG
(01334) 475063 (tel/fax)
Mon-Sat 10-1, 2:30-5, Thur close
Small. Spec: Scot. Buys: Anytime. cc: AV. BR: Leuchars. "Probably the finest selection of Scottish antique maps & prints for sale."
Owner: David Waugh

BOUQUINISTE
31 Market Street
St. Andrews KY16 9NS
(01334) 476724
Mon-Sat 10-5 (Winter, Thur close)
Est. 1982. Medium. Gen Stock. Buys: Ring first. BR: Leuchars. "All s'hand. Also postcards."
Owners: Mr & Mrs Anderson

A. & F. McILREAVY RARE & INTERESTING BOOKS
57 South Street
St. Andrews KY16 9QR
(01334) 472487
Mon-Sat 9:30-5
Est. 1976. Medium. Gen Stock and Nat Hist, Art, Lit. Cat: 2 pa: Gen. Buys: Anytime. cc: AVJ. BR: Leuchars. "Formerly in Melbourne."
Owners: Fiona & Alan McIlreavy

QUARTO BOOKSHOP
8 Golf Place
St. Andrews KY16 9JA
(01334) 474616
Mon-Sat 10-1, 2:15-5:30
Est. 1969. Medium. Spec: Golf: also Gen Stock and Scot, Acad. Buys: Ring first. Book search. BR: Leuchars. "4 golf courses in St. Andrews. We also do a wide range of new golf books & new serious pbks."
Owner: Margaret Squires

STIRLING

R. & B. D. McCUTCHEON
30 Spittal Street
Stirling FK8 1DU
(01786) 461771
Mon-Sat 10-5
Est. 1964. Large. Gen Stock. Buys: Anytime. BR: Stirling. "Large selection of both coloured, mounted and Black/White unmounted antique prints always available. Good selection of postcards, posters, ephemera. 2 floors."
Owners: R. & B.D. McCutcheon

STRATHCARRON

BLYTHSWOOD BOOKSHOP
Lochcarron
Strathcarron IV54 8YD
(01520) 722337 (tel/fax)
Mon-Fri 9-5:30 (Sat, phone first)
Est. 1988. Small. Spec: Religious: also Gen Stock. Cat: 4 pa: Rel (dep on supply). Buys: Ring first. Book search. cc: AVAm. BR: Strathcarron. "Turn left at West end of Lochcarron village. We sell Evangelical books in aid of Christian charity."
Manager: Peter Reynolds

WEST LINTON

LINTON BOOKS
Deanfoot Road
West Linton EH46 7DY
(01968) 660339
Same
Apr-Sept 11-6, Oct-Mar 2-5
Est. 1994. Medium. Spec: Scot, Fict: also Countryside, Chld. Buys: Anytime. Book search. BR: Carstairs Junction. "Also maps, prints, scores, postcards. Framing & bookbinding service. New books and Talking books. Photocopying service."
Owner: Derek Watson

WIGTOWN

THE BOOKSHOP
17 North Main Street
Wigtown DG8 9HL
(01988) 402499 (tel/fax)
Mon-Sat 9-5
Large. Spec: Scot: also Gen Stock. Buys: Anytime. Book search. "6 miles off A75. Near Newton Stewart. Gallery (pictures), Bric-a-Brac, antiques. Browsers welcome."
Owner: John Carter

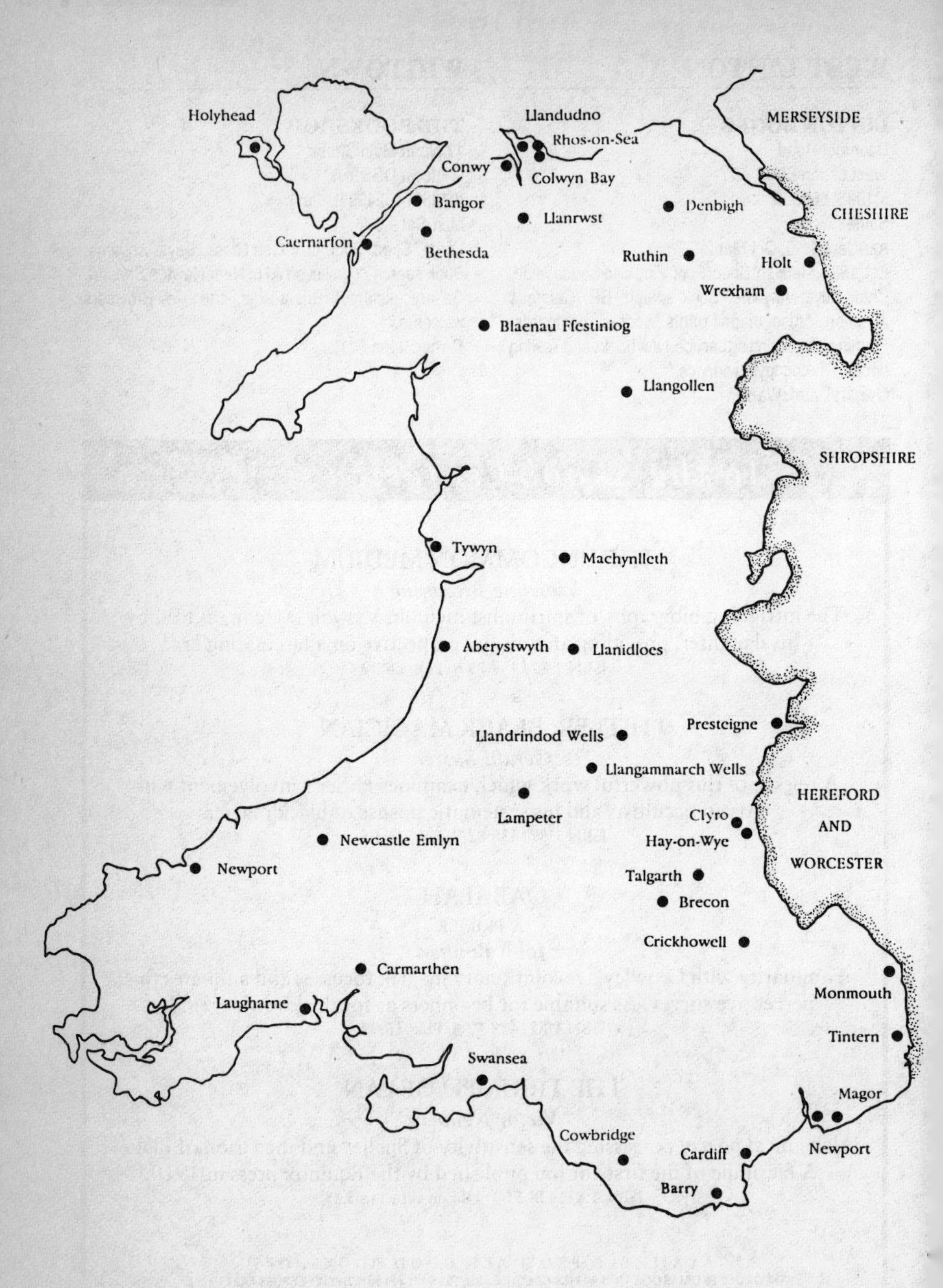
Holyhead
Llandudno
Rhos-on-Sea
Conwy
Colwyn Bay
MERSEYSIDE
Bangor
Llanrwst
Denbigh
CHESHIRE
Caernarfon
Bethesda
Ruthin
Holt
Wrexham
Blaenau Ffestiniog
Llangollen
SHROPSHIRE
Tywyn
Machynlleth
Aberystwyth
Llanidloes
Presteigne
Llandrindod Wells
Llangammarch Wells
HEREFORD
AND
WORCESTER
Lampeter
Clyro
Hay-on-Wye
Newcastle Emlyn
Newport
Talgarth
Brecon
Crickhowell
Carmarthen
Monmouth
Laugharne
Tintern
Swansea
Magor
Cowbridge
Cardiff
Newport
Barry

WALES

ABERYSTWYTH

YSTWYTH BOOKS

7 Princess Street
Dyfed
Aberystwyth SY23 1DX
(01970) 617511
Mon-Sat 10-5:15, Wed close
Est. 1977. Medium. Gen Stock and Lit, Hist, Tech. Buys: Anytime. BR: Aberystwyth. "Up market, well-organised stock and new books. No postal business."
Owner: Mrs H. Hinde

BANGOR

USEFUL BOOKS

122 High Street
Bangor
(01248) 352695/(01286) 678668
Mon-Sat 9:30-5 (Jan-Apr, Wed 9:30-1)
Medium. Spec: Welsh (in Eng): also Gen Stock and Lit, Theol, Railways. Buys: Ring first. BR: Bangor. "100 yds from Cathedral."
Owner: Mrs Christine Williams

BETHESDA

A.E. MORRIS

40 High Street
Bethesda LL57 3AN
(01248) 602533
Mon-Sat 10-5:30 (Winter 10-5 or by appt)
Est. 1987. Medium. Gen Stock and Leather-bound books, Plate books. Buys: Anytime. cc: AV. BR: Bangor. "If closed, please ring doorbell."
Owner: A.E. Morris

BLAENAU FFESTINIOG

SIOP LYFRAU'R HEN BOST

45 Stryd Fawr
Gwynedd
Blaenau Ffestiniog LL41 3AA
(01766) 831802
Mon-Sat 9:30-5:30
Est. 1982. Medium. Spec: Wales, Hist: also Gen Stock. Buys: Anytime. BR: Blaenau Ffestiniog.
Owner: Elin Angharad

BRECON

D.G. & A.S. EVANS (BOOKS, MAPS, PRINTS)

7 The Struet
Brecon LD3 7LL
(01874) 622714
Mon-Sat 9-1, 2-5, Wed 9-1
Est. 1972. Small. Spec: Wales: also Gen Stock. Buys: Anytime. cc: Am. BR: Abergavenny. "Maps, prints, and books - Wales, antiques, art."
Owners: Ann & Gwyn Evans

CAERNARFON

BALCONY BOOKSHOP

The Old Market Hall
Palace Street, Gwynedd
Caernarfon LL55 1RR
(01286) 677688
Mon-Sat 11-5 (Win, Thur close)
Est. 1988. Medium. Gen Stock and Lit, Atqn. Buys: Anytime. Book search. BR: Bangor. "Some Welsh books and new books."
Owners: P. Hunter, L. Stanley & J. Tydeman

CARDIFF

CAPITAL BOOKSHOP

27 Morgan Arcade
Cardiff CF1 2AF
(01222) 388423
Mon-Fri 10-5:30
Est. 1980. Medium. Spec: Wales: also Gen Stock and Lit, Hist, Trav. Buys: Anytime. Book search. BR: Cardiff Central. "City centre, 5 min from BR. Fast turnover. Welsh interest speciality. Price range 20p-£2,000."
Owner: Andrew Mitchell

LAND OF THE GREEN GINGER
Salisbury Road
Cathays
Cardiff CF2 4AA
(01222) 226300
Mon-Sat 10-6
Est. 1993. Small. Gen Stock. Buys: Ring first. "Near the university. General stock, aimed towards the academic market."
Owner: Kevin Cram

PONTCANNA OLD BOOKS, MAPS & PRINTS
1 Pontcanna Street
Cardiff CF1 9HQ
(01222) 641047
Mon-Sat 10-5:30
Medium. Spec: Welsh, Mil Hist: also Gen Stock and Illus. Cat: 4 pa: Mil. Buys: Anytime. cc: V. BR: Cardiff Central. "20 min walk from centre, or bus to Llandaf Fields/Pontcanna. Also maps and prints."
Owners: M. Bartlett & A. Beynon

ROATH BOOKS
188 City Road
Roath
Cardiff CF2 3JF
(01222) 490523
Mon-Sat 10:30-5:30
Est. 1977. Medium. Gen Stock and Chld. Buys: Anytime. BR: Cardiff Central. "Children's books, comics, anuuals, etc. especially 1920s, 30s & 40s."
Owner: Mr Viv Cooper

TROUTMARK BOOKS
41/43 Castle Arcade
Cardiff
(01222) 382814
Mon-Sat 10-5:30
Est. 1995. Medium. Spec: Pbk Fict, Educational Non-Fict: also Gen Stock and Comics, Magazines, Psy. Buys: Anytime. BR: Cardiff Central. "Situated in Castle Arcade, opp. Cardiff Castle. 2 floors of quality books & magazines. We exchange, buy or sell."
Owner: Mr C. Rogers

WHITCHURCH BOOKS LTD
67 Merthyr Road
Whitchurch
Cardiff CF4 1DD
(01222) 521956 (tel/fax)
Mon-Sat 9:45-6
Est. 1994. Medium. Spec: Arch: also Gen Stock and Hist. Cat: 8 pa: Arch, Hist. Buys: Ring first. Book search. cc: AVEJ. BR: Llandaff. "Off M4 at Junction 32. South on A4054 (signposted Whitchurch) 1 mile."
Directors: G. Canvin & M. Hunt

CARMARTHEN

CARMARTHEN BOOKS
1 St. Mary Street
Off Guildhall Square
Carmarthen SA17 1TN
(01267) 235676/(01566) 685778
Mon-Sat (ring first)
Est. 1982. Medium. Spec: Atqn: also Gen Stock and Illus, Wales. Buys: Anytime. cc: AV. BR: Carmarthen. "Town centre - plenty of parking."
Owners: L.R. & H.M. Privett

PICTON BOOKS
28 Lammas Street
Carmarthen SA31 3AL
(01267) 232940
Mon-Sat 9:30-5
Medium. Gen Stock. Buys: Anytime. Book search. cc: AV. BR: Carmarthen.
Owner: Mrs M. Stretch

CLYRO

MARIJANA DWORSKI BOOKS
Wye Pottery
Clyro HR3 5LB
(01497) 821613 (tel/fax)
Mon-Fri 10-5:30 (phone first)
Small. Spec: For. Dictionaries & Grammar, E. Eur: Cat: 3 pa: listed subjs. Buys: Ring first. BR: Hereford/ Abergavenny. "1 1/2 mi from Hay, on main A438 Brecon-Hereford. Ample parking. Wide range of languages, Slavonic and E. Eur. Early and modern phrasebooks. Good stock of E. Eur acad and travel."
Owner: Marijana Dworski

COLWYN BAY

BAY BOOKSHOP
14 Seaview Road
Clwyd
Colwyn Bay LL29 8DG
(01492) 531642
Mon-Sat 9-5:30
Est. 1973. Large. Gen Stock. Buys: Anytime. BR: Colwyn Bay. "Opp. Colwyn Centre. Good parking. Large selection , s'hand, new, and Atqn books, also ephermera and postcards."
Owner: A.S. Morley

COLWYN BOOKS
66 Abergele Road
Colwyn Bay LL29 7PP
(01492) 530683
Mon-Sat 9-6 (Winter, Wed close)
Est. 1989. Medium. Spec: Theol, France: also Gen Stock. Buys: Anytime. Book search. BR: Colwyn Bay. "On main road through town at east end. WBA."
Owner: J. Owen

CONWY

THE BOOKSHOP (CONWY)
21 High Street
Conwy LL32 8DE
(01492) 592137
Mon-Sat 10-6, Sun 11-1 (Win, Mon-Sat 10-5, ec Wed)
Medium. Spec: Maritime: also Gen Stock and Lit, Trav. Buys: Anytime. BR: Llandudno Junction.
Owners: Dorothy & David Crewe

COWBRIDGE

ARCADE BOOKSHOP
Northgate Way
High Street
Cowbridge CF7 7AE
(01443) 774500
Tue-Sat 10-5
Est. 1993. Medium. Gen Stock. Buys: Anytime. Book search. BR: Bridgend.
Owner: Phil Davies

CRICKHOWELL

MONMOUTH HOUSE BOOKS
The Cheese Press
18 High Street
Crickhowell
(01873) 811122
Fax (01600) 780532
Mon-Sat 9-5, Wed 9-12:30 (Sun hours vary)
Est. 1985. Small. Spec: Atec: also Gen Stock and Arch. Cat: 4 pa: Atec. Buys: Ring first. Book search. cc: AVAmD. BR: Abergavenny. "Other stock is held at Monmouth House, Llanfapley, Abergavenny, Gwent NP7 8SN (01600) 780236."
Owner: Richard Sidwell

DENBIGH

FAGIN'S BOOKSHOP
43 Vale Street
Denbigh LL16 3AH
(01745) 816774
Tue-Sat 10-5
Est. 1993. Large. Spec: Trav, Hist: also Gen Stock. Buys: Ring first. "Large premises with interesting, varied and well laid-out general stock."
Owner: Joseph A. Heacock

HAY-ON-WYE

ADDYMAN BOOKS
39 Lion Street
Hay-on-Wye HR3 5AA
(01497) 821136
Mon-Sat 10-6 (Sun 11-6, ring first)
Est. 1987. Large. Spec: 1sts, Lit: also Gen Stock. Cat: 2 pa: 1sts, Lit. Buys: Anytime. cc: V. BR: Hereford.
Owners: Derek Addyman & Anne Brichto

C. ARDEN (BOOKSELLER)
Radnor House
Church Street
Hay-on-Wye HR3 5DQ
(01497) 820471 (tel/fax)
Mon-Sun 10:30-5:30 (in season)
Est. 1994. Medium. Spec: Nat Hist, Biol: also Gen Stock and Ornith, Botany, Gard. Cat: 3-4 pa: Spec subjs. Buys: Ring first. BR: Hereford. "Also 'New Naturalist' series."
Owner: C. Arden

J. GEOFFREY ASPIN
The Rare Bookshop
27 Castle Street
Hay-on-Wye HR3 5DF
(01497) 820437
Mon-Sat 10-5:30 (Winter 11-5)
Est. 1963. Large. Spec: Continental Atqn, Old & rare Bibles: also Gen Stock and Prayer Books, Classics, Eng Lit. Cat: 1 pa: Continental, 1 pa: Eng. Buys: Anytime. cc: AVJS. BR: Hereford. "Prices range from 30p-£5,000."
Owner: J. Geoffrey Aspin

B & K BOOKS OF HAY-ON-WYE
Riverside
Newport Street
Hay-on-Wye HR3 5BG
(01497) 821004 (tel/fax)
Mon-Sat 9-5
Est. 1962. Small. Spec: Bees/Apiculture etc: also JH Fabre, Morris Maeterlinck. Cat: 2 pa: Bees. Buys: Ring first. BR: Hereford. "Smallest b'shop in Hay with the largest range of titles on bees in the world."
Owners: Betty & Karl Showler

BOOK WAREHOUSE
The Old Drill Hall
25 Lion Street
Hay-on-Wye HR3 5AD
(01497) 821679
Fax (01497) 821681
Mon-Sat 10-5:30, Sun 10:30-5 (later on in B/Hols & Summer)
Est. 1994. Large. Gen Stock. Buys: Anytime. cc: AVAmD. BR: Hereford. "Thousands of books on all subjects in 3000 square feet, 2 floors and a cellar. Also maps & ephemera."
Owner: Castle Street Books

THE BOOKSHOP
The Pavement
Hay-on-Wye HR3 5BU
(01497) 821341
Mon-Sun 9-8
Large. Gen Stock. Buys: Ring first. Book search. cc: AV. BR: Hereford.
Owners: R. Thompson & A.W.E. Cooke

RICHARD BOOTH BOOKS
44 Lion Street
Hay-on-Wye HR3 5AA
(01497) 821322
Fax (01497) 821150
Mon-Sat 9-8 (Winter 9-5:30) Sun 11:30-5:30
Est. 1961. Large. Spec: Theol, Topog: also Gen Stock and USA, Lit, Periodicals. Buys: Anytime. Book search. cc: AVAm. BR: Hereford. "The famous b'shop of Hay, over 400,000 books."
Owner: Richard Booth

BOURNVILLE BOOKS
19 Brecon Road
Hay-on-Wye HR3 5DY
(01497) 820002
Mon-Sun 9-8 (Winter 9-6)
Small. Spec: Atqn. Buys: Ring first. BR: Hereford. "300 yards from town centre. Dealers in old and Atqn books."

BOZ BOOKS
13A Castle Street
Hay-on-Wye HR3 5DF
(01497) 821277 (tel/fax)
Mon-Sat 10-1, 2-5 (Nov-Mar, ring first)
Medium. Spec: Dickens, Austen & Brontes: also Gen Stock and 1sts & Early editions, C19th authors. Cat: 1 pa: Lit. Buys: Anytime. cc: AV. BR: Hereford. "Always interested in buying good quality books across all fields."
Owner: Peter Harries

CASTLE STREET BOOKS
23 Castle Street
Hay-on-Wye HR3 5DF
(01497) 820160
Mon-Sat 10-1, 2-5:30, Sun 11-4:30 (later in Summer)
Medium. Spec: Art, Collecting: also Gen Stock and Mills & Boon, Large Print. Buys: Ring first. Book search. cc: AVAmD. BR: Hereford. "Good parking. New books, stationery, maps & prints."
Owner: Edward Foreman

THE CHILDREN'S BOOKSHOP
Toll Cottage
Pontvaen
Hay-on-Wye HR3 5EW
(01497) 821083 (tel/fax)
Mon-Sun 9:30-5:30 (eve by appt)
Medium. Spec: Chld: Cat: occ. Buys: Ring first. Book search. cc: AV. BR: Hereford. "1 mile from main car park on B4350 (Clifford Road). Parking available. The only bookshop in Hay that only sells children's books. Cater for both children & collectors."
Owner: Judith Gardner

THE CHILDREN'S BOOKSHOP NO.2
The Backfold
Hay-on-Wye HR3 5DL
(01497) 821655
Mon-Sun 10-5:30
Est. 1994. Small. Spec: Chld. Buys: Ring first. BR: Hereford. "Small stock aimed at children rather than collectors."
Owner: Judith Gardner

FRANCIS EDWARDS
The Old Cinema
Castle Street
Hay-on-Wye HR3 5DF
(01497) 820071
Fax (01497) 821900
Mon-Sat 9-7, Sun 11:30-5:30
Est. 1855. Medium. Spec: Trav, Art: also Gen Stock and Lit, Nat Hist, Acad. Cat: 35 pa: listed subjs, Recent acquisitions. Buys: Anytime. Book search. cc: AVAmD. "Also world's largest outside b'shop of cheap books."
Owner: Hay Cinema Bookshop Ltd

FISHER'S BOOKSHOP
6 Broad Street
Hay-on-Wye HR3 5DB
(01497) 821554
Mon-Sun 10-6 (later in Summer)
Est. 1994. Large. Gen Stock. Buys: Anytime. BR: Hereford. "Large stock of quality s'hand & Atqn books on most subjects."

HAY CASTLE (BOOTH BOOKS)
Hay Castle
Hay-on-Wye HR3 5DL
(01497) 820503
Fax (01497) 821314
Mon-Sun 9:30-5:30 (Winter 9-5:30) close 25 Dec
Est. 1987. Medium. Spec: Art, Photo: also American Indians, Cinema, Fine Bindings. Buys: Anytime. Book search. cc: AV. BR: Hereford. "Large area of gen stock at 50p outside."
Owner: Hope Booth

HAY CINEMA BOOKSHOP
Castle Street
Hay-on-Wye HR3 5DF
(01497) 820071
Fax (01497) 821900
Mon-Sat 9-7, Sun 11:30-5:30
Large. Gen Stock. Buys: Anytime. Book search. cc: AVAmD. BR: Hereford. "Converted cinema. Running stock of 200,000 on gen. subjects. 2 floors, inc. Francis Edwards."
Owner: Hay Cinema Bookshop Ltd

HAY-ON-WYE BOOKSELLERS
14 High Town
Hay-on-Wye HR3 5PR
(01497) 820875
Mon-Sun 9-5:30 (Summer, longer hours)
Est. 1976. Large. Gen Stock and Atqn, Fine bindings. Buys: Anytime. BR: Hereford.
Owners: Messrs M. & G. Bullock

INDEPENDENT TOURIST INFORMATION CENTRE & FIVE STAR BOOKSHOP
Backfold
Hay-on-Wye HR3 5AJ
(01497) 820164
Fax (01497) 821314
Mon-Sun 9-5:30
Est. 1989. Small. Spec: SF, Horror: also Trans, Avia, Astronomy. Buys: Anytime. Book search. cc: AV. BR: Hereford. "Honesty 50p general section open 24 hours. Postcards, stamps & cigarette cards."
Owner: Booth Books (Richard Booth)

LION STREET BOOKS
36 Lion Street
Hay-on-Wye HR3 5AB
(01497) 820121 (tel/fax)
Mon-Sun 10-6
Est. 1995. Medium. Spec: Boxing, Mil, Anarchism: also Gen Stock and Kennedy Assassination, American Indian. Cat: 6 pa: Boxing. Buys: Anytime. Book search. BR: Hereford. "Single items and collections quoted."
Owner: Mark Williams

MARCHES GALLERY
Lion Street (corner of High Town)
Hay-on-Wye HR3 5AA
(01497) 821451
Mon-Sat 10-5 (Sun, ring first)
Est. 1994. Small. Spec: Theol, Church Hist: also Gen Stock. Buys: Ring first. BR: Hereford. "Paintings and drawings by Trevor Taylor."
Owners: B. & E. Carter

THE OLD PENGUIN BOOKSHOP
22 Broad Street
Hay-on-Wye HR3 5DB
(01497) 821225
Mon-Sat 10:30-6 (Sun in Summer)
Medium. Spec: Pbks, Peng: also Mod Fict, Classics, Crime. Buys: Anytime. BR: Hereford.
Owners: A. Halsey & R. Hayles

OUTCAST BOOKS
12 Oxford Road
Hay-on-Wye HR3 5AJ
(01497) 820265
Thur-Sat 10-5 (otherwise ring)
Small. Spec: Psy: also Gen Stock and Soc Studs. Cat: occ: Psychotherapy. Buys: Anytime. Book search. BR: Hereford. "Small gen s'hand stock with emphasis on applied soc. stud. and human relations."
Owner: David Howard

PHOTOGRAPHIC BOOKSHOP - BLINKING IMAGES
Oxford Road
Hay-on-Wye HR3 5DG
(01497) 820171 (tel/fax)
Mon-Sun 10-5
Est. 1994. Small. Spec: Photo: Cat: Lists: Photo. Buys: Anytime. Book search. cc: AVS. BR: Hereford. "Every aspect of Photography. Worldwide mail order. Prices from 50p."
Owner: Haydn Pugh

THE POETRY BOOKSHOP
West House
Broad Street
Hay-on-Wye HR3 5DB
(01497) 820305
Mon-Sun 10:30-6 (off season Sun close)
Est. 1979. Medium. Spec: Poetry: Cat: 4-5 pa: Poetry. Buys: Ring first. Book search. BR: Hereford.
Owner: Alan Halsey

ROSE'S BOOKS
14 Broad Street
Hay-on-Wye HR3 5DB
(01497) 820013
Mon-Sat 9:30-5:30
Est. 1981. Small. Gen Stock and Chld, Illus. Buys: Ring first. BR: Hereford. "By the clocktower. Also new books and greeting cards."
Owner: Maria Bradshaw

TRANSPORT BOOKSHOPS (BOOTH BOOKS)
Hay Castle
Hay-on-Wye HR3 5DL
(01497) 820503
Fax (01497) 821314
Mon-Sun 9:30-5:30, close 25 Dec
Est. 1988. Small. Spec: Trans, Industrial Arch. Buys: Ring first. Book search. cc: AVAm. BR: Hereford. "We stock only the subjects specialised above but carry a wide range in them."

WEST HOUSE BOOKS
Broad Street
Hay-on-Wye HR3 5DB
(01497) 821225
Mon-Sun 10:30-6
Est. 1990. Medium. Spec: Chld, Mysticism and Myth: Cat: 3 pa: 1 each in listed subjs. Buys: Anytime. Book search. BR: Hereford. "Large selection of Chld's and Illus annuals, etc. Emphasis on Arthuriana and Celtica in the mythology section."
Owner: Rosie Hayles

MARK WESTWOOD BOOKS
High Town
Hay-on-Wye HR3 5AE
(01497) 820068
Mon-Sat 10:30-5:30 (Sun in Summer)
Medium. Spec: Acad: also Gen Stock and Atqn, Tech. Cat: 4 pa: History of Ideas, Med. Buys: Anytime. BR: Hereford.
Owner: Mark Westwood

HOLT nr. Wrexham

CASTLE BOOKSHOP
Castle Street
Holt (nr. Wrexham) LL13 9YW
(01829) 270382
Fax (01892) 271087
Thur-Sat 10-5
Est. 1987. Large. Spec: Welsh Topog and Lang: also Gen Stock and Cheshire, Arch, Clocks & Silver. Cat: 12 pa: Wales, Borders, Arch. Buys: Ring first. Book search. BR: Wrexham/Chester. "Own forecourt parking. 5 miles Wrexham, 8 miles Chester."
Owners: N., E. & S. Moore

HOLYHEAD

ANGLESEY BOOKS
1 Thomas Street
Anglesey, Gwynedd
Holyhead LL65 1RR
(01407) 760988
Fax (01407) 810121
Mon-Sat 10-4:30 (ec Tue)
Est. 1981. Medium. Spec: Mount, Trav: also Wales. Cat: 2-3 pa: Mount, Cent Asia. Buys: Ring first. Book search. cc: A. BR: Holyhead. "Easy parking."
Owner: Jack Baines

LAMPETER

WEST WALES BOOKS
Railway Hotel
Dyfed
Lampeter SA48 7PA
(01570) 423778
Mon-Sat 10-6 (Sun in Summer)
Est. 1990. Medium. Gen Stock and Atqn, Acad. Buys: Anytime. Book search. cc: AV. BR: Carmarthen. "Interested in buying books on all academic subjects. Also new books orders."
Manager: Cris Kheser-John

LAUGHARNE

CORRAN BOOKS LTD
King Street
Laugharne SA33 4RY
(01994) 427444
Mon-Sun 11-5 (later in July & Aug)
Large. Spec: Welsh: also Dylan Thomas, Atqn, Loc. Buys: Ring first. Book search. " 'The bookshop that's as long as many a High Street' (Sunday Telegraph). Antique maps, prints & postcards. 1sts incl. Dylan Thomas - Laugharne was his home."
Owner: Jane Tremlett

LLANDIDLOES

GREAT OAK BOOKSHOP
35 Great Oak Street
Powys
Llandidloes SY18 6BW
(01686) 412959
Mon-Sat 9:30-5:30
Small. Gen Stock and Welsh. Buys: Anytime. Book search. BR: Llandrindod Wells. "Used records, tapes, and sheet music, new books, maps, and cards."
Owner: Dr A. Scrase

LLANDRINDOD WELLS

CASTLE HILL BOOKS
Ground floor, Trafford House
Temple Street, Powys
Llandrindod Wells LD1 5HG
(01544) 231195/231161
Mon-Sat 10-5, Wed close
Medium. Spec: Arch, Loc Hist: also Gen Stock and Br Topog. Cat: occ. Buys: Ring first. Book search. cc: AV. BR: Llandrindod Wells. "Easy parking."
Owner: Peter Newman

LLANDUDNO

DAVID E. HUGHES
21 Madoc Street
Llandudno LL30 2TL
(01492) 877700
Mon-Sat 9-5
Est. 1968. Medium. Gen Stock. Buys: Ring first. BR: Llandudno.
Owner: David E. Hughes

LLANGAMMARCH WELLS

CAMMARCH BOOKS
Llangammarch Wells LD4 4EB
(01591) 620517
Tue-Sun 10-5:30
Est. 1994. Medium. Spec: Theol, Hist of Rel: also Gen Stock. Cat: on req. Buys: Anytime. BR: Llangammarch Wells. "No parking problems. Gen stock of s'hand & Atqn books."
Owner: Celia Villa-Landa

LLANGOLLEN

BOOKS
Above Maximes Cafe
17 Castle Street
Llangollen LL20 8NY
(01978) 860334
Mon-Sun 10-5 (close 25 Dec, longer Summer hours)
Est. 1983. Large. Spec: Peng, SF: also Gen Stock and Lit Crit. Buys: Anytime. cc: AV. BR: Chester. "Books on most subjects. Browsers welcome. Why not visit our cafe where we serve our own home-made food."
Owner: Tibor Sever

LLANRWST

PROSPECT BOOKS & PRINTS
18 Denbigh Street
Llanrwst LL26 0AA
(01492) 640111
Tue-Sat 9-5
Est. 1987. Spec: Guns: also Gen Stock. Cat: 4 pa: Firearms & Edged weapons. Buys: Anytime. BR: Llanrwst.
Owner: M. Dingle & M. Kitching

MACHYNLLETH

COCH-Y-BONDDU BOOKS
Coedcae
Penegoes, Powys
Machynlleth SY20 8NN
(01654) 702837
Mon-Sat 9-5 (or by appt)
Medium. Spec: Fishing, Field Sports: also Big Game Hunting, Falconry, Sporting Dogs. Buys: Anytime. Book search. cc: AV. BR: Machynlleth. "2 miles from Machynlleth on the Newtown Road. Very large specialist stock including new books and remainders. Ring first if making a long trip."
Owner: Paul Morgan

DYFI VALLEY BOOKSHOP
6 Heol Y Doll
Powys
Machynlleth SY20 8BQ
(01654) 703849
Mon-Sat 9-6, Thur close (Sun in Summer) (ring first)
Est. 1988. Small. Spec: Wales, Countryside: also Gen Stock and Firearms, Archery, Fieldsports. Buys: Anytime. Book search. BR: Machynlleth. "5 min from BR."
Owner: Barbara Beeby

MAGOR nr. Newport

COOKING THE BOOKS
Croft Cottage
The Square, Gwent
Magor nr. Newport MP6 3HY
(01633) 881899
Mon, Thur-Sat 9-5:30 (ring first)
Est. 1991. Medium. Spec: Cookery: Cat: 1 every 3 wks: Cookery. Buys: Anytime. Book search. BR: Llanfihangel Rogiet. "Strong out-of-print section as well as s'hand and Atqn. Back numbers of food magazines, and ephemera."
Owner: Mr B. Cashman

MONMOUTH

STEPHEN'S BOOKSHOP
3 Church Street
Monmouth NP5 3BX
(01600) 713701
Mon-Sat 10-1, 2-5, Thur close
Est. 1968. Small. Gen Stock. Buys: Ring first. BR: Newport. "Also new books, maps & prints."
Owner: Stephen Porter

NEWCASTLE EMLYN

FRED COOPER BOOKS
1 Emlyn Square
Newcastle Emlyn SA38 9BG
(01239) 711230 (tel/fax)
Mon-Sat 9-5:30
Medium. Gen Stock. Buys: Anytime. Book search. cc: AV. BR: Carmarthen. "Friendly shop with a constantly changing stock (inc. pbks) covering all subjects. Browsers welcome. Also new books & bargains."
Owner: Dr Fred Cooper

NEWPORT

BOOKENDS
195 Upper Dock Street
Newport NP1
(01633) 222086
Mon-Sat 9-5:30
Est. 1991. Large. Gen Stock. Buys: Anytime. cc: AV. BR: Newport. "Near Kingshead Hotel. 4 storey bookshop - the largest in Gwent."
Owners: R. Thompson & A.W.E. Cooke

CARNINGLI CENTRE
East Street
Dyfed
Newport SA42 0SY
(01239) 820724
Mon-Sat 9:30-5:30 ec Wed
Est. 1982. Medium. Gen Stock and Theol, Fict, Biog. Buys: Anytime. cc: AV. BR: Fishguard/Haverfordwest. "Newport is set in the heart of the beautiful Pembrokeshire Coast National Park. We are in the main street."
Owner: Mr C.J. Field

TROUTMARK BOOKS
Newport Market
The Gallery, High Street
Newport
(01633) 216208
Mon-Sun 9-5
Est. 1992. Medium. Spec: Pbk Fict, Magazines: also Gen Stock and Non-Fict, Role-playing Games, Hbk Fict. Buys: Ring first. BR: Newport. "Upstairs in Newport Indoor Market. Mail Order available - callers welcome. We exchange, buy & sell."
Manager: Gary Greenwood

PRESTEIGNE

TONY BIRD BOOKS
2 Hereford Street
Powys
Presteigne LD8
(01544) 260316
Mon-Sun 9-6
Est. 1988. Small. Spec: Br Topog: also Gen Stock and Nat Hist. Buys: Anytime. cc: AV. BR: Knighton. "50p to £150, all subjects. Also collectables."
Owner: Tony Bird

RHOS-ON-SEA, COLWYN BAY

RHOS POINT BOOKS
85 The Promenade
Clwyd
Rhos-on-Sea, Colwyn Bay
(01492) 545236
Mon-Sun 10-5:30 (Win, Mon close)
Est. 1986. Medium. Gen Stock and Atqn. Buys: Anytime. BR: Colwyn Bay. "Shop at centre of Promenade, near pedestrian crossing."
Owners: Gwyn & Beryl Morris

RUTHIN

SPREAD EAGLE BOOKS
Upper Clwyd Street
Ruthin LL15 1HY
(01824) 703840
Mon-Sat 9:30-5:30
Est. 1978. Medium. Spec: Atqn, Thomas Pennant: also Gen Stock and Wales & Marches, Lit. Cat: 4 pa: Atqn. Buys: Ring first. Book search. BR: Chester. "On A525 between Wrexham and Rhyl, and A494 between Mold and Corwen. Also new books and Maps. Old inn, just off square. On-street parking & car parks nearby."
Owners: Keith & Janet Kenyon-Thompson

SWANSEA

DYLAN'S BOOKSTORE
Salubrious Passage
W. Glamorgan
Swansea SA1 3RT
(01792) 655255/360438
Mon-Sat 10ish-5ish
Est. 1971. Medium. Gen Stock and Dylan Thomas. Cat: oc. BR: Swansea. "Parking. Large adjacent store room open by appt."
Owner: Jeff Towns

DYLAN'S BOOKSTORE
Ty-Llen National Literature Centre
Somerset Place
Swansea
(01792) 463980
Tue-Sun 11-5:30 (occ. late opening)
Est. 1994. Small. Gen Stock. Buys: Ring first. "Atqn, s'hand & new books."
Owner: Jeff Towns

ROBERTS BOOKSHOP
12 Dillwyn Street
Swansea SA1 4AQ
(01792) 655525
Mon-Sat 9:30-5, ec Thur
Small. Spec: Theol, Fict: also Gen Stock. Buys: Anytime. BR: Swansea High Street.
Owner: R. Leonard

ROWLANDS BOOKSHOP
16 St. Helen's Road
Swansea
(01792) 654427
Mon-Sat 9-4:30
Est. 1968. Medium. Gen Stock and Novels, Non-Fict, Ref. BR: Swansea High Street. "Above Music Exchange dealing in musical instruments & equipment, records, CDs, videos, etc."
Owner: Christine Rowlands

TALGARTH

ASHBURNHAM BOOKS at the STRAND BOOKSHOP
Regent Street
Talgarth LD3 0DB
(01874) 711195 (tel/fax)
Mon-Sat 9-6 (Winter, 9:30-5:30, Wed close)
Est. 1985. Large. Spec: SF, Nat Hist: also Gen Stock and Fict, Chld. Buys: Anytime. Book search. BR: Abergavenny/Hereford. "18 miles from Abergavenny & 32 miles from Hereford. Serve tea & snacks. Small selection of s'hand stamps & greeting cards."
Owners: R. & A. Cardwell

TINTERN

STELLA BOOKS
Monmouth Road
Tintern NP6 6SE
(01291) 689755
Mon-Sun 9-5:30
Medium. Spec: Nat Hist, Chld: also Gen Stock and UK Topog, Illus, Wye Valley & District. Cat: 4 pa. Buys: Ring first. Book search. cc: AV. BR: Chepstow. "200 yards from Tintern Abbey. Picturesque setting by river."
Owner: Maria Bradshaw

TYWYN

TOWN & GOWN BOOKSHOP
Shop 9
Seafront Arcade
Tywyn LL36 0DG
(01341) 250542
Afternoons (in season)
Est. 1987. Small. Spec: Acad, Crime: also Gen Stock and Biog, Theol, Pre-War Fict. Buys: Ring first. BR: Tywyn. "BR 22 yds. Phone (eves) before making special journey."
Owner: Mr M.H. Ford

WREXHAM

GLYN'S BOOKS
1 Overton Arcade
High Street
Wrexham LL13 8LL
(01978) 355797
Mon-Sat 10-5, Wed close
Est. 1986. Medium. Spec: Lit: also Gen Stock and Mod 1sts. Buys: Ring first. Book search. cc: AV. BR: Wrexham Central. "Major international booksearch service - no fees."
Owner: Glyn Watson

NORTHERN IRELAND

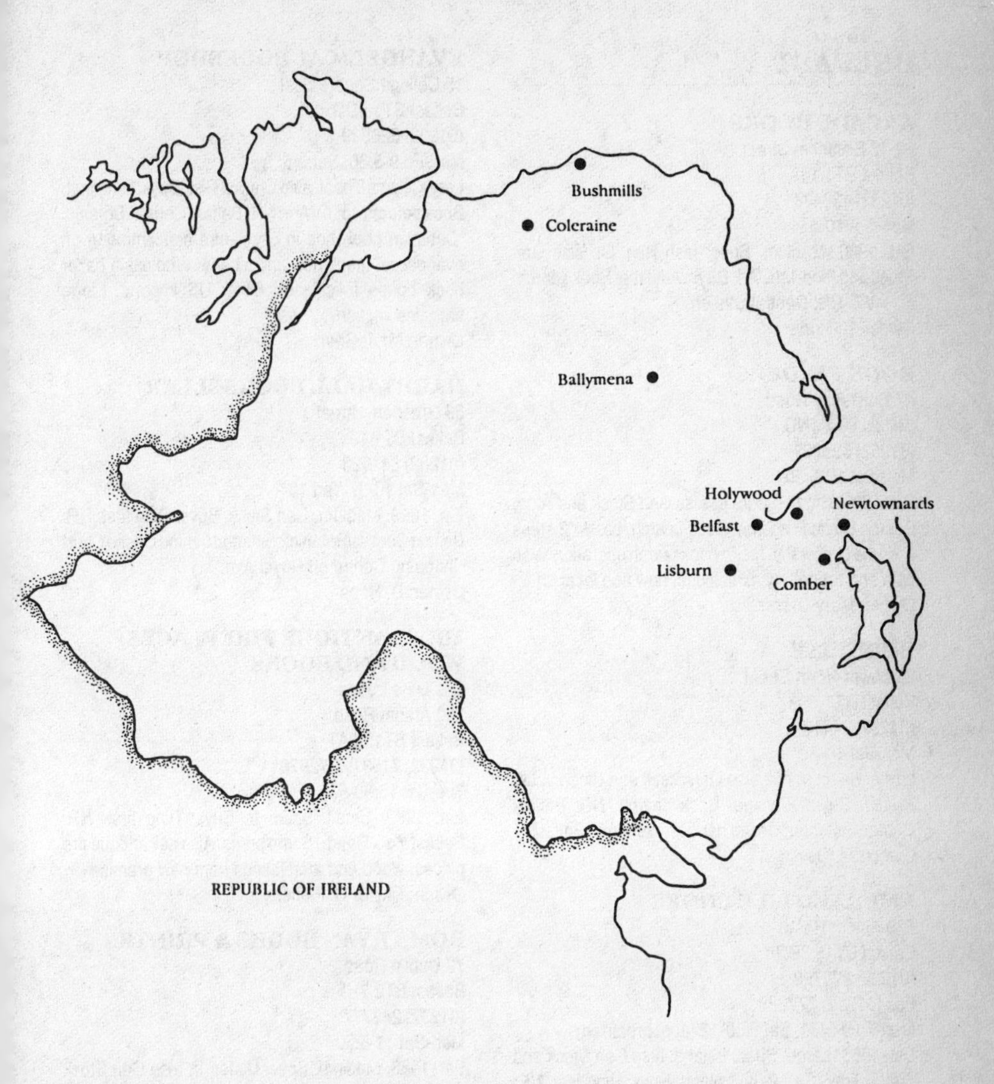

NORTHERN IRELAND

BELFAST

ARCADE BOOKS
10-12 Gresham Street
Belfast BT1 1JA
(01232) 438474
Mon-Sat 10-5
Est. 1980. Medium. Spec: Irish Hist, Lit: also Gen Stock and Mod 1sts, Art. Buys: Anytime. Book search. cc: AVE. BR: Central Station.
Owner: B. Hope

BOOK FINDERS
47 University Road
Belfast BT7 1ND
(01232) 328269
Mon-Sat 10-5:30
Est. 1986. Small. Spec: Ir: also Gen Stock and Atqn, Poetry. Buys: Ring first. Book search. cc: V. "2 steps from the University. Major booksearch operation. Also cafe and art gallery exhibitions, new and local art."
Owner: Mary Denvir

BOOKRITE
25 Lower North Street
Belfast BT1
(01232) 244137
Mon-Sat 10-5
Large. Spec: Ir, Mil: also Gen Stock and Cinema, Lit, Health. Buys: Anytime. Book search. NR: Belfast Central/Botanic. "Best s'hand bookshop in Belfast."
Owner: M. Devlin

EMERALD ISLE BOOKS
539 Antrim Road
Belfast BT15 3BU
(01232) 370798
Fax (01232) 777288
Mon-Fri 9-5:30, Sat 9:30-12 (appt preferred)
Est. 1963. Large. Spec: Ireland: also Gen Stock and Theol, Trav. Cat: 2 pa: Ireland. Buys: Ring first. NR: Belfast Central.
Owner: John A. Gamble

EVANGELICAL BOOKSHOP
15 College Square East
Belfast BT1 6DD
(01232) 320529
Mon-Fri 9-5:30, Sat 9-5
Large. Spec: Theol: also Church Hist. Buys: Ring first. Book search. cc: AVAm. NR: Belfast Central/Botanic. "Christian bookshop in city centre concentrating on evangelical theol, new and s'hand. Wholesale baker book house (Michigan). Other US imports. Large bargains section."
Owner: Mr J. Grier

HARRY HALL BOOKSELLER
39 Gresham Street
Belfast BT1 1JL
(01232) 241923
Mon-Sat 10-5, Wed 10-2
Est. 1899. Medium. Gen Stock. Buys: Ring first. NR: Belfast Central/Botanic. "Situated behind Castle Court Shopping Centre off Royal Ave."
Owner: B. Hope

MEWS ANTIQUE FIREPLACES, WOOD AND BOOKS
The Gate Lodge
260 Antrim Road
Belfast BT15 2AT
(01232) 715319/772970
Tue-Sat 10:30-5
Est. 1989. Small. Spec: Ir. Buys: Ring first. NR: Belfast York Road. "Some prints. Also sell antique fire places, wood and arch fittings from new premises."
Owner: Phyllis O' Flaherty

ROMA RYAN BOOKS & PRINTS
73 Dublin Road
Belfast BT2 7HF
(01232) 242777
Mon-Sat 11-5:30
Est. 1983. Medium. Spec: Ulster, Ir: also Gen Stock and Lit, Art, Illus. Buys: Anytime. Book search. cc: AVAmD. NR: Belfast Botanic. "Convenient car parks. Steady turnover. Also sells maps and prints."
Owner: Roma Ryan

WAR ON WANT BOOKSHOP
1 Rugby Avenue
Belfast BT7 1RD
(01232) 232064
Mon-Fri 10:30-4:30, Sat 10-1:30
Est. 1969. Medium. Gen Stock. Buys: Ring first. NR: Belfast Botanic. "Student texts. A diversity of books and the most competitive prices in the city."
Manager: Mr S. Boswell

WORLD OF BOOKS
329 Woodstock Road
Belfast BT6 8PT
(01232) 454272
Mon-Sat 10-5:30, Wed 10-5
Est. 1984. Medium. Spec: Theol: also Gen Stock and Metaphysics. Buys: Anytime. NR: Belfast Central. "10 min from city centre on city Bus 33. Only bookshop in the east of the city."
Owner: Wesley Armstrong

BUSHMILLS

CAUSEWAY BOOKS
110 Main Street
Bushmills
(012657) 32596
Mon-Fri 10-5:30, Sat 10-6
Est. 1983. Medium. Spec: Ir: also Gen Stock. Buys: Ring first.
Owner: David Speers

COLERAINE

THE COLERAINE BOOKSHOP
5 Stone Row
Coleraine BT52 1EP
(01265) 52557
Mon-Sat 10-1, 2-5, ec Thur
Est. 1976. Medium. Spec: Ir: also Gen Stock and Lit, Hist. Buys: Ring first. NR: Coleraine. "50 yards from the Abbey Street car park. New books of local interest."
Owner: John McClements

COMBER

WORLD OF BOOKS
44 Castle Street
Comber
Down
(01247) 874397
Mon-Sat 10-5:30, Wed 10-5
Medium. Spec: Theol: also Gen Stock and Metaphysics. Buys: Anytime. "Bus from Belfast to Comber."
Owner: Wesley Armstrong

HOLYWOOD

WORLD OF BOOKS
13 Downshire Road
Holywood
Down
(01232) 427099
Mon-Sat 10-5:30, Wed 10-5
Medium. Spec: Theol: also Gen Stock and Metaphysics. Buys: Anytime. "Bus from Belfast to Holywood city centre."
Owner: Wesley Armstrong

LISBURN

THE BOOK NOOK
15 Antrim Street
Lisburn
(01846) 607394
Mon-Sat 9:30-5:30
Est. 1987. Medium. Spec: Ir: also Gen Stock and Mil, 1sts. Buys: Ring first. Book search. NR: Lisburn. "Near town centre. Bargain books."
Owner: Norman Mulholland

NEWTOWNARDS

WORLD OF BOOKS
37 West Street
Newtownards
(01247) 820588
Mon-Sat 10-5:30, Wed 10-5
Medium. Spec: Theol: also Gen Stock and Metaphysics. Buys: Anytime. "Bus from Belfast to Newtownards city centre."
Owner: Wesley Armstrong

Channel Islands

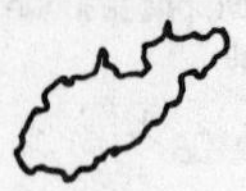

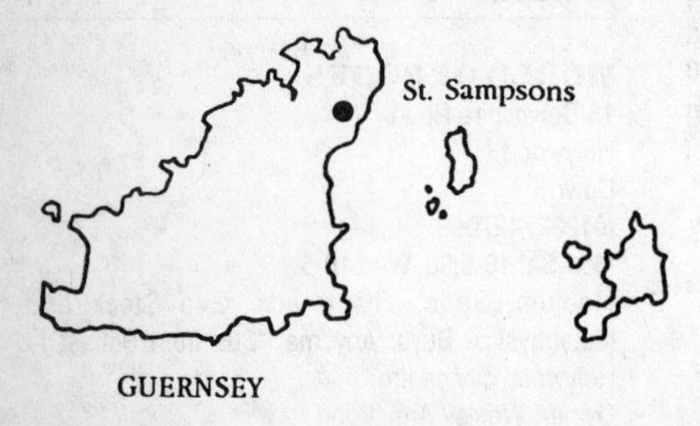

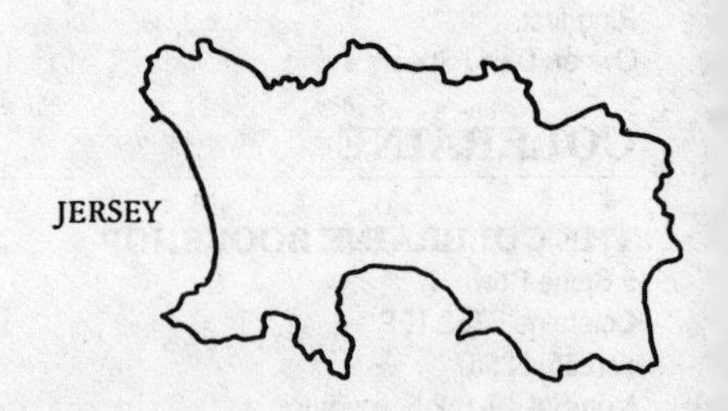

ST. SAMPSONS (GUERNSEY)

OLD CURIOSITY SHOP

Commercial Road
(Off the bridge)
St. Sampsons (Guernsey)
(01481) 45324/45091
Tue-Sat 10-5, Thur close
Est. 1978. Small. Spec: Channel Is: also Gen Stock. Buys: Ring first. "Also antiques, collectables, postcards, and prints."
Owner: Mrs Adele Stevens-Cox

ISLE OF MAN

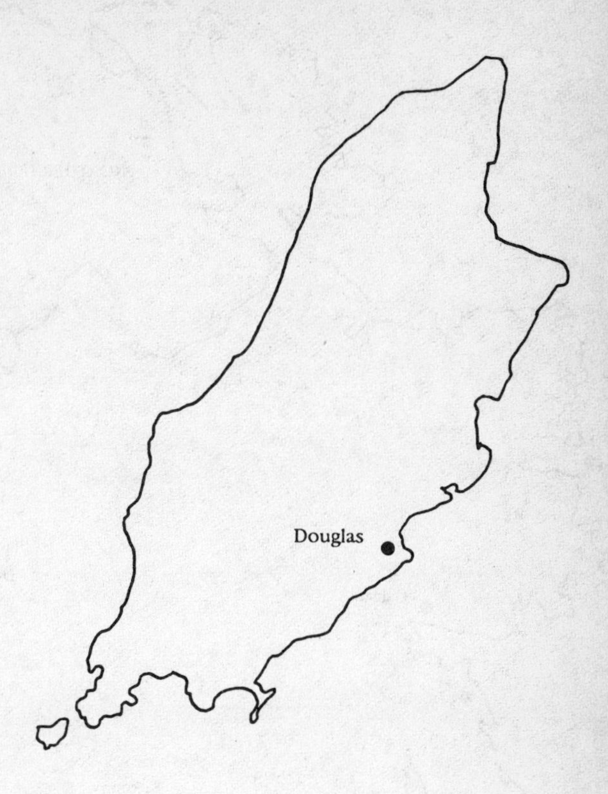

DOUGLAS

GARRETT'S ANTIQUARIAN BOOKS
Peter Luis Building
9 Duke Street
Douglas
(01624) 629660
Tue-Sat 10-4:30
Est. 1988. Small. Spec: Manx: also Gen Stock. Buys: Anytime. BR: Douglas.
Owner: Mr John Hall

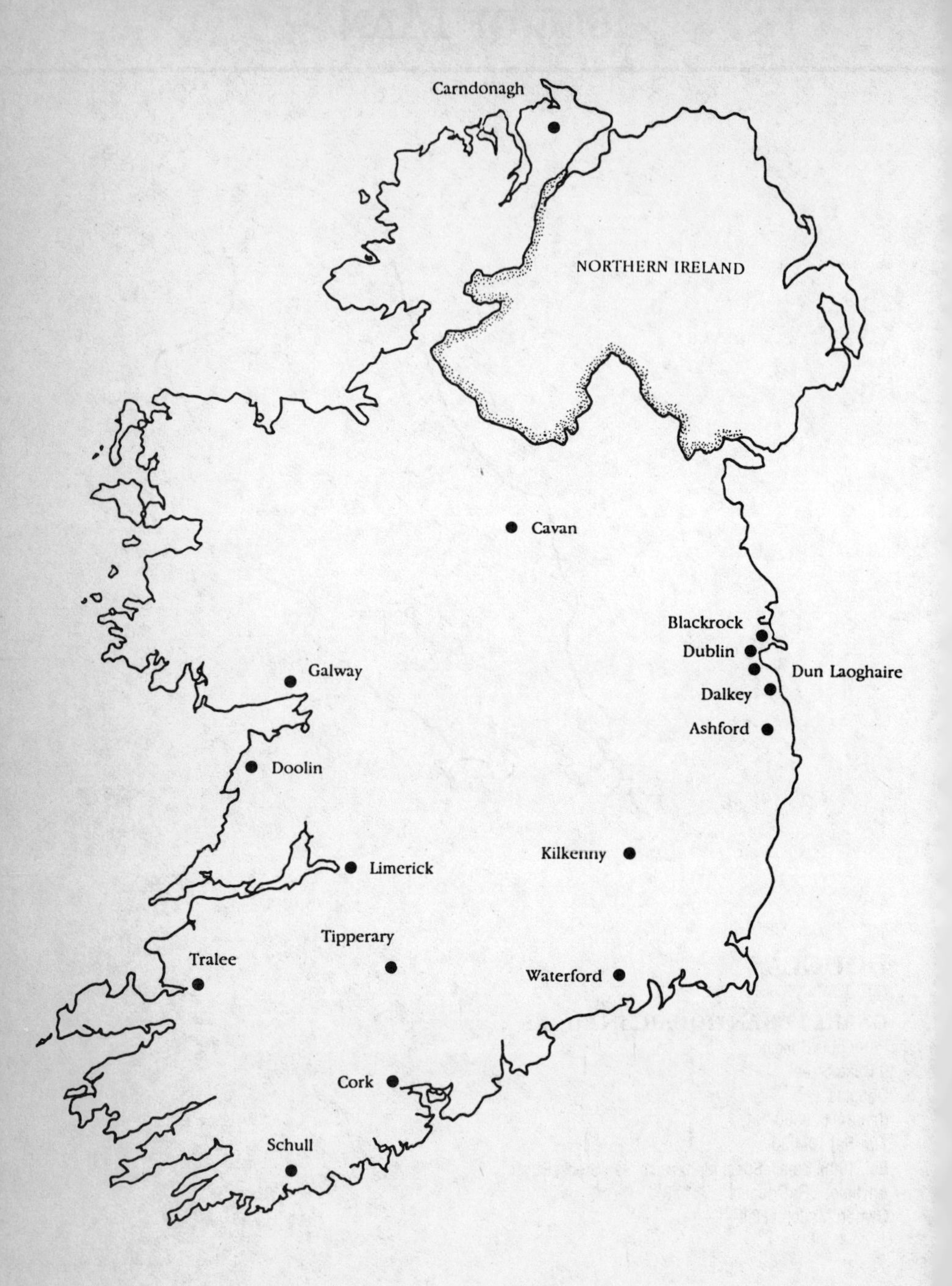
Carndonagh
NORTHERN IRELAND
Cavan
Blackrock
Dublin
Dun Laoghaire
Dalkey
Ashford
Galway
Doolin
Kilkenny
Limerick
Tipperary
Tralee
Waterford
Cork
Schull

Republic of Ireland

ASHFORD

VARTRY BOOKS
Mount Usher Books
Ashford
Wicklow
(00 353 404) 40490
Mon-Sat 12-6, Sun 2-6
Est. 1984. Medium. Spec: Ir: also Gen Stock and Chld. Buys: Anytime. Rail: Wicklow. "Situated at the entrance to Mount Usher Gardens."
Owner: Mark Sinnott

BLACKROCK

CARRAIG BOOKS LTD
73 Main Street
Blackrock
Dublin
(00 353 1) 288 2575
Mon-Fri 9:30-1, 2-5:30, Sat 10-5:30
Est. 1968. Large. Spec: Ir: also Gen Stock and RC, Lit, Hist. Cat: 10 pa. Buys: Anytime. cc: AV. Dart: Blackrock. "Opposite library."
Owners: Sean Day & L. Keegan

CARDONAGH

THE BOOKSHOP
Carnfair Arcade
Carndonagh
Donegal
(00 353 77) 74719/74389
Fax (00 353 77) 74313
Mon-Sat 2-7
Medium. Spec: Mod 1sts, Ir: also Gen Stock and Trav, Sci, C19th Lit. Buys: Ring first. Book search. cc: AVAmD. "By bus only. 20 miles north of Perry. Only s'hand bookshop in Donegal. 1/2 price sales at Easter, Aug, Dec."
Owner: Michael Herron

CAVAN

CAVAN BOOK CENTRE
Main Street
Cavan
(049) 62882
Tues-Sat 10-6
Est. 1984. Medium. Spec: Irish Interest, Rel: also Gen Stock and Biog, Lit, Trav. Buys: Anytime. Book search.
Owner: Beatrice Maloney

CORK

CONNOLLY'S BOOKSHOP
Paul Street
Cork
(00 353 21) 275366
Mon-Sat 10-6
Est. 1978. Medium. Gen Stock. Buys: Anytime. cc: V. Dart: Cork. "2 floors of used books, new books, & remainders."
Owner: Adrian Connolly

LEE BOOKSTORE
10 Lavitts Quay
Cork
(00 353 21) 272307
Tue-Sat 10-1, 2-5:30
Est. 1947. Medium. Spec: Ir Lit: also Gen Stock and Hist, Topog. Buys: Ring first. Book search. Dart: Cork. "Also some steel engravings."
Owner: Gerald McSweeney

DALKEY

THE EXCHANGE BOOKSHOP
34 Castle Street
Dalkey
Dublin
(00 353 1) 285 3805 (tel/fax)
Mon-Sat 9:15-6:15, Sun 1-6
Est. 1975. Medium. Gen Stock. Buys: Ring first. cc: VAm. Dart: Dalkey. "Dalkey Dart Station (4 min). Exchanging - cash purchase, ring first. Also new books & cards."
Director: Michael Simons

DOOLIN

DOOLIN DINGY BOOKS
Fisher Street
Doolin
Clare
(00 353 65) 74449
Mon-Sun 9-9 (Oct-Apr by appt only)
Small. Spec: Ir, Amer, & Eng Lit: also Gen Stock and Lit, Hist. Cat: 1-2 pa: Ir. Buys: Anytime. Book search. "20 mi from Ennis, close to world famous O'Connors Pub in heart of Doolin - home of traditional music. Small shop incorporating crafts, paintings, prints."
Owner: Cynthia Sinnott Griffin

DUBLIN

CATHACH BOOKS
10 Duke Street
Dublin 2
(00 353 1) 671 8676 (tel/fax)
Mon-Sat 9:30-6
Est. 1955. Medium. Spec: Ir. Cat: 1 pa: Ir. Buys: Ring first. cc: AVAm. Dart: Para Street. "Also sells maps & prints."
Owner: Edna Cunningham

CHAPTERS
70 Middle Abbey Street
Dublin 1
(00 353 1) 872 3297
Mon-Sat 9-7, Thur 9-8, Sun 1-6
Est. 1983. Medium. Gen Stock and Ir, Atqn. Buys: Ring first. cc: AV. Dart: Connolly Station. "A good wide range of stock. Music shop at No.54."
Owner: William Kinsella

DANDELION BOOKS
72 Aungier Street
Dublin 2
(00 353 1) 478 4759
Mon-Sat 10:30-6:30, Sun 2-6
Est. 1986. Medium. Spec: SF, New Age: also Gen Stock and Mod Lit, Irish Interest, Arts. Buys: Anytime. cc: AVE. Dart: City Centre. "5 min walk form Trinity College, Dublin. We pride ourselves on our comprehensive stock, friendly atmosphere, and knowledgeable staff."
Manager: Padraig O' Mealoid

DUFFY'S BOOKSHOP
4 South Lenster Street
Dublin 2
(00 353 1) 676 6836
Fax (00 3531) 676 6788
Mon-Sat 9-6
Medium. Spec: Ir, Pbks: also Gen Stock. Buys: Anytime. cc: AV. "Substantial range of s'hand pbks, remainder bargains, Fict, Non-Fict. No academic books."
Owner: Edward Creevey

GREEN'S BOOKSHOP LTD
16 Clare St
Dublin 2
(00 353 1) 676 2554
Fax (00 353 1) 678 9091
Mon-Fri 9-5:30, Sat 9-5
Est. 1843. Medium. Spec: Ir: also Gen Stock. Cat: 5-6 pa: Ir. Buys: Ring first. Book search. cc: AVAmD. Dart: Pearse Street. "New books, school books, & pbks also sold."
Owner: Eric Pembrey

FRED HANNA LTD
27-29 Nassau Street
Dublin 2
(00 353 1) 677 1255
Fax (00 353 1) 671 4330
Mon-Sat 9-5:30
Est. 1895. Small. Spec: Ir: also Gen Stock and Peng, Plate books, Fine Bindings. Cat: occ. Buys: Anytime. Book search. cc: AV. "New & s'hand shop in 3 buildings and on 2 floors. Atqn dept is the basement of No. 29. Quick turnover."
Owner: Fred Hanna

RATHMINES BOOKSHOP
211 Lower Rathmines Road
Dublin 6
(00 353 1) 496 1064
Mon-Sat 10-9, Sun 1-7
Est. 1988. Large. Gen Stock. Buys: Anytime. Book search. cc: AV. Bus: Imp. No. 83. "Large selec. of everything. Recycle - buy a s'hand book."
Owner: James Kinsella

STOKES BOOKS
19 Margaret Arcade
South Great Georges Street
Dublin 2
(00 353 1) 671 3584
Mon-Sat 10-6
Est. 1983. Medium. Spec: Ir: also Gen Stock and Phil. Cat: 1 pa: Ir. Buys: Anytime. Book search. Dart: Tara Street.
Owner: Stephen Stokes

TRINITY COLLEGE STUDENT UNION BOOKSHOP COOPERATIVE
TCD House 6
Dublin Town 2
(00 353 16) 776545
Mon-Fri 9:30-5:30
Small. Spec: Acad: also Gen Stock and Novels. Buys: Anytime. "Through the Arch and left, 1st floor."
Owner: Cooperative

GEORGE WEBB
5 & 6 Crampton Quay
Dublin 2
(00 353 1) 677 7489
Mon-Sat 9-5:30
Est. 1800. Medium. Spec: Ir: also Gen Stock and Ir Lit & Hist, Rems, Acad. Cat: occ: Ir. Buys: Ring first. Book search. cc: AV. Dart: Euston Street. "Reasonable. Also have plate books."
Owner: Fred Hanna

THE WINDING STAIR BOOKSHOP & CAFE
40 Lower Ormond Quay
Dublin 1
(00 353 1) 873 3292
Mon-Sat 10-6
Est. 1982. Large. Gen Stock. Buys: Ring first. Book search. Dart: Tara Station. "Next to the north side of Ha' Penny Bridge."
Owner: Kevin Connolly

DUN LAOGHAIRE

NAUGHTON BOOKSHOP
8 Marine Terrace
Dun Laoghaire
Dublin
(00 353 1) 280 4392
Mon-Sat 9:30-5:30
Est. 1978. Medium. Spec: Ir: also Gen Stock. Buys: Ring first. Book search. cc: AVAm. Dart: Dun Loaghaire. "Good s'hand bookshop on the way to James Joyce's Tower and Sandycove. Strong in Joyce items."
Owner: Susan Naughton

GALWAY

BYRNE'S BOOKSHOP
The Cornerstone
Middle Street
Galway
(00 353 91) 61766
Mon-Sat 9-6 (Summer 9-7) Fri 9-8, July and Aug, Sun 12-6
Large. Gen Stock. Buys: Anytime. Rail: Galway.
Owner: Charles Byrne

KENNY'S BOOKSHOP
Merchant's Road
Galway
(00 353 91) 62739
Fax (00 353 91) 68544
Mon-Sat 9-1, 2-5:30
Est. 1994. Large. Gen Stock. Buys: Anytime. Book search. "Gen stock £1-£10."

KENNY'S BOOKSHOP & ART GALLERY
High Street
Galway
(00 353 91) 62739
Fax (00 353 91) 68544
Mon-Sat 9-6
Est. 1940. Large. Spec: Ir: also Gen Stock and Lit, Hist, Soc Sci. Cat: 12 pa: Ir. Buys: Anytime. Book search. cc: AVAmD. Dart: Galway. "Very large range of books. Also Atqn maps and prints."
Owner: The Kenny Family

KILKENNY

OSSORY BOOKSHOP
67 High Street
Kilkenny
(00 353 56) 21893
Mon-Sun 10-6
Large. Spec: Ir, Atqn: also Gen Stock and Mil Hist. Cat: occ. Buys: Anytime. Book search. cc: AV. "New and s'hand books. Also bargain remainders."
Owner: Richard Kinsella

LIMERICK

TONY CLARKE (NEW & SECONDHAND BOOKSHOP)
12 Thomas Street
Limerick
(00 353 61) 410199
Mon-Sat 9:30-5:30
Medium. Gen Stock. Buys: Anytime. cc: AV. Rail: Limerick.
Owner: Mary Treacy

TONY CLARKE BOOKS
20 Thomas Street
Limerick
(00 353 61) 414852
Fax (00 353 61) 410442
Mon-Sat 9-5:45
Medium. Spec: School books. Buys: Ring first. Book search. cc: AV. Rail: Limerick.
Owner: Tony Clarke

MICHAEL DINEEN
95 Lower Henry Street
Limerick
(00 353 61) 413326
Mon-Sat 10-5:30
Small. Gen Stock. Buys: Anytime. Book search. cc: AV. "City centre Limerick. Pbks and hbks."
Owner: Michael Dineen

O'BRIEN BOOKSHOP
Bedford Row
Limerick
(00 353 61) 412833
Mon-Sat 10:30-5:30
Est. 1987. Medium. Spec: Ir: also Gen Stock. Buys: Anytime. Book search. cc: Am. Dart: Limerick City. "In the city centre, 1/2 mile away from rail."
Owner: John O'Brien

GEORGE STACPOOLE
Adare
Limerick
(00 353 61) 396409
Fax (00 353 61) 396733
Mon-Sat 10-5:30
Small. Spec: Ir, Sport: also Gen Stock. Buys: Anytime. Book search. cc: AVAmD. Rail: Limerick. "This shop not only has books, but also one of the largest collections of prints, watercolours, etc. in Ireland. Also antiques."
Owner: George Stacpoole

SCHULL

FUSCHIA BOOKS
Schull
(00 353 28) 28118
Mon-Sun 10-6 (Winter, Mon-Sat 11-4)
Medium. Spec: Ir: also Gen Stock. Buys: Anytime. Book search.
Owner: Mary Mackey

TIPPERARY

PENNYFARTHING BOOKSHOP
Pennyfarthing Arcade
Main Street
Tipperary
(00 353 62) 51124
Mon-Sat 11-6 (Lent 10-6)
Small. Spec: Rel, RC, Hist (Local): also Gen Stock and Cuba, Cosmography, Male Infibulation. Dart: Limerick Junction. "Will trade in Irish books. Shop & books for sale cheap. Goodwill priceless, no key money. Landlord nice. Girls good looking. Buyers literate and devout. Go for it."
Owner: Rudy Trew

TRALEE

BILLY NOLAN, DAUGHTER & SON
The Treasure Chest, 14 Dominic Street
Tralee
Kerry
(00 353 66) 22095 (tel/fax)
Mon-Sat 9:30-1, 2-6
Est. 1966. Medium. Gen Stock and Pbks. Buys: Anytime. cc: AVAm. Dart: Tralee.
Owner: William Nolan

WATERFORD

GLADSTONE'S BOOKSHOP
12 Gladstone Street
Waterford
(00 353 51) 70423
Mon-Sat 10-6, Fri 10-9, Sun 2-6
Est. 1988. Medium. Gen Stock and Avia, War, Art. Buys: Anytime. Rail: Waterford.
Owner: K. Kinsella

Late Entries

OXFORDSHIRE

THE PARLOUR BOOKSHOP

30 Wantage Road
Didcot OX11 0BT
(01235) 818989
Fax (01235) 814494
Mon-Fri 9:30-12:45, 1:45-4:30
Medium. Gen Stock. Buys: ring first. Est 1995. BR: Didcot. "Located in shopping parade just past Shell garage on B4493. Parking a pleasure - private fore-court."

LINCOLNSHIRE

ST. PAUL'S STREET BOOKSHOP

7 St. Paul's Street
Stamford PE9 2BE
(01780) 482748
Fax (01778) 380538
Mon-Sat 10-5
Medium. Spec: Motoring, Motor Sport: also Gen Stock, Loc Topog. Cat: 5 pa: Motoring. Buys: ring first. Est 1988. cc: MVE. BR: Stamford. "Eastern end of town centre in same road as Stamford Boys' School. Used to be Bridge Bookshop in Deeping St. James."
Owners: Jim & Brenda Blessett

DERBYSHIRE

HIGH STREET BOOKSHOP

9A High Street
Buxton SK17 6ET
(01298) 22246
Mon-Sat 9:30-5, Wed 9:30-1
Small. Gen Stock. Buys: ring first. Book search. Est 1995. BR: Buxton. "Opposite the Market Place in Higher Buxton. Some new and collectable books. Also buy in new books."
Owner: Mike Smith.

HEREFORD & WORCESTER

THE PAPERBACK EXCHANGE

12/13 St Peter's Street
Hereford HR1 2LE
(01432) 356902 (Tel/Fax)
Mon-Sat 9-5:30
Medium. Spec: Biog, Hist, New Age: also Gen Stock. Buys: ring first. Est 1993. cc:MVES. "New/secondhand bookshop. Mainstream."
Manager: Mrs Frankie Devereux

THE PAPERBACK EXCHANGE

70 Broad Street
Worcester WR1 3LY
(01905) 26689 (Tel/Fax)
Mon-Sat 9-5:30
Medium. Spec: Biog, Hist, New Age: also Gen Stock. Buys: ring first. Est 1993. cc: MVES. "New/secondhand bookshop. Mainstream."
Manager: Mrs Juna Vaughan

SOMERSET

THE PAPERBACK EXCHANGE

56 High Street
Taunton TA1 3PT
(01823) 323003 (Tel/Fax)
Mon-Sat 9-5:30
Medium. Spec: Biog, Hist, New Age: also Gen Stock. Buys: ring first. Est 1993.cc: MVES. "New/secondhand bookshop. Mainstream."
Manager: Mrs Lindsey Hobson

WEST MIDLANDS

THE PAPERBACK EXCHANGE

24 Market Way
Coventry CV1 1DL
(01203) 555152 (Tel/Fax)
Mon-Sat 9-5:30
Medium. Spec: Biog, Hist, New Age: also Gen Stock. Buys: ring first. Est 1993.cc: MVES. "New/secondhand bookshop. Mainstream."
Manager: Robert Skinner

THE PAPERBACK EXCHANGE

1 Church Street
Rugby CV21 1PH
(01788) 562737 (Tel/Fax)
Mon-Sat 9-5:30
Medium. Spec: Biog, Hist, New Age: also Gen Stock. Buys: ring first. Est 1993. cc: MVES. "New/secondhand bookshop. Mainstream."
Manager: Mrs Lisa Tyree

SURREY

FARNCOMBE BOOKS
131 Kings Road
Farncome
Godalming GU7
(01483) 861168
Tue 10-1, Wed-Fri 10-5, Sat 9:30-5
Med. Spec: Cookery also Gen Stock and Travel, Poetry, Fict, Mod 1sts,Nat Hist, Biog. Buys: ring first, Est 1996. "Also annuals annd classics." BR: Godalming.
Owner: Kevin Hooper

EAST SUSSEX

THE COPY SHOP
Church Road
Newick BN8 4JX
(01825) 723556
Mon-Fri 9-5
"Very small stock but continually changing."
Manager: Mr J. Pattenden

INDEX OF SHOPS

THE
CENTRAL
AFRICAN
ARCHIVES
LIBRARY
LVX
IN TENEBRIS
SIT NOMINE DIGNA

INDEX OF SUBJECTS

INDEX OF SUBJECTS

INDEX OF SUBJECTS

INDEX OF SUBJECTS

Index of Towns

Wrest Park.

NOTES

NOTES

NOTES

NOTES

NOTES

NOTES

NOTES

NOTES

NOTES

ROUTE PLANNER
REPUBLIC OF IRELAND & NORTHERN IRELAND

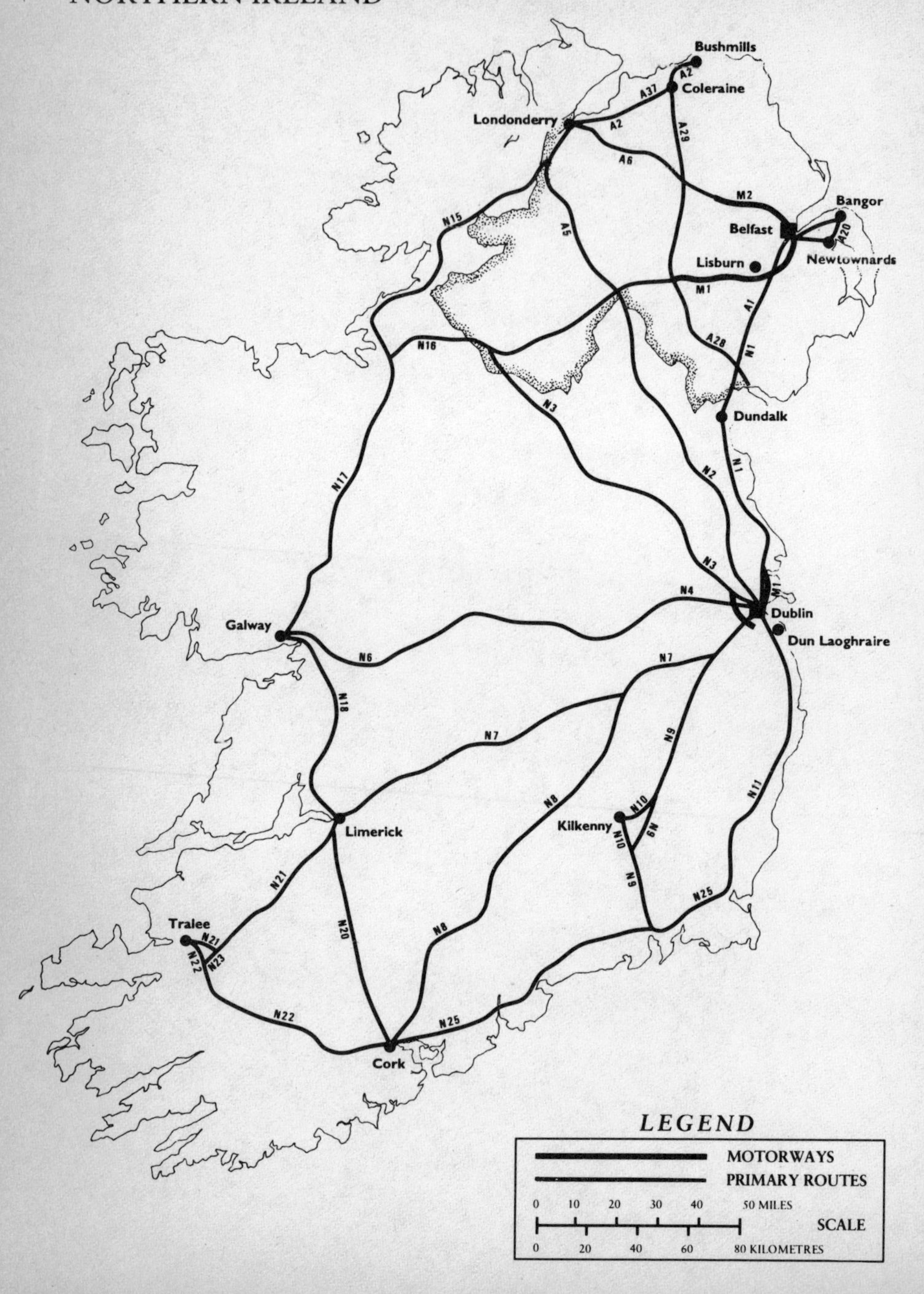